# Cooperative Math
## Engaging Structures & Activities

Ranae Stites &
Amanda Buethe

Kagan

*Kagan Publishing*
P.O. Box 72008
San Clemente, CA 92673-2008
**1(800) 933-2667**
**www.KaganOnline.com**

ISBN: 978-1-933445-06-9

# Cooperative Math PreK–2
## Introduction

**A**s testing dominated our classrooms and increased across grade levels, we began looking for ready-made activities to fit the NCTM standards. However, finding hands-on activities that fit the standards was very difficult.

We began our efforts by putting a notebook together that contained the cooperative learning strategies that met the national standards. Using the activities in our classrooms with our students, we could immediately see that it was very beneficial. All students were engaged in the activities, having fun, and learning important information.

As a result, we published our first book *Cooperative Math 3–5*. We felt the need for lower elementary students to experience enagaging math activities with Kagan Structures as well. Thus, we created our second book, *Cooperative Math PreK–2*.

In this book, you will find selected Kagan Cooperative Learning Structures. You will receive step-by-step instructions and practical tips on how to use each structure with the given activity.

*Cooperative Math PreK–2* is designed to give teachers a needed resource that aligns with the national standards. Activities in this book are ready-made and easy to use. They are carefully planned around the national standards. Each chapter is organized by structure. For each structure, a number of activities for each strand are provided.

This book has one goal: to provide teachers with ready-made, hands-on activities that will help students increase mathematical knowledge and skills, and reach national mathematics standards. By engaging in these cooperative math activities, students understand and use the math skills needed in today's society.

The activities in this book, along with the Kagan Cooperative Learning Structures, are beneficial to all children. All students are engaged in the learning activities, even those who are quiet or those who traditionally perform poorly. All students are given the chance to become a leader and take ownership with the needed skills.

It is our job as teachers to prepare our students with the needed skills to succeed not only in school, but in life. This book will meet those needs, based on the NCTM standards.

# About the Authors

**R**anae Stites draws on 17 years of teaching experience ranging from 1st to 8th grade. She has a Master's degree in curriculum instruction and completed a post-Master's program. Ranae is currently teaching 3rd grade and has for several years. In the past and present years, she has incorporated Kagan Cooperative Learning in her classroom. Ranae co-authored *Cooperative Math* for grades 3–5 and is also a consultant for the math program taught in her district. She has ventured to Arkansas, Iowa, Missouri, and Oklahoma as a consultant.

**A**manda Buethe has taught grades 3–6 and is currently teaching 6th grade in Sidney, Nebraska. She received her B.A. at Bethany College and completed her Master's degree in curriculum instruction from Wichita State University. Amanda is the co-author of *Cooperative Math* for grades 3–5. Kagan Cooperative Learning has long been an instrumental part of Amanda's classroom.

# Acknowledgments

I would like to dedicate this book to my family—my husband Troy, and my three wonderful children: Taylor, TJ, and Tyson. —*Ranae*

To my wonderful husband, Bruce, and my family and friends for always being supportive with anything I choose to do. —*Amanda*

Thanks go to Dr. Jackie Minor, Laurie Kagan, Miguel Kagan, and all the great staff at Kagan Publishing for the feedback and the opportunity to share this book with others; Alex Core and Becky Herrington for book design; Jeremie Rujanawech for math illustrations and design; Erin Kant for the illustrations of the cover and Kagan Structures; and Kim Fields, copy editor.

We would like to thank the wonderful people in USD 418, especially Dr. Watson for his insight.

# NCTM Standards for Grades PreK-2*

## Number and Operations

*In prekindergarten through grade 2 all students should:*

- Understand numbers, ways of representing numbers, relationships among numbers, and number systems.
- Understand meanings of operations and how they relate to one another.
- Compute fluently and make reasonable estimates.

## Algebra

*In prekindergarten through grade 2 all students should:*

- Understand patterns, relations, and functions.
- Represent and analyze mathematical situations and structures using algebraic symbols.
- Use mathematical models to represent and understand quantitative relationships.
- Analyze change in various contexts.

## Geometry

*In prekindergarten through grade 2 all students should:*

- Analyze characteristics and properties of two- and three-dimensional geometric shapes and develop mathematical arguments about geometric relationships.
- Specify locations and describe spatial relationships using coordinate geometry and other representational systems.
- Apply transformations and use symmetry to analyze mathematical situations.
- Use visualization, spatial reasoning, and geometric modeling to solve problems.

## Measurements

*In prekindergarten through grade 2 all students should:*

- Understand measurable attributes of objects and the units, systems, and processes of measurement.
- Apply appropriate techniques, tools, and formulas to determine measurements.

## Data Analysis and Probability

*In prekindergarten through grade 2 all students should:*

- Formulate questions that can be addressed with data and collect, organize, and display relevant data to answer them.
- Select and use appropriate statistical methods to analyze data.
- Develop and evaluate inferences and predictions that are based on data.
- Understand and apply basic concepts of probability.

*Standards are from the National Council of Teachers of Mathematics Website at http://standards.nctm.org/*

# Table of Contents

# Aligning Structures to NCTM Standards

| Activities by Structure | Number and Operations | Algebra | Geometry | Measurement | Data Analysis and Probability |
|---|:---:|:---:|:---:|:---:|:---:|
| **Fan-N-Pick** | | | | | |
| 1.1 Base Ten Blocks | ● | | | | |
| 1.2 Ordinal Numbers | ● | | | | |
| 1.3 Count the Coins | ● | | | | |
| 1.4 Naming Patterns | | ● | | | |
| 1.5 Properties of Operation | | ● | | | |
| 1.6 Relative Position | | | ● | | |
| 1.7 Transformations | | | ● | | |
| 1.8 Measurement | | | | ● | |
| **Find Someone Who** | | | | | |
| 2.1 Cardinal Numbers | ● | | | | |
| 2.2 Find the Missing Number | | ● | | | |
| 2.3 Ordering Objects | | ● | | | |
| 2.4 Shape Attributes | | | ● | | |
| 2.5 Environmental Shapes | | | ● | | |
| 2.6 2-D Shapes | | | ● | | |
| 2.7 Measurement | | | | ● | |
| 2.8 Repetition Measuring | | | | ● | |
| **Match Mine** | | | | | |
| 3.1 Match My Number Sentence | ● | | | | |
| 3.2 Match My Shape Design | | | ● | | |
| 3.3 Match My Coordinate Grid | | | ● | | |
| 3.4 Match My Location | | | ● | | |
| 3.5 Match My Time | | | | ● | |

Cooperative Math • Kagan Publishing • (800) 933-2667 • www.KaganOnline.com **Activities/Standards**

| Activities by Structure | Number and Operations | Algebra | Geometry | Measurement | Data Analysis and Probability |
|---|---|---|---|---|---|
| **Mix-Freeze-Group** | | | | | |
| 4.1 Subtraction Situations | ● | | | | |
| 4.2 Fractions | ● | | | | |
| 4.3 Ordinal Numbers | ● | | | | |
| 4.4 Number Words | ● | | | | |
| 4.5 Money | ● | | | | |
| 4.6 Shapes #1 | | | ● | | |
| 4.7 Shapes #2 | | | ● | | |
| **Quiz-Quiz-Trade** | | | | | |
| 5.1 How Many? | ● | | | | |
| 5.2 Addition Facts | ● | | | | |
| 5.3 Subtraction Facts | ● | | | | |
| 5.4 Naming 2-D Shapes | | | ● | | |
| 5.5 Naming 3-D Shapes | | | ● | | |
| 5.6 Coordinate Points | | | ● | | |
| 5.7 Likely or Unlikely? | | | | | ● |
| **Sage-N-Scribe** | | | | | |
| 6.1 Fact Families | ● | | | | |
| 6.2 Addition Situations | ● | | | | |
| 6.3 Estimate and Calculate | ● | | | | |
| 6.4 Growing Patterns | | ● | | | |
| 6.5 Direction and Distance | | | ● | | |
| 6.6 Symmetry #1 | | | ● | | |
| 6.7 Symmetry #2 | | | ● | | |
| 6.8 Match the Time | | | | ● | |
| 6.9 Measuring with Dinosaurs | | | | ● | |
| 6.10 Graphs | | | | | ● |

# Aligning Structures to NCTM Standards continued

| Activities by Structure | Number and Operations | Algebra | Geometry | Measurement | Data Analysis and Probability |
|---|:---:|:---:|:---:|:---:|:---:|
| **Showdown** | | | | | |
| 7.1  Number Words and Numerals | ● | | | | |
| 7.2  Basic Fractions | ● | | | | |
| 7.3  Equal Groups | ● | | | | |
| 7.4  Addition and Subtraction | ● | | | | |
| 7.5  Sort the Objects | | ● | | | |
| 7.6  Is It Symmetrical? | | | ● | | |
| 7.7  What Time Is It? | | | | ● | |
| 7.8  Make a Graph | | | | | ● |

# COOPERATIVE MATH

# Structure 1

# Fan-N-Pick

# Fan-N-Pick

**Students play a card game to respond to questions.**

## Instructions

*Each team receives a set of question cards.*

**1** Student #1 holds question cards in a fan and says, "Pick a card, any card!"

**2** Student #2 picks a card, reads the question aloud, and allows five seconds of think time.

**3** Student #3 answers the question.

**4** Student #4 checks the answer. If the answer is correct, Student #4 praises the student who answered. If the answer is incorrect, Student #4 tutors the student who answered.

**5** Students rotate roles, one person clockwise, for each new round.

*Modifications: Fan-N-Pick can be played in pairs. Student #1 fans; Student #2 picks and reads; Student #1 answers; Student #2 tutors or praises; students switch roles.*

## ★★ Boosting Engagement ★★

Fan-N-Pick keeps everyone actively involved in learning math. All teammates have a role for each problem. That means now everyone is on task and no one can tune out. Teammates count on each other to do their part so they can play this fun learning "game." And when a student needs help, he or she has the support of teammates to help him or her learn the math skills.

# Fan-N-Pick Activities

## Number and Operations

## Algebra

## Geometry

## Measurement

## Answer Key ...........................68

# Fan-N-Pick
# Primary Tips

## General Tips

- Limit number of concepts being reviewed. It is okay for primary students to practice concepts multiple times.
- Laminate cards for durability.
- Fold card in half to conceal the answer.
- Content should be a review of material previously taught.

## Before
### Teaching the Structure

- Start with a visual of the structure. Use the visual to explain the steps.
- Show how to use *Fan-N-Pick* by modeling how to fan the cards, coach, praise, and rotate roles.
  - ★ **Tips on "Coaching"**
    - Give students examples of coaching phrases without giving their partner the answer. For example: "Count with me." Coaching is always specific to the task so the teacher must model specific coaching phrases that match the content. Phrases like "keep trying" or "try again" are encouraging statements, not coaching.
    - Student coaches could also use manipulatives to help show things such as addition/subtraction, counting, etc.

## Before
### Teaching the Structure *(continued)*

★ **Tips on "Praising"**
- Give specific praise or cheer that all students do when done quizzing/answering (examples: high five, a round of applause, thumbs up, "Great job!"). Watch to make sure the praising does not distract students from the content.

★ **Tips on "Fanning the cards"**
- Model with four students. Demonstrate how to fan the cards.
- For primary students, have them choose a set number of cards to fan if they cannot hold all of them at once.

★ **Tips on "Picking a card"**
- Model asking the question. Demonstrate how to hold the card and ask the question. If the answer is on the back, remind students to show the question side only to their teammates.
- The listening student puts his or her hands behind his or her back and looks directly at the asking student. Make sure their shoulders are "squared up."

## During
### Doing the Structure

- Start with short amounts of time. If the structure continues for too long, students may start to get loud and off task.
- Listen for good coaching and praising. Stop the group if appropriate and hold up a team or pair as a model. Do this during the structure so that other students can practice what you have emphasized.

## After
### Processing the Structure

- Talk about what went well. Demonstrate if needed.
- Note any problems.
- Set goals for next time.

# Fan-N-Pick
# Activities

## Base Ten Blocks

*Base ten* is a concrete representation of numbers in which each place has ten times the value of the next place to its right. Students name the number represented by the base ten blocks. Student #1 fans the cards and says, "Pick a card, any card."

Student #2 picks a card, shows the side of the card with the *base ten blocks*, and allows five seconds of think time for Student #3. Student #3 names the number represented by the *base ten blocks*. Student #4 checks, coaches, and praises. Rotate roles for each new problem.

**NCTM Standard: Numbers and Operations Standard PreK–2**
★ Understand numbers, ways of representing numbers, relationships among numbers, and number systems.
• Uses multiple models to develop initial understandings of place value and the base-ten number system.

**pp. 9–24**

## Activity 1.2

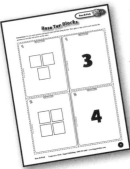

## Ordinal Numbers

An *ordinal number* is a number that tells you the position of people or things that are in order. Students name the position of the colored circle. Student #1 fans the cards and says, "Pick a card, any card." Student #2 picks a card, shows the side of the card with the *ordinal numbers*, and allows five seconds of think time for Student #3. Student #3 names the number represented by the *ordinal numbers*. Student #4 checks, coaches, and praises. Rotate roles for each new problem.

**NCTM Standard: Numbers and Operations Standard PreK–2**
★ Understand numbers, ways of representing numbers, relationships among numbers, and number systems.
• Develop understanding of the relative position and magnitude of whole numbers and of ordinal and cardinal numbers and their connections.

**pp. 25–30**

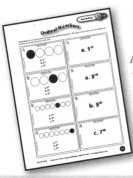

## Activity 1.3

# Count the Coins

Students identify the front and back of the penny, nickel, dime, and quarter. Students count the total amount of money shown on the card. Student #1 fans the cards and says, "Pick a card, any card." Student #2 picks a card, shows the side of the card with the coins, and allows five seconds of think time for Student #3. Student #3 names the amount represented by the coins. Student #4 checks, coaches, and praises. Rotate roles for each new problem.

**NCTM Standard: Number and Operations Standard PreK–2**
★ Compute fluently and make reasonable estimates.
• Develop fluency with basic number combinations for addition and subtraction.

pp. 31–37

## Activity 1.4

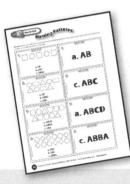

# Naming Patterns

A *pattern* is a sequence of shapes or numbers that repeat or change in a regular manner. Students name the pattern shown on the card. Student #1 fans the cards and says, "Pick a card, any card." Student #2 picks a card, shows the side of the card with the *named pattern*, and allows five seconds of think time for Student #3. Student #3 names the pattern represented by the pictures. Student #4 checks, coaches, and praises. Rotate roles for each new problem.

**NCTM Standard: Algebra Standard PreK–2**
★ Understands patterns, relations, and functions.
• Recognize, describe, and extend patterns, such as sequences of sounds and shapes or simple numeric patterns, and translate from one representation to another.

pp. 38–43

## Activity 1.5

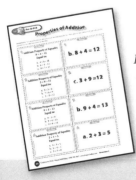

# Properties of Addition

*Properties of addition* match a number sentence. Students find the number sentence on the card. Student #1 fans the cards and says, "Pick a card, any card." Student #2 picks a card, shows the side of the card with the number sentence, and allows five seconds of think time for Student #3. Student #3 names the number sentence that matches the given number sentence. Student #4 checks, coaches, and praises. Rotate roles for each new problem.

**NCTM Standard: Algebra PreK–2**
★ Represent and analyze mathematical situations and structures using algebraic symbols.
• Illustrate general principles and properties of operations such as commutativity using specific numbers.

pp. 44–49

# Fan-N-Pick
## Activities continued

## Activity 1.6

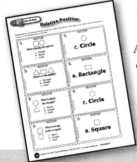

### Relative Position

A *relative position* is a location that describes spatial relationships. Students identify relative positions such as above, beside, after. Student #1 fans the cards and says, "Pick a card, any card." Student #2 picks a card, shows the side of the card with the *relative position,* and allows five seconds of think time for Student #3. Student #3 names the shape represented by the *relative position.* Student #4 checks, coaches, and praises. Rotate roles for each new problem.

**NCTM Standard: Geometry Standard PreK–2**
★ Specify locations and describe spatial relationships using coordinate geometry and other representational systems.
• Describe, name, and interpret relative positions in space and apply ideas about relative position.

pp. 50–55

## Activity 1.7

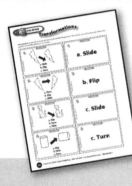

### Transformations

A *transformation* is a rule for moving every point in a plane figure to a new location. Students identify which *transformation* has occurred: translate (slide), flip, rotate (turn). Student #1 fans the cards and say, "Pick a card, any card." Student #2 picks a card, shows the side of the card with the *transformation,* and allows five seconds of think time for Student #3. Student #3 tells which *transformation* has occurred. Student #4 checks, coaches, and praises. Rotate roles for each new problem.

**NCTM Standard: Number and Operations Standard PreK–2**
★ Compute fluently and make reasonable estimates.
• Develop fluency with basic number combinations for addition and subtraction.

pp. 56–61

## Activity 1.8

### Measurement

A *measurement* is a comparison to some other known unit. Students measure to the nearest inch and centimeter. Students measure the line with the appropriate unit. Student #1 fans the cards and says, "Pick a card, any card." Student #2 picks a card, shows the side of the card with the *measurement,* and allows five seconds of think time for Student #3. Student #3 names the number represented by the *measurement.* Student #4 checks, coaches, and praises. Rotate roles for each new problem.

**NCTM Standard: Measurement Standard PreK–2**
★ Apply appropriate techniques, tools, and formulas to determine measurements.
• Uses tools to measure.

pp. 62–67

# Base Ten Blocks

**Instructions:** Cut out each question and answer pair and fold along the line. Then, glue or tape card so each card has the question on one side and answer on the other.

# Base Ten Blocks

**Instructions:** Cut out each question and answer pair and fold along the line. Then, glue or tape card so each card will have the question on one side and answer on the other.

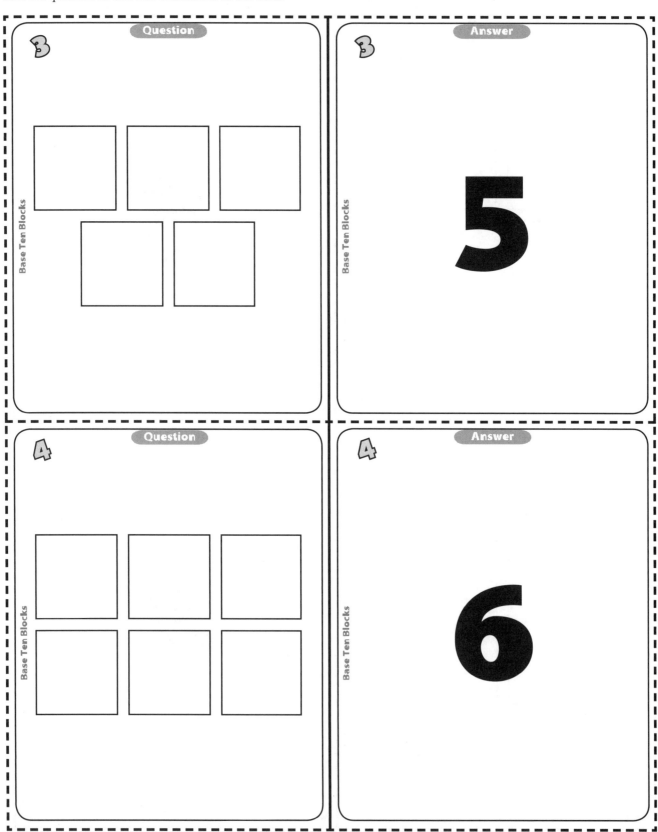

# Base Ten Blocks

**Instructions:** Cut out each question and answer pair and fold along the line. Then, glue or tape card so each card will have the question on one side and answer on the other.

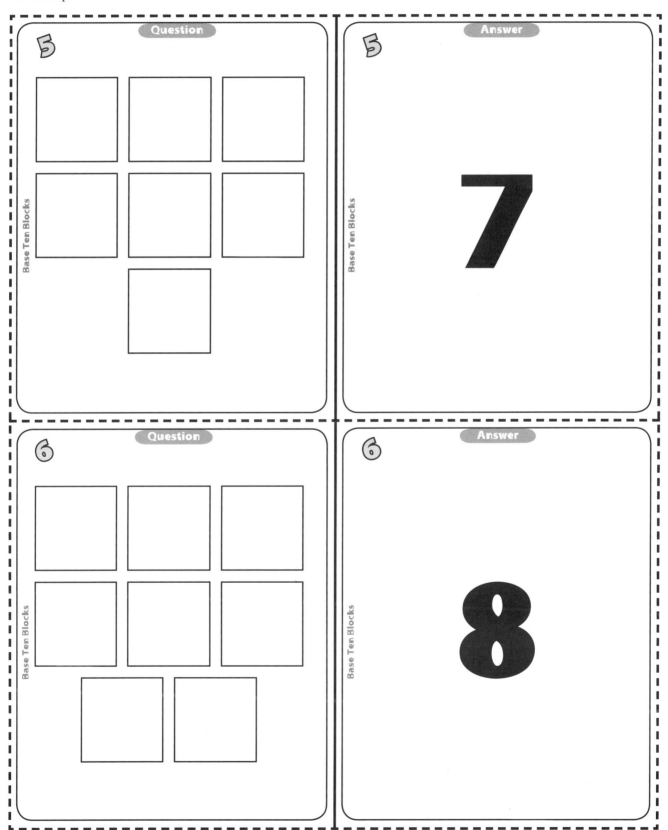

# Base Ten Blocks

**Instructions:** Cut out each question and answer pair and fold along the line. Then, glue or tape card so each card will have the question on one side and answer on the other.

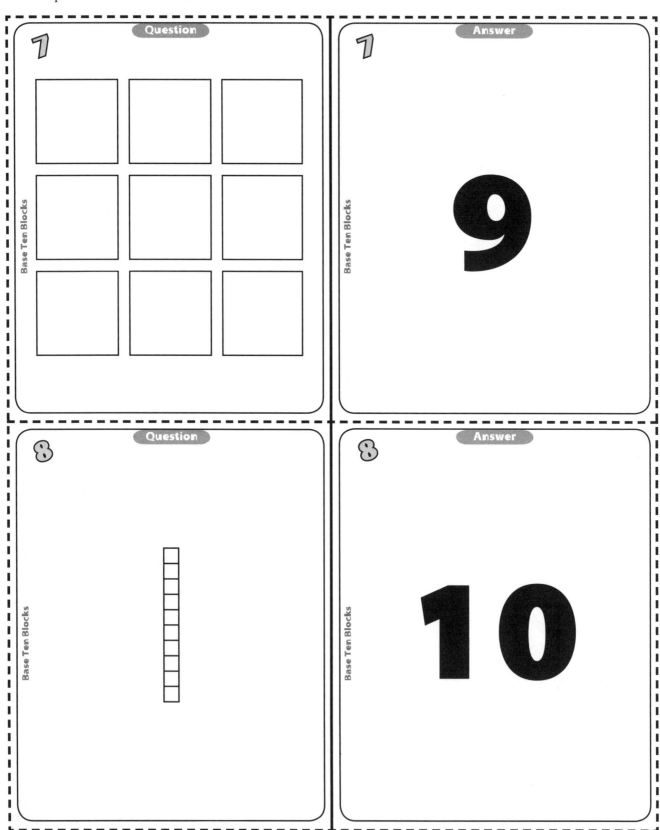

# Base Ten Blocks

**Instructions:** Cut out each question and answer pair and fold along the line. Then, glue or tape card so each card will have the question on one side and answer on the other.

# Base Ten Blocks

**Instructions:** Cut out each question and answer pair and fold along the line. Then, glue or tape card so each card will have the question on one side and answer on the other.

**11** Question

Base Ten Blocks

**11** Answer

Base Ten Blocks

# 40

**12** Question

Base Ten Blocks

**12** Answer

Base Ten Blocks

# 50

# Base Ten Blocks

**Instructions:** Cut out each question and answer pair and fold along the line. Then, glue or tape card so each card will have the question on one side and answer on the other.

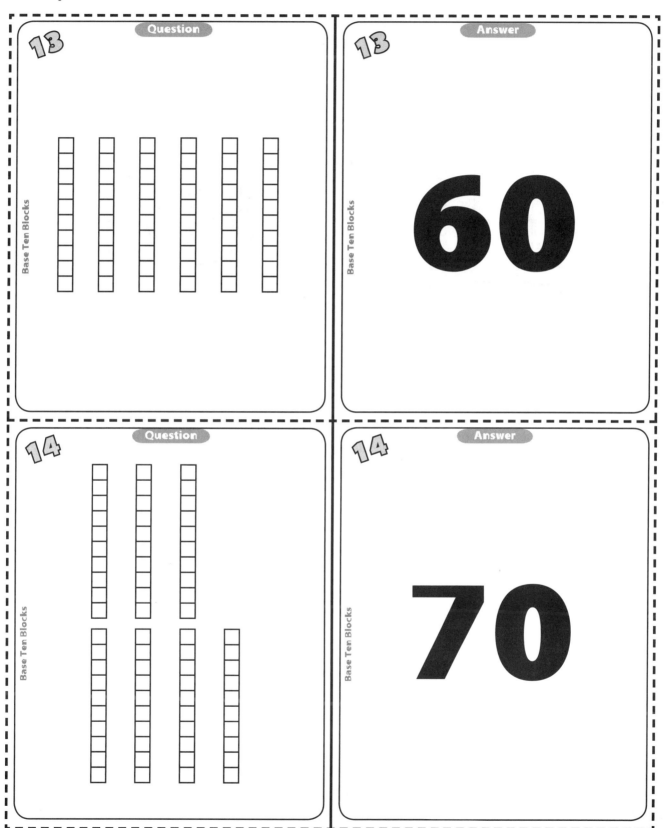

# Base Ten Blocks

**Instructions:** Cut out each question and answer pair and fold along the line. Then, glue or tape card so each card will have the question on one side and answer on the other.

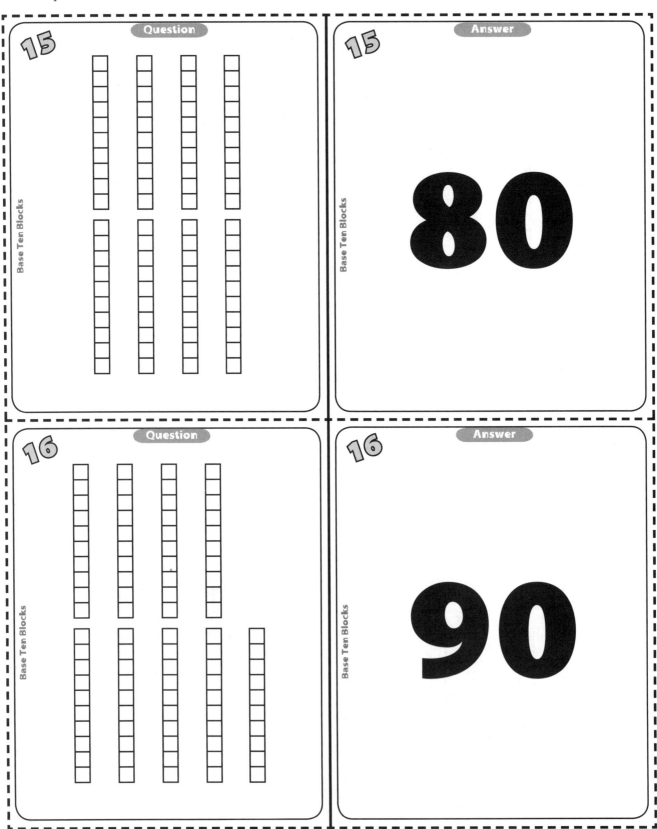

# Base Ten Blocks

**Instructions:** Cut out each question and answer pair and fold along the line. Then, glue or tape card so each card will have the question on one side and answer on the other.

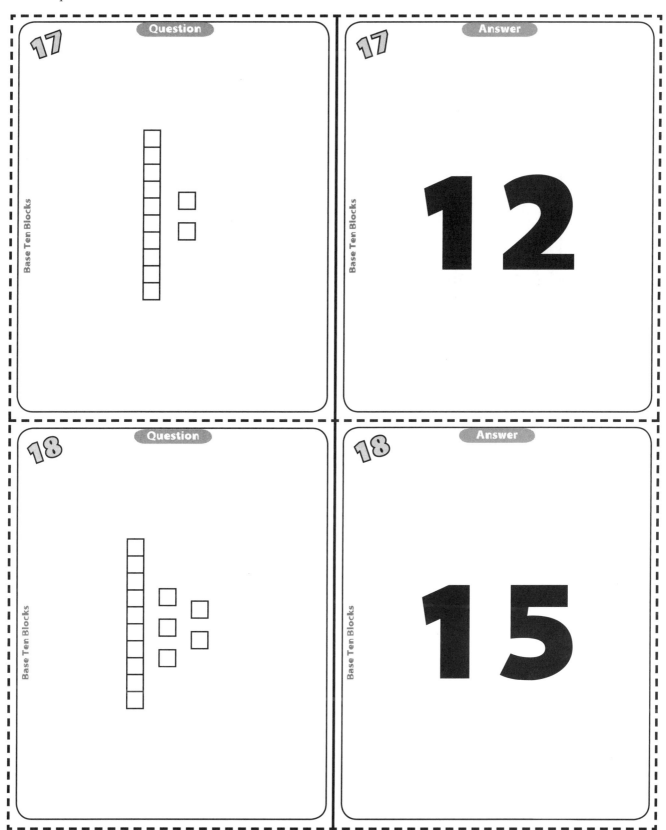

**17** Question

Base Ten Blocks

**17** Answer

Base Ten Blocks

**12**

**18** Question

Base Ten Blocks

**18** Answer

Base Ten Blocks

**15**

# Base Ten Blocks

**Instructions:** Cut out each question and answer pair and fold along the line. Then, glue or tape card so each card will have the question on one side and answer on the other.

**19** Question

Base Ten Blocks

**19** Answer

**17**

Base Ten Blocks

**20** Question

Base Ten Blocks

**20** Answer

**29**

Base Ten Blocks

# Base Ten Blocks

**Instructions:** Cut out each question and answer pair and fold along the line. Then, glue or tape card so each card will have the question on one side and answer on the other.

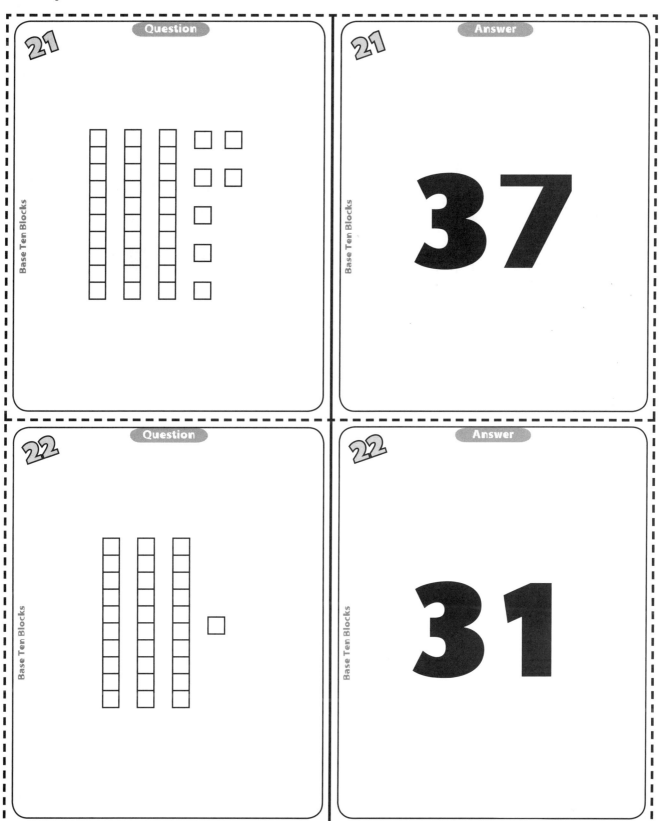

# Base Ten Blocks

**Instructions:** Cut out each question and answer pair and fold along the line. Then, glue or tape card so each card will have the question on one side and answer on the other.

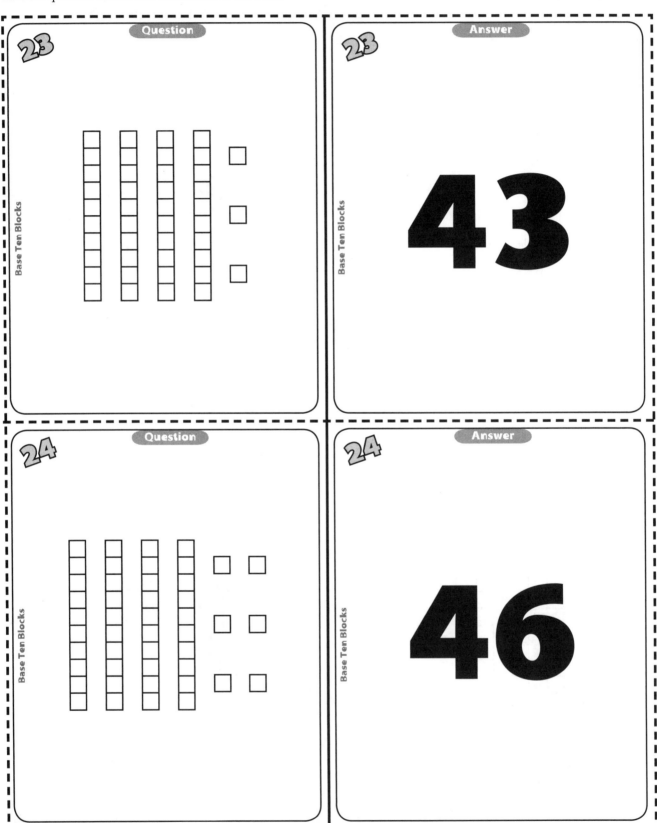

**23** Question

Base Ten Blocks

**23** Answer

Base Ten Blocks

**43**

**24** Question

Base Ten Blocks

**24** Answer

Base Ten Blocks

**46**

# Base Ten Blocks

**Instructions:** Cut out each question and answer pair and fold along the line. Then, glue or tape card so each card will have the question on one side and answer on the other.

# Base Ten Blocks

**Instructions:** Cut out each question and answer pair and fold along the line. Then, glue or tape card so each card will have the question on one side and answer on the other.

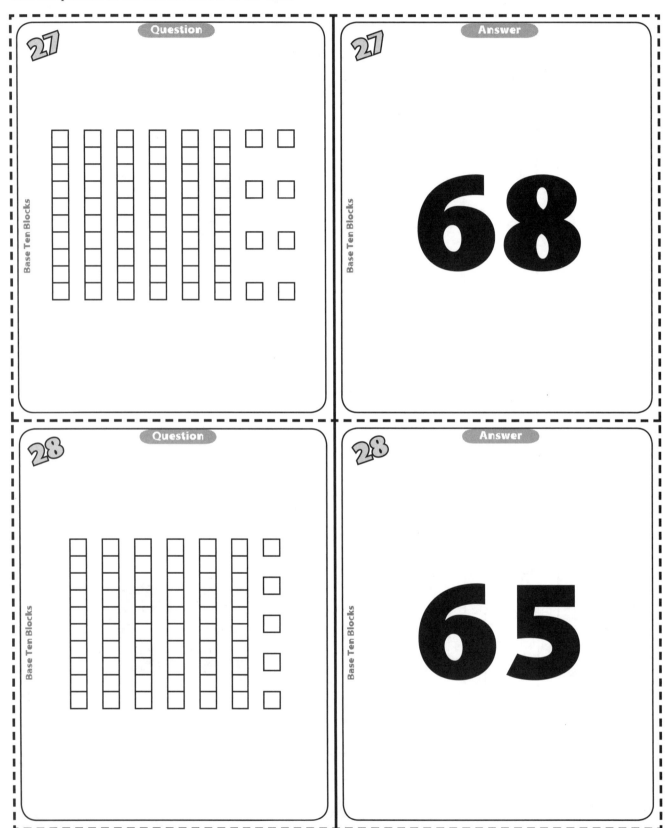

**27**   Question

Base Ten Blocks

**27**   Answer

**68**

Base Ten Blocks

**28**   Question

Base Ten Blocks

**28**   Answer

**65**

Base Ten Blocks

# Base Ten Blocks

**Instructions:** Cut out each question and answer pair and fold along the line. Then, glue or tape card so each card will have the question on one side and answer on the other.

**29** Question

Base Ten Blocks

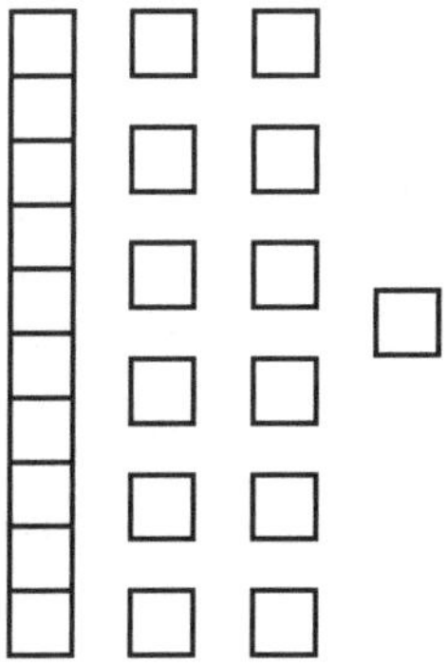

**29** Answer

Base Ten Blocks

23

**30** Question

Base Ten Blocks

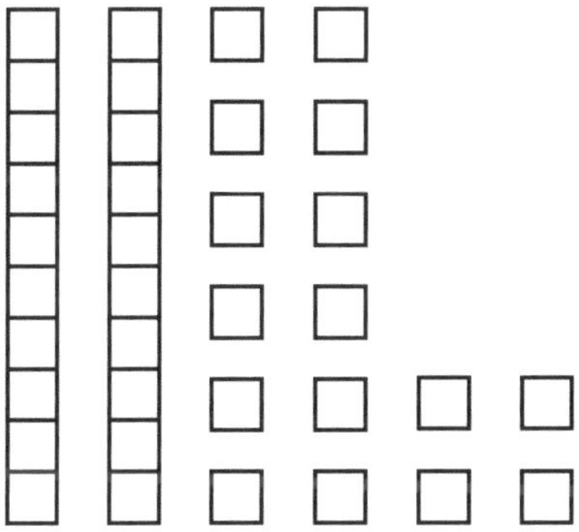

**30** Answer

Base Ten Blocks

36

# Base Ten Blocks

**Instructions:** Cut out each question and answer pair and fold along the line. Then, glue or tape card so each card will have the question on one side and answer on the other.

| | |
|---|---|
| **31** Question | **31** Answer |
| Base Ten Blocks | Base Ten Blocks **34** |
| **32** Question | **32** Answer |
| Base Ten Blocks | Base Ten Blocks **100** |

# Ordinal Numbers

**Instructions:** Cut out each question and answer pair and fold along the line. Then, glue or tape card so each card will have the question on one side and answer on the other.

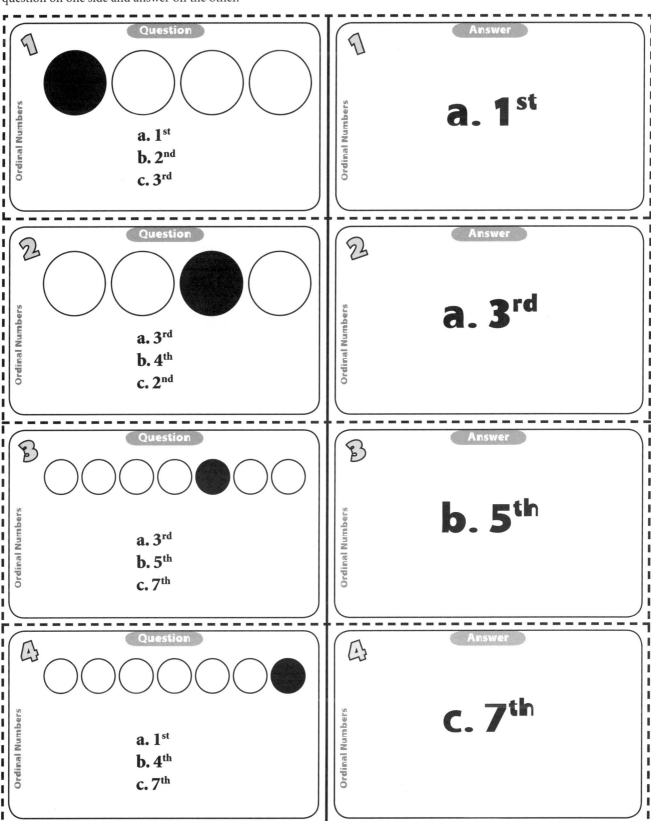

# Ordinal Numbers

**Instructions:** Cut out each question and answer pair and fold along the line. Then, glue or tape card so each card will have the question on one side and answer on the other.

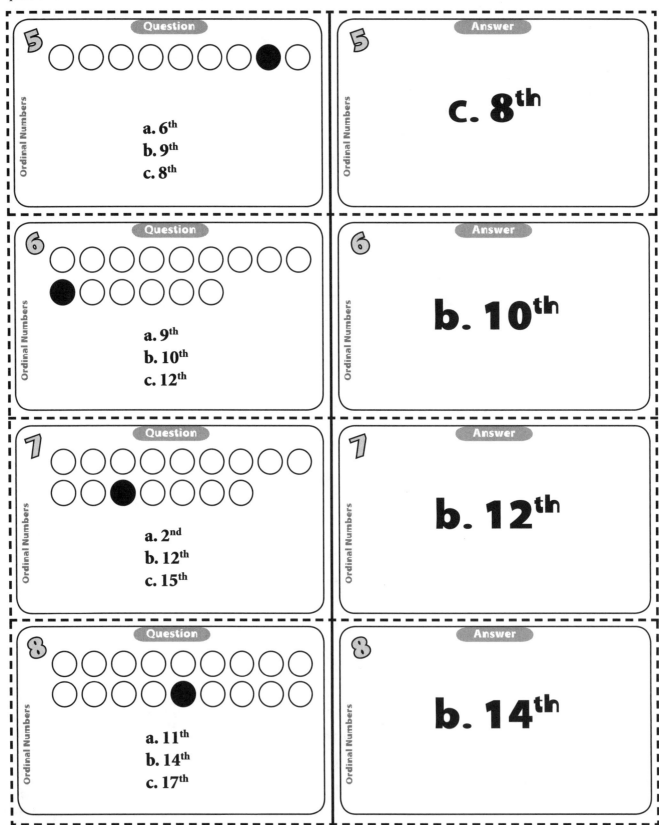

# Ordinal Numbers

**Instructions:** Cut out each question and answer pair and fold along the line. Then, glue or tape card so each card will have the question on one side and answer on the other.

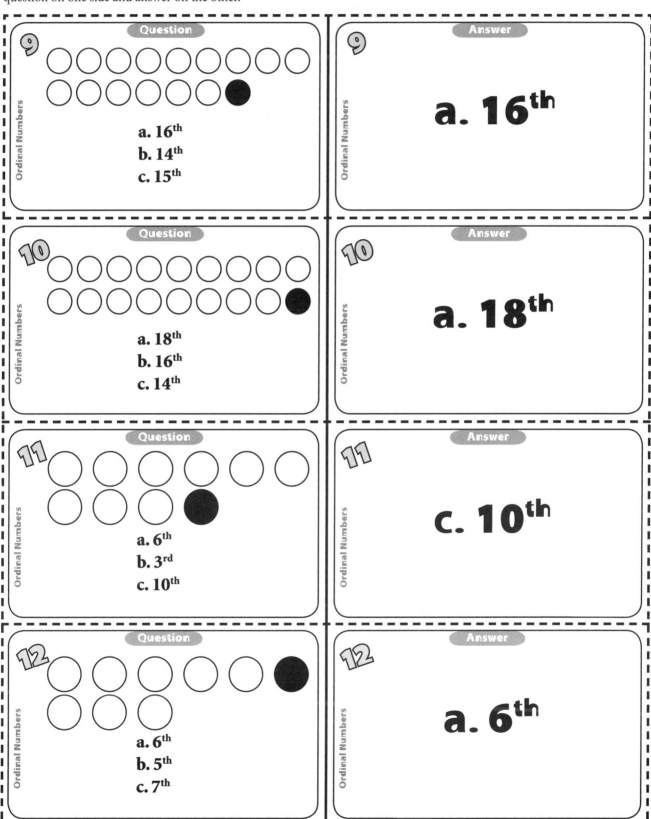

**9** Question
Ordinal Numbers

a. 16th
b. 14th
c. 15th

**9** Answer
Ordinal Numbers

a. 16th

**10** Question
Ordinal Numbers

a. 18th
b. 16th
c. 14th

**10** Answer
Ordinal Numbers

a. 18th

**11** Question
Ordinal Numbers

a. 6th
b. 3rd
c. 10th

**11** Answer
Ordinal Numbers

c. 10th

**12** Question
Ordinal Numbers

a. 6th
b. 5th
c. 7th

**12** Answer
Ordinal Numbers

a. 6th

# Ordinal Numbers

**Instructions:** Cut out each question and answer pair and fold along the line. Then, glue or tape card so each card will have the question on one side and answer on the other.

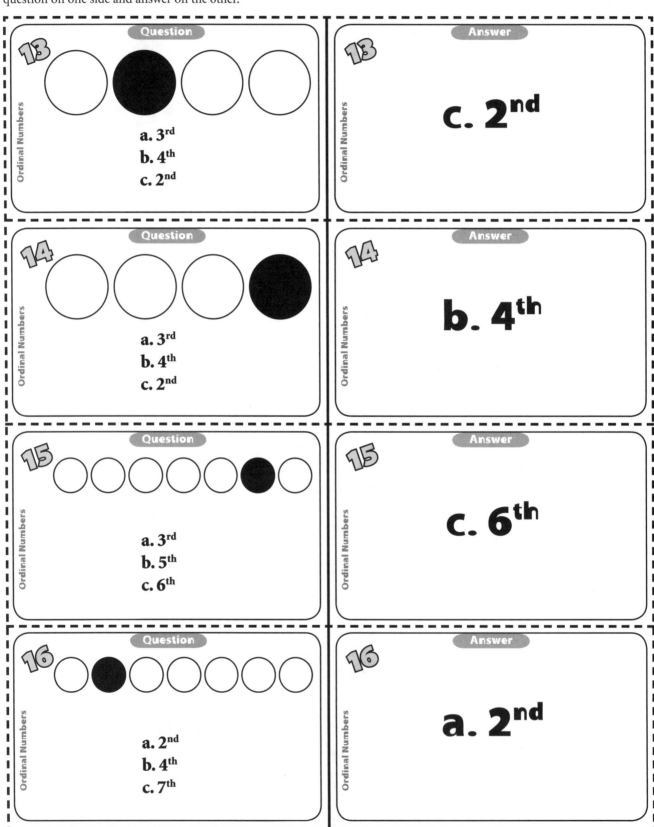

**13** Question

a. 3<sup>rd</sup>
b. 4<sup>th</sup>
c. 2<sup>nd</sup>

**13** Answer

c. 2<sup>nd</sup>

**14** Question

a. 3<sup>rd</sup>
b. 4<sup>th</sup>
c. 2<sup>nd</sup>

**14** Answer

b. 4<sup>th</sup>

**15** Question

a. 3<sup>rd</sup>
b. 5<sup>th</sup>
c. 6<sup>th</sup>

**15** Answer

c. 6<sup>th</sup>

**16** Question

a. 2<sup>nd</sup>
b. 4<sup>th</sup>
c. 7<sup>th</sup>

**16** Answer

a. 2<sup>nd</sup>

Ordinal Numbers

# Ordinal Numbers

**Instructions:** Cut out each question and answer pair and fold along the line. Then, glue or tape card so each card will have the question on one side and answer on the other.

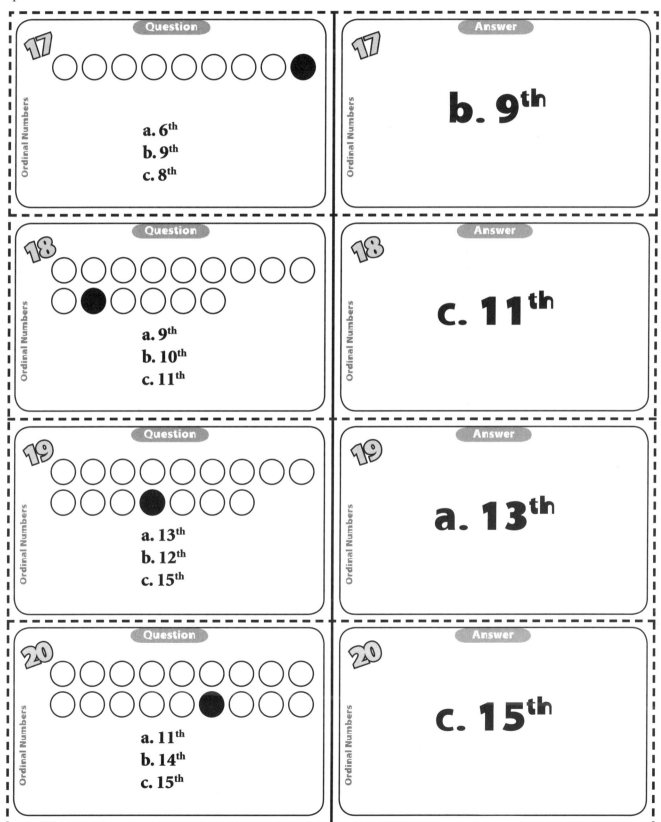

17 **Question**

a. 6th
b. 9th
c. 8th

17 **Answer**

b. 9th

18 **Question**

a. 9th
b. 10th
c. 11th

18 **Answer**

c. 11th

19 **Question**

a. 13th
b. 12th
c. 15th

19 **Answer**

a. 13th

20 **Question**

a. 11th
b. 14th
c. 15th

20 **Answer**

c. 15th

# Ordinal Numbers

**Instructions:** Cut out each question and answer pair and fold along the line. Then, glue or tape card so each card will have the question on one side and answer on the other.

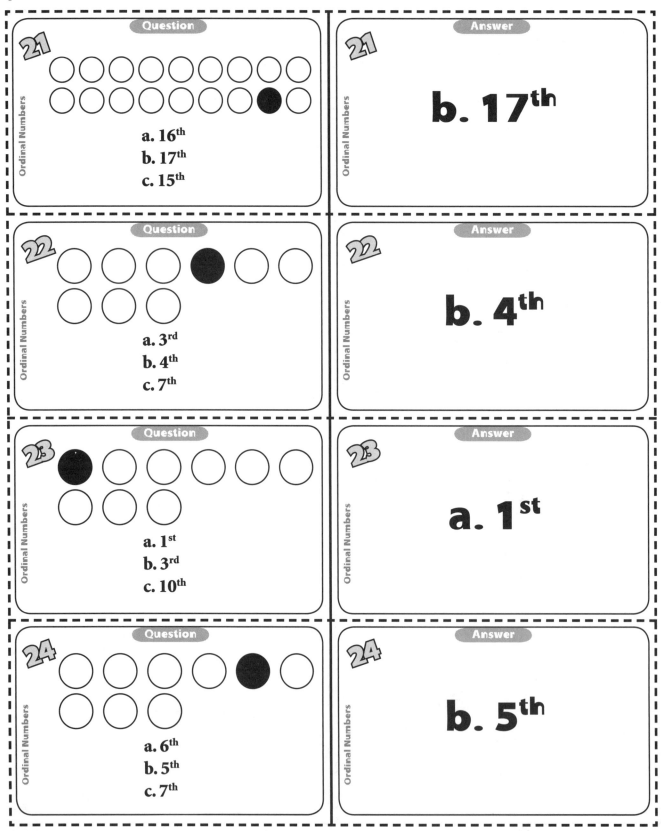

**21**
Question

Ordinal Numbers

a. 16th
b. 17th
c. 15th

**21**
Answer

Ordinal Numbers

b. 17th

**22**
Question

Ordinal Numbers

a. 3rd
b. 4th
c. 7th

**22**
Answer

Ordinal Numbers

b. 4th

**23**
Question

Ordinal Numbers

a. 1st
b. 3rd
c. 10th

**23**
Answer

Ordinal Numbers

a. 1st

**24**
Question

Ordinal Numbers

a. 6th
b. 5th
c. 7th

**24**
Answer

Ordinal Numbers

b. 5th

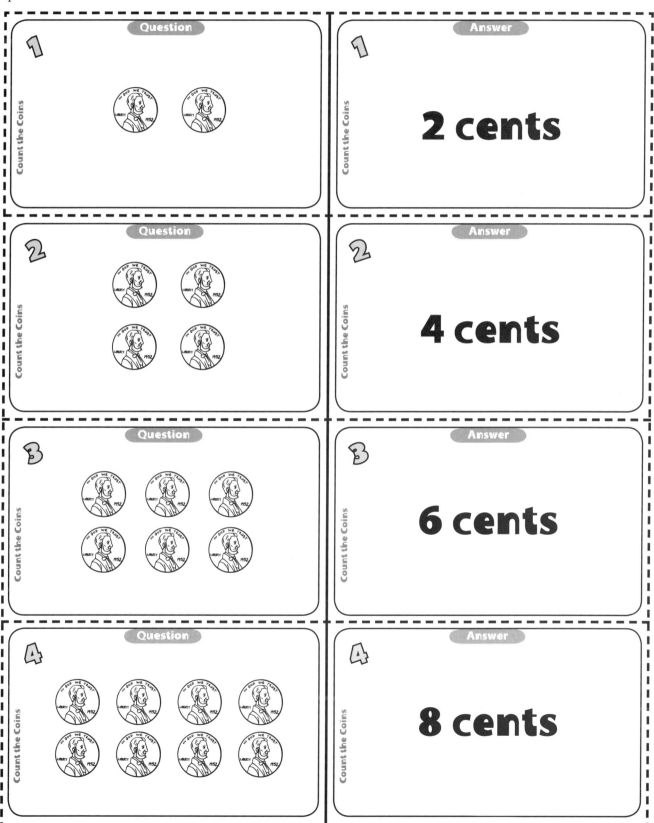

# Count the Coins

**Instructions:** Cut out each question and answer pair and fold along the line. Then, glue or tape card so each card will have the question on one side and answer on the other.

# Count the Coins

**Instructions:** Cut out each question and answer pair and fold along the line. Then, glue or tape card so each card will have the question on one side and answer on the other.

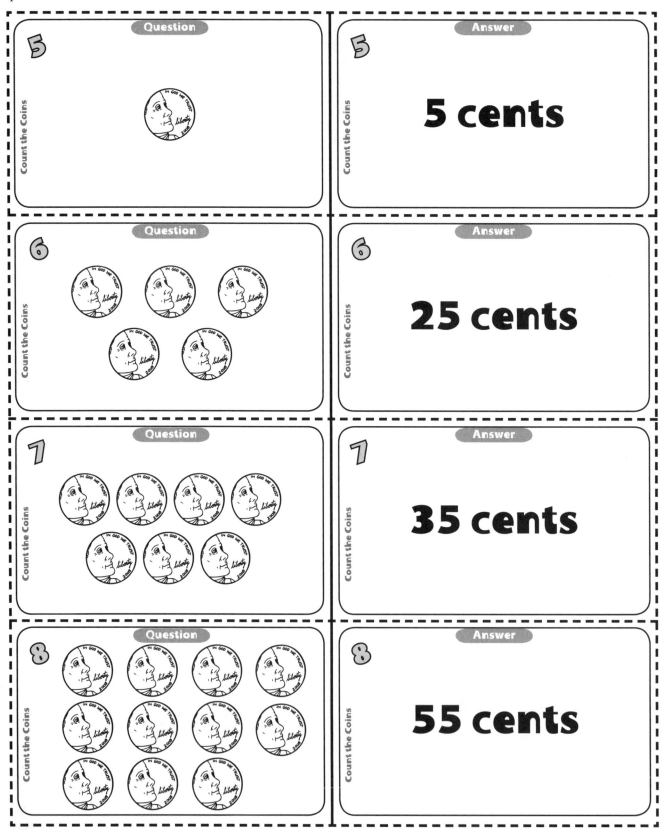

| Question | Answer |
|---|---|
| **5** Count the Coins | **5** Count the Coins **5 cents** |
| **6** Count the Coins | **6** Count the Coins **25 cents** |
| **7** Count the Coins | **7** Count the Coins **35 cents** |
| **8** Count the Coins | **8** Count the Coins **55 cents** |

# Count the Coins

**Instructions:** Cut out each question and answer pair and fold along the line. Then, glue or tape card so each card will have the question on one side and answer on the other.

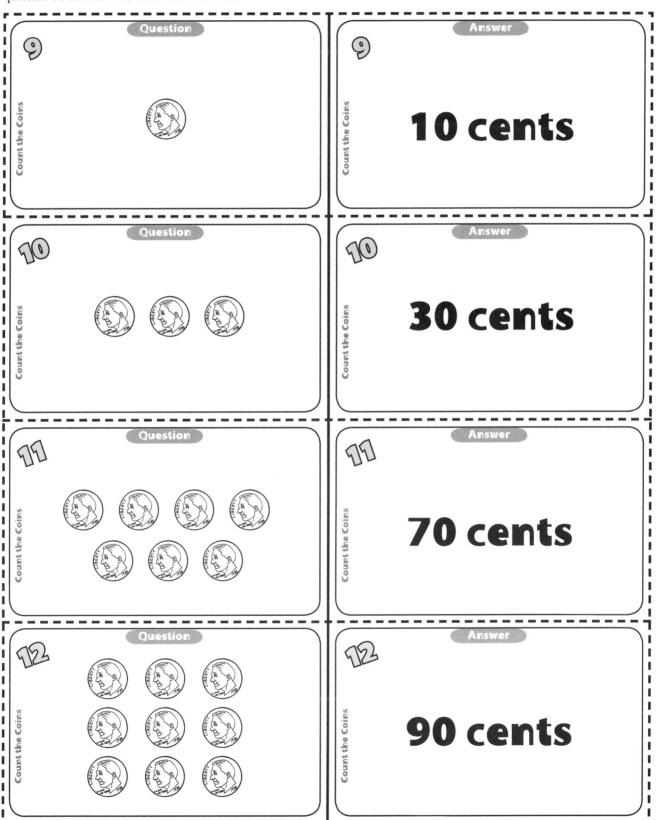

| | |
|---|---|
| **Question** 9 *Count the Coins* | **Answer** 9 *Count the Coins* **10 cents** |
| **Question** 10 *Count the Coins* | **Answer** 10 *Count the Coins* **30 cents** |
| **Question** 11 *Count the Coins* | **Answer** 11 *Count the Coins* **70 cents** |
| **Question** 12 *Count the Coins* | **Answer** 12 *Count the Coins* **90 cents** |

# Count the Coins

**Instructions:** Cut out each question and answer pair and fold along the line. Then, glue or tape card so each card will have the question on one side and answer on the other.

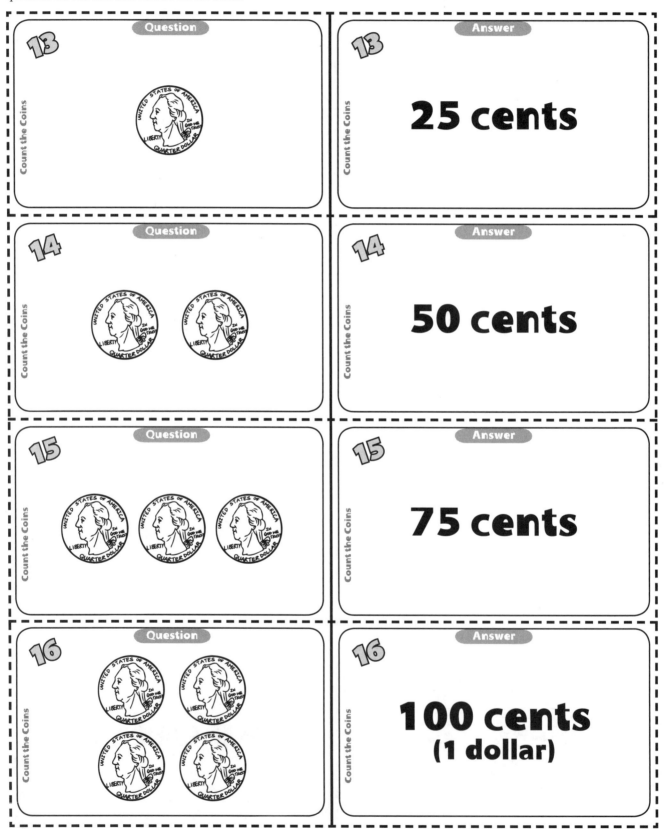

**13** Question — Count the Coins

**13** Answer — Count the Coins — **25 cents**

**14** Question — Count the Coins

**14** Answer — Count the Coins — **50 cents**

**15** Question — Count the Coins

**15** Answer — Count the Coins — **75 cents**

**16** Question — Count the Coins

**16** Answer — Count the Coins — **100 cents** (1 dollar)

# Count the Coins

**Instructions:** Cut out each question and answer pair and fold along the line. Then, glue or tape card so each card will have the question on one side and answer on the other.

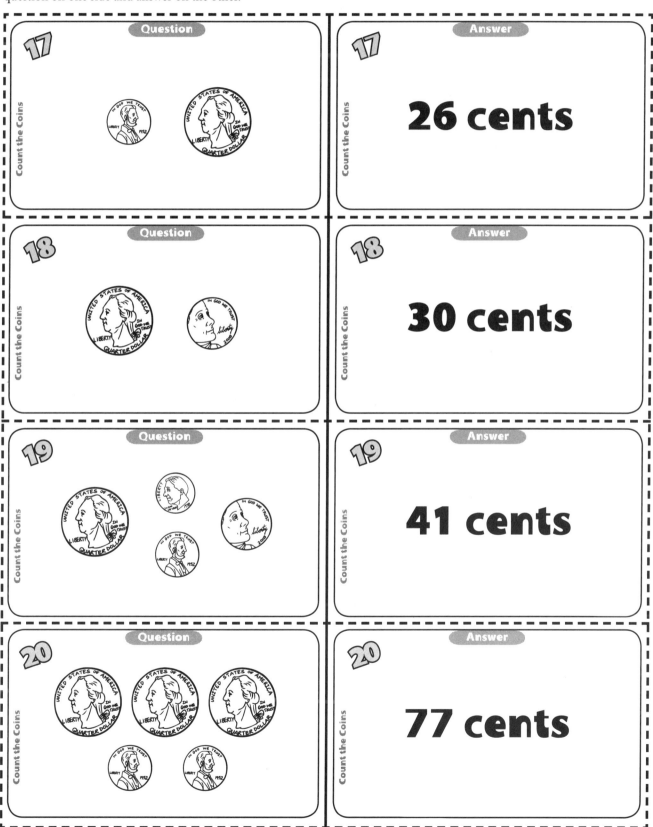

| Question 17 — Count the Coins | Answer 17 — Count the Coins |
|---|---|
| | **26 cents** |
| Question 18 — Count the Coins | Answer 18 — Count the Coins |
| | **30 cents** |
| Question 19 — Count the Coins | Answer 19 — Count the Coins |
| | **41 cents** |
| Question 20 — Count the Coins | Answer 20 — Count the Coins |
| | **77 cents** |

# Count the Coins

**Instructions:** Cut out each question and answer pair and fold along the line. Then, glue or tape card so each card will have the question on one side and answer on the other.

**21** Question — Count the Coins

**21** Answer — Count the Coins

## 65 cents

**22** Question — Count the Coins

**22** Answer — Count the Coins

## 74 cents

**23** Question — Count the Coins

**23** Answer — Count the Coins

## 86 cents

**24** Question — Count the Coins

**24** Answer — Count the Coins

## 90 cents

# Count the Coins

**Instructions:** Cut out each question and answer pair and fold along the line. Then, glue or tape card so each card will have the question on one side and answer on the other.

| Question | Answer |
|----------|--------|
| 25 — Count the Coins | 25 — Count the Coins — **20 cents** |
| 26 — Count the Coins | 26 — Count the Coins — **49 cents** |
| 27 — Count the Coins | 27 — Count the Coins — **61 cents** |
| 28 — Count the Coins | 28 — Count the Coins — **82 cents** |

# Naming Patterns

**Instructions:** Cut out each question and answer pair and fold along the line. Then, glue or tape card so each card will have the question on one side and answer on the other.

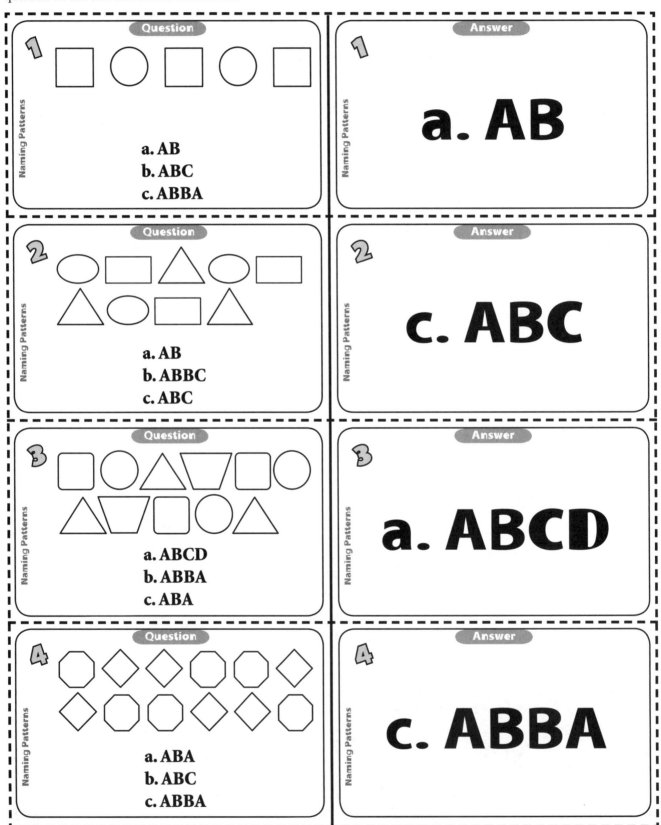

**Question 1**
Naming Patterns

a. AB
b. ABC
c. ABBA

**Answer 1**
Naming Patterns

## a. AB

**Question 2**
Naming Patterns

a. AB
b. ABBC
c. ABC

**Answer 2**
Naming Patterns

## c. ABC

**Question 3**
Naming Patterns

a. ABCD
b. ABBA
c. ABA

**Answer 3**
Naming Patterns

## a. ABCD

**Question 4**
Naming Patterns

a. ABA
b. ABC
c. ABBA

**Answer 4**
Naming Patterns

## c. ABBA

# Naming Patterns

**Instructions:** Cut out each question and answer pair and fold along the line. Then, glue or tape card so each card will have the question on one side and answer on the other.

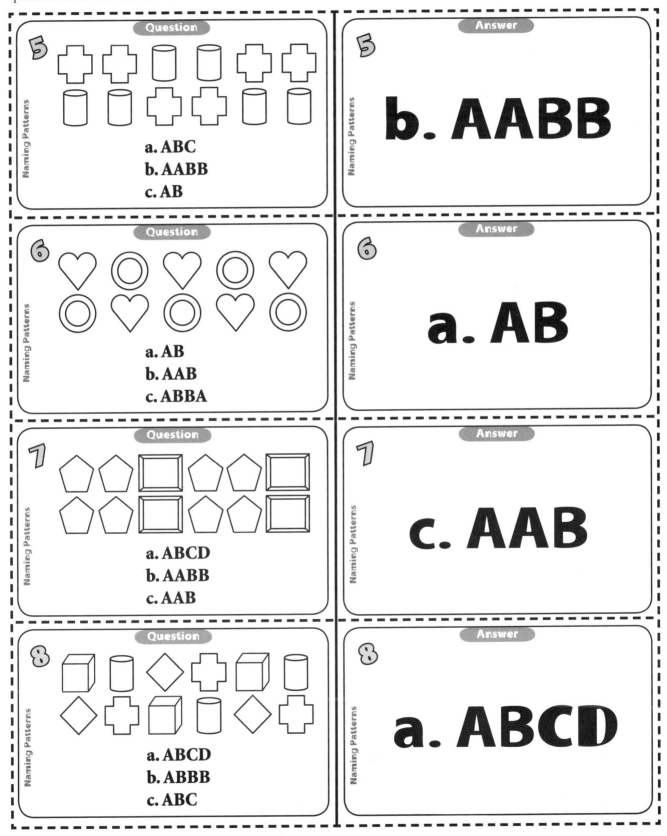

Question 5 — Naming Patterns
a. ABC
b. AABB
c. AB

Answer 5 — **b. AABB**

Question 6 — Naming Patterns
a. AB
b. AAB
c. ABBA

Answer 6 — **a. AB**

Question 7 — Naming Patterns
a. ABCD
b. AABB
c. AAB

Answer 7 — **c. AAB**

Question 8 — Naming Patterns
a. ABCD
b. ABBB
c. ABC

Answer 8 — **a. ABCD**

# Naming Patterns

**Instructions:** Cut out each question and answer pair and fold along the line. Then, glue or tape card so each card will have the question on one side and answer on the other.

**Question**

9

a. AAB
b. ABA
c. ABBC

**Answer**

9

# b. ABA

**Question**

10

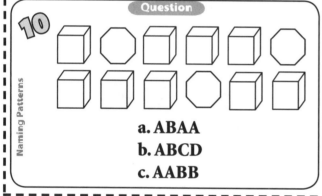

a. ABAA
b. ABCD
c. AABB

**Answer**

10

# a. ABAA

**Question**

11

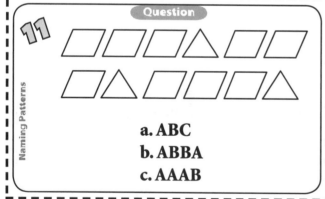

a. ABC
b. ABBA
c. AAAB

**Answer**

11

# c. AAAB

**Question**

12

a. ABCC
b. ABB
c. ABC

**Answer**

12

# a. ABCC

# Naming Patterns

**Instructions:** Cut out each question and answer pair and fold along the line. Then, glue or tape card so each card will have the question on one side and answer on the other.

**Question 13**

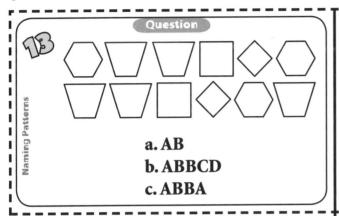

a. AB
b. ABBCD
c. ABBA

**Answer 13**

b. ABBCD

**Question 14**

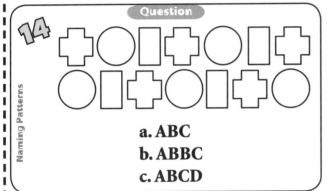

a. ABC
b. ABBC
c. ABCD

**Answer 14**

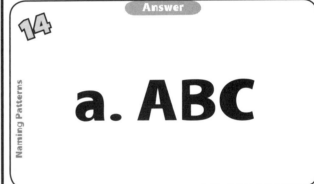

a. ABC

**Question 15**

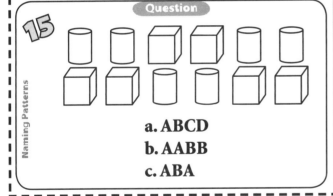

a. ABCD
b. AABB
c. ABA

**Answer 15**

b. AABB

**Question 16**

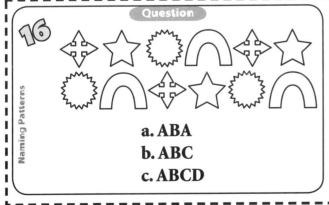

a. ABA
b. ABC
c. ABCD

**Answer 16**

c. ABCD

# Naming Patterns

**Instructions:** Cut out each question and answer pair and fold along the line. Then, glue or tape card so each card will have the question on one side and answer on the other.

---

**Question** 17

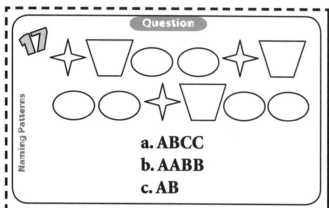

a. ABCC
b. AABB
c. AB

**Answer** 17

## a. ABCC

---

**Question** 18

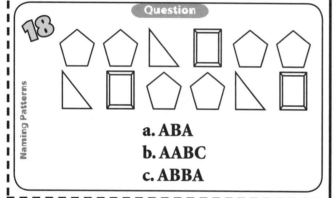

a. ABA
b. AABC
c. ABBA

**Answer** 18

## b. AABC

---

**Question** 19

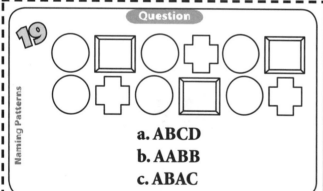

a. ABCD
b. AABB
c. ABAC

**Answer** 19

## c. ABAC

---

**Question** 20

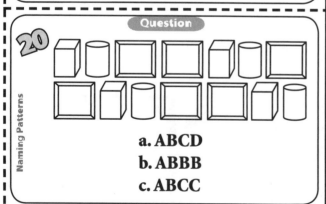

a. ABCD
b. ABBB
c. ABCC

**Answer** 20

## c. ABCC

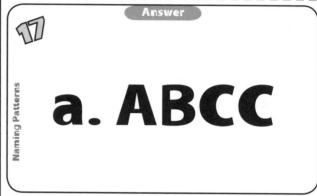

# Naming Patterns

**Instructions:** Cut out each question and answer pair and fold along the line. Then, glue or tape card so each card will have the question on one side and answer on the other.

**Question**

21

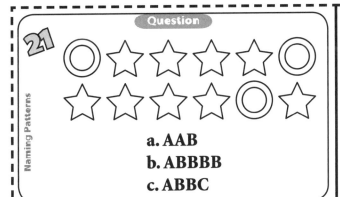

a. AAB
b. ABBBB
c. ABBC

**Answer**

21

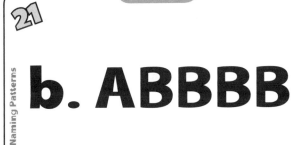

**b. ABBBB**

**Question**

22

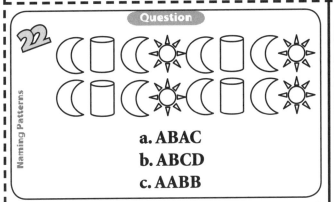

a. ABAC
b. ABCD
c. AABB

**Answer**

22

**a. ABAC**

**Question**

23

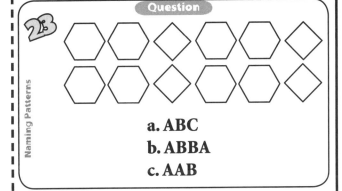

a. ABC
b. ABBA
c. AAB

**Answer**

23

**c. AAB**

**Question**

24

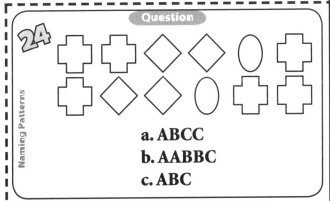

a. ABCC
b. AABBC
c. ABC

**Answer**

24

**b. AABBC**

# Properties of Addition

**Instructions:** Cut out each question and answer pair and fold along the line. Then, glue or tape card so each card will have the question on one side and answer on the other.

**Question** 1

**1** Addition Property of Equality
$8 + 4 = 12$
**Equal to:**

a. $4 + 6 = 10$
b. $8 + 4 = 12$
c. $8 + 3 = 11$

*Properties of Addition*

---

**Answer** 1

**1** b. $8 + 4 = 12$

*Properties of Addition*

---

**Question** 2

**2** Addition Property of Equality
$3 + 9 = 12$
**Equal to:**

a. $9 - 3 = 6$
b. $3 + 6 = 9$
c. $3 + 9 = 12$

*Properties of Addition*

---

**Answer** 2

**2** c. $3 + 9 = 12$

*Properties of Addition*

---

**Question** 3

**3** Addition Property of Equality
$9 + 4 = 13$
**Equal to:**

a. $9 - 3 = 6$
b. $9 + 4 = 13$
c. $8 + 6 = 14$

*Properties of Addition*

---

**Answer** 3

**3** b. $9 + 4 = 13$

*Properties of Addition*

---

**Question** 4

**4** Addition Property of Equality
$2 + 3 = 5$
**Equal to:**

a. $2 + 3 = 5$
b. $5 - 4 = 1$
c. $3 + 5 = 8$

*Properties of Addition*

---

**Answer** 4

**4** a. $2 + 3 = 5$

*Properties of Addition*

# Properties of Addition

**Instructions:** Cut out each question and answer pair and fold along the line. Then, glue or tape card so each card will have the question on one side and answer on the other.

---

**Question 5**

**Addition Property of Equality**

$6 + 5 = 11$

**Equal to:**

a. $5 + 4 = 9$
b. $6 + 5 = 11$
c. $6 + 2 = 8$

*Properties of Addition*

**Answer 5**

$$b. \; 6 + 5 = 11$$

*Properties of Addition*

---

**Question 6**

**Addition Property of Equality**

$5 + 4 = 9$

**Equal to:**

a. $6 + 4 = 10$
b. $9 + 4 = 13$
c. $5 + 4 = 9$

*Properties of Addition*

**Answer 6**

$$c. \; 5 + 4 = 9$$

*Properties of Addition*

---

**Question 7**

**Addition Property of Equality**

$7 + 5 = 12$

**Equal to:**

a. $7 + 5 = 12$
b. $12 + 5 = 17$
c. $5 + 5 = 10$

*Properties of Addition*

**Answer 7**

$$a. \; 7 + 5 = 12$$

*Properties of Addition*

---

**Question 8**

**Addition Property of Equality**

$10 + 2 = 12$

**Equal to:**

a. $4 + 8 = 12$
b. $10 + 1 = 11$
c. $10 + 2 = 12$

*Properties of Addition*

**Answer 8**

$$c. \; 10 + 2 = 12$$

*Properties of Addition*

---

# Properties of Addition

**Instructions:** Cut out each question and answer pair and fold along the line. Then, glue or tape card so each card will have the question on one side and answer on the other.

| | |
|---|---|
| **9** **Question** | **9** **Answer** |
| **Adding 0 Property** $$4 + 0 =$$ a. 4 b. 0 c. 10 | # a. 4 |
| **10** **Question** | **10** **Answer** |
| **Adding 0 Property** $$0 + 1 =$$ a. 0 b. 6 c. 1 | # c. 1 |
| **11** **Question** | **11** **Answer** |
| **Adding 0 Property** $$15 + 0 =$$ a. 15 b. 0 c. 7 | # a. 15 |
| **12** **Question** | **12** **Answer** |
| **Adding 0 Property** $$0 + 12 =$$ a. 9 b. 12 c. 10 | # b. 12 |

*Properties of Addition* (side labels on each card)

# Properties of Addition

**Instructions:** Cut out each question and answer pair and fold along the line. Then, glue or tape card so each card will have the question on one side and answer on the other.

**Question**

**13**

*Properties of Addition*

### Order Property of Addition
3 + 6 = 9
**Same As:**

a. 6 + 9 = 15
b. 3 + 9 = 12
c. 6 + 3 = 9

---

**Answer**

**13**

*Properties of Addition*

## c. 6 + 3 = 9

---

**Question**

**14**

*Properties of Addition*

### Order Property of Addition
5 + 4 = 9
**Same As:**

a. 4 + 5 = 9
b. 9 + 4 = 13
c. 2 + 9 = 11

---

**Answer**

**14**

*Properties of Addition*

## a. 4 + 5 = 9

---

**Question**

**15**

*Properties of Addition*

### Order Property of Addition
2 + 9 = 11
**Same As:**

a. 11 + 2 = 13
b. 9 + 2 = 11
c. 2 + 9 = 11

---

**Answer**

**15**

*Properties of Addition*

## b. 9 + 2 = 11

---

**Question**

**16**

*Properties of Addition*

### Order Property of Addition
7 + 5 = 12
**Same As:**

a. 5 + 7 = 12
b. 7 + 12 = 19
c. 5 + 5 = 10

---

**Answer**

**16**

*Properties of Addition*

## a. 5 + 7 = 12

---

# Properties of Addition

**Instructions:** Cut out each question and answer pair and fold along the line. Then, glue or tape card so each card will have the question on one side and answer on the other.

---

**17** Question

### Order Property of Addition
$$5 + 3 = 8$$
**Same As:**

a. $8 + 3 = 11$
b. $3 + 3 = 6$
c. $3 + 5 = 8$

*Properties of Addition*

---

**17** Answer

## c. $3 + 5 = 8$

*Properties of Addition*

---

**18** Question

### Order Property of Addition
$$4 + 6 = 10$$
**Same As:**

a. $6 + 4 = 10$
b. $10 + 4 = 14$
c. $4 + 10 = 14$

*Properties of Addition*

---

**18** Answer

## a. $6 + 4 = 10$

*Properties of Addition*

---

**19** Question

### Order Property of Addition
$$7 + 6 = 13$$
**Same As:**

a. $13 + 6 = 19$
b. $6 + 7 = 13$
c. $7 + 6 = 13$

*Properties of Addition*

---

**19** Answer

## b. $6 + 7 = 13$

*Properties of Addition*

---

**20** Question

### Order Property of Addition
$$8 + 2 = 10$$
**Same As:**

a. $2 + 10 = 12$
b. $8 + 10 = 18$
c. $2 + 8 = 10$

*Properties of Addition*

---

**20** Answer

## c. $2 + 8 = 10$

*Properties of Addition*

---

# Properties of Addition

**Instructions:** Cut out each question and answer pair and fold along the line. Then, glue or tape card so each card will have the question on one side and answer on the other.

---

**21** Question

*Properties of Addition*

## Adding 0 Property

$9 + 0 =$

a. 9
b. 0
c. 10

**21** Answer

*Properties of Addition*

## a. 9

---

**22** Question

*Properties of Addition*

## Adding 0 Property

$0 + 6 =$

a. 0
b. 6
c. 8

**22** Answer

*Properties of Addition*

## b. 6

---

**23** Question

*Properties of Addition*

## Adding 0 Property

$7 + 0 =$

a. 8
b. 0
c. 7

**23** Answer

*Properties of Addition*

## c. 7

---

**24** Question

*Properties of Addition*

## Adding 0 Property

$0 + 9 =$

a. 9
b. 0
c. 10

**24** Answer

*Properties of Addition*

## a. 9

---

# Relative Position

**Instructions:** Cut out each question and answer pair and fold along the line. Then, glue or tape card so each card will have the question on one side and answer on the other.

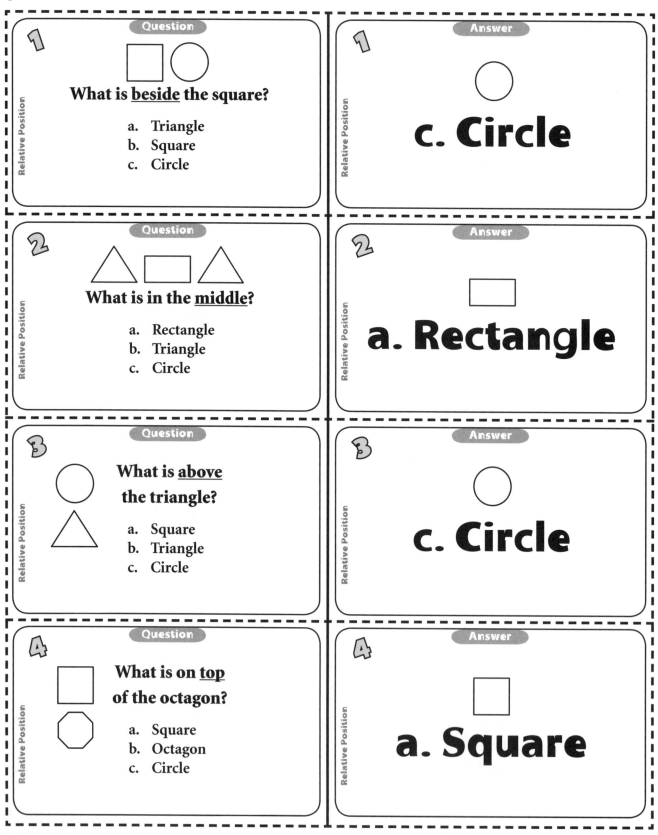

# Relative Position

**Instructions:** Cut out each question and answer pair and fold along the line. Then, glue or tape card so each card will have the question on one side and answer on the other.

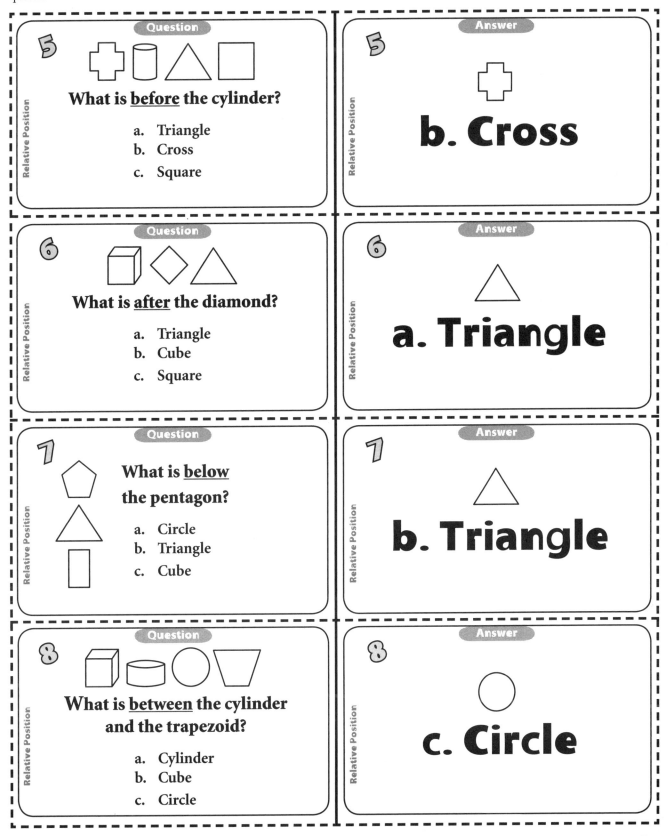

**5** **Question**

What is **before** the cylinder?

a. Triangle
b. Cross
c. Square

**5** **Answer**

b. Cross

**6** **Question**

What is **after** the diamond?

a. Triangle
b. Cube
c. Square

**6** **Answer**

a. Triangle

**7** **Question**

What is **below** the pentagon?

a. Circle
b. Triangle
c. Cube

**7** **Answer**

b. Triangle

**8** **Question**

What is **between** the cylinder and the trapezoid?

a. Cylinder
b. Cube
c. Circle

**8** **Answer**

c. Circle

Relative Position

# Relative Position

**Instructions:** Cut out each question and answer pair and fold along the line. Then, glue or tape card so each card will have the question on one side and answer on the other.

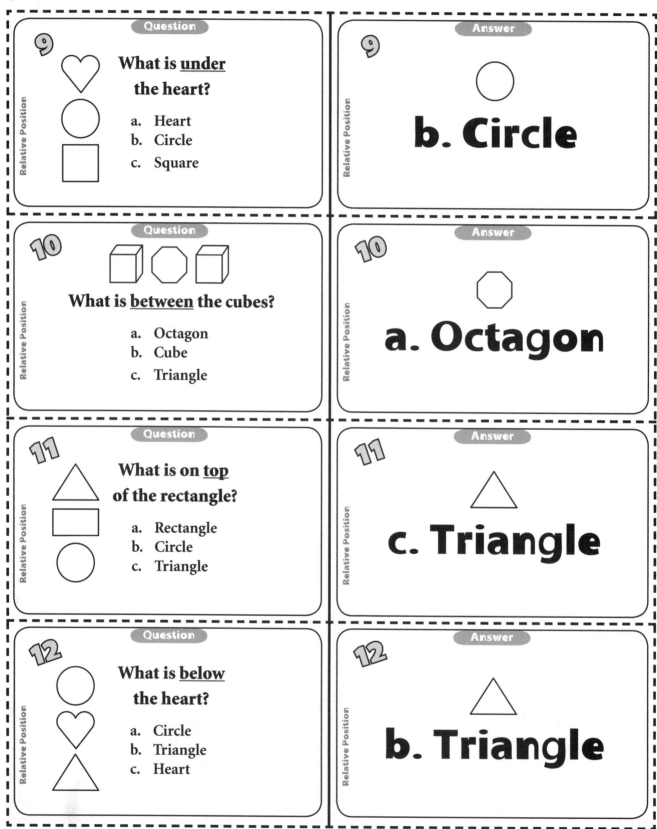

**Question 9**

What is <u>under</u> the heart?

a. Heart
b. Circle
c. Square

**Answer 9**

b. Circle

**Question 10**

What is <u>between</u> the cubes?

a. Octagon
b. Cube
c. Triangle

**Answer 10**

a. Octagon

**Question 11**

What is on <u>top</u> of the rectangle?

a. Rectangle
b. Circle
c. Triangle

**Answer 11**

c. Triangle

**Question 12**

What is <u>below</u> the heart?

a. Circle
b. Triangle
c. Heart

**Answer 12**

b. Triangle

# Relative Position

**Instructions:** Cut out each question and answer pair and fold along the line. Then, glue or tape card so each card will have the question on one side and answer on the other.

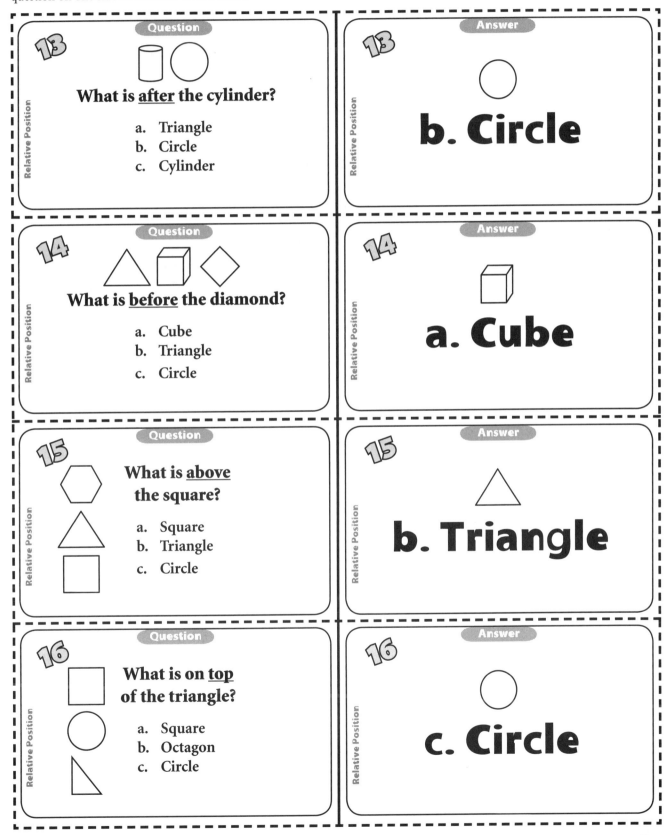

**13** Question

What is <u>after</u> the cylinder?

a. Triangle
b. Circle
c. Cylinder

**13** Answer

b. Circle

**14** Question

What is <u>before</u> the diamond?

a. Cube
b. Triangle
c. Circle

**14** Answer

a. Cube

**15** Question

What is <u>above</u> the square?

a. Square
b. Triangle
c. Circle

**15** Answer

b. Triangle

**16** Question

What is on <u>top</u> of the triangle?

a. Square
b. Octagon
c. Circle

**16** Answer

c. Circle

# Relative Position

**Instructions:** Cut out each question and answer pair and fold along the line. Then, glue or tape card so each card will have the question on one side and answer on the other.

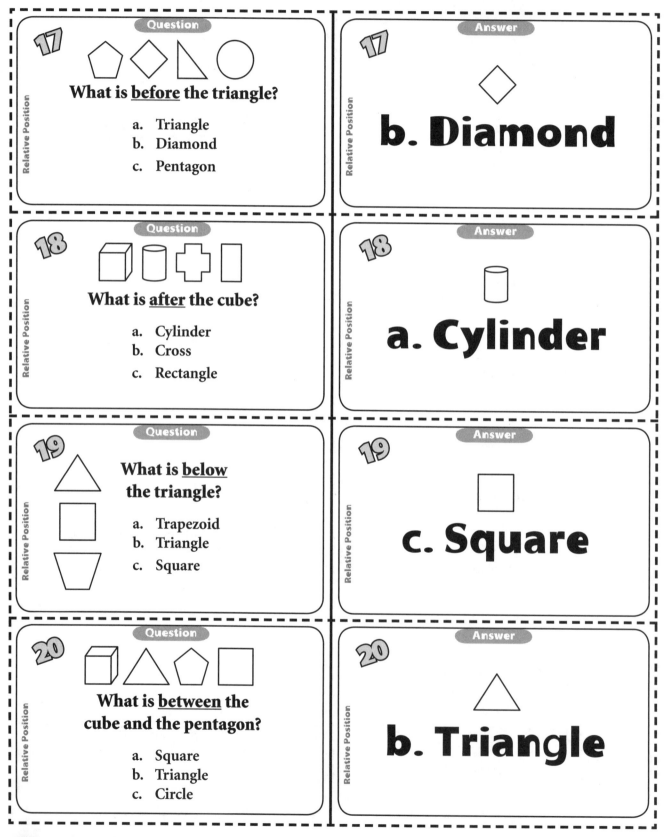

**17** Question

What is <u>before</u> the triangle?

    a.  Triangle
    b.  Diamond
    c.  Pentagon

**17** Answer

**b. Diamond**

**18** Question

What is <u>after</u> the cube?

    a.  Cylinder
    b.  Cross
    c.  Rectangle

**18** Answer

**a. Cylinder**

**19** Question

What is <u>below</u> the triangle?

    a.  Trapezoid
    b.  Triangle
    c.  Square

**19** Answer

**c. Square**

**20** Question

What is <u>between</u> the cube and the pentagon?

    a.  Square
    b.  Triangle
    c.  Circle

**20** Answer

**b. Triangle**

# Relative Position

**Instructions:** Cut out each question and answer pair and fold along the line. Then, glue or tape card so each card will have the question on one side and answer on the other.

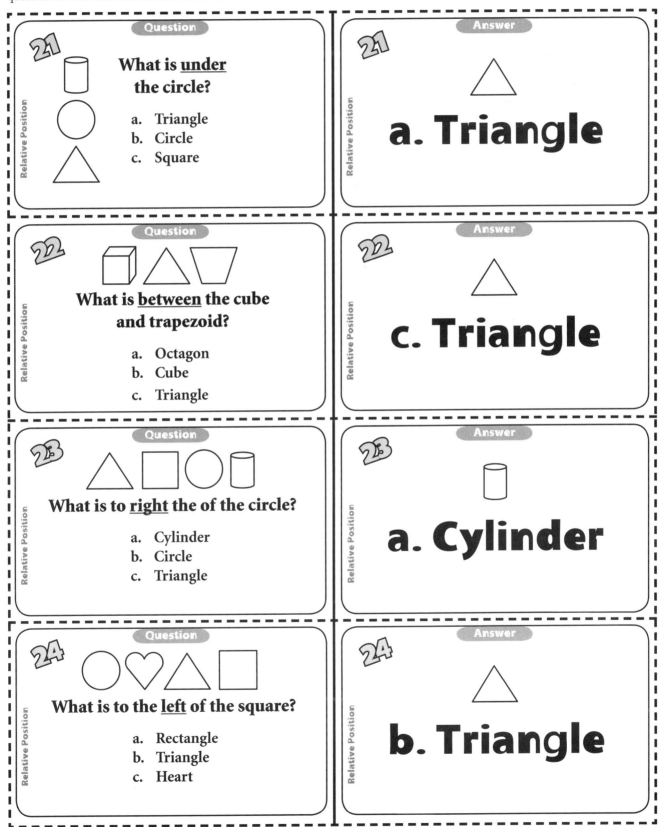

**Relative Position**

**21 Question**

What is <u>under</u> the circle?

a. Triangle
b. Circle
c. Square

**21 Answer**

a. Triangle

**22 Question**

What is <u>between</u> the cube and trapezoid?

a. Octagon
b. Cube
c. Triangle

**22 Answer**

c. Triangle

**23 Question**

What is to <u>right</u> the of the circle?

a. Cylinder
b. Circle
c. Triangle

**23 Answer**

a. Cylinder

**24 Question**

What is to the <u>left</u> of the square?

a. Rectangle
b. Triangle
c. Heart

**24 Answer**

b. Triangle

# Transformations

**Instructions:** Cut out each question and answer pair and fold along the line. Then, glue or tape card so each card will have the question on one side and answer on the other.

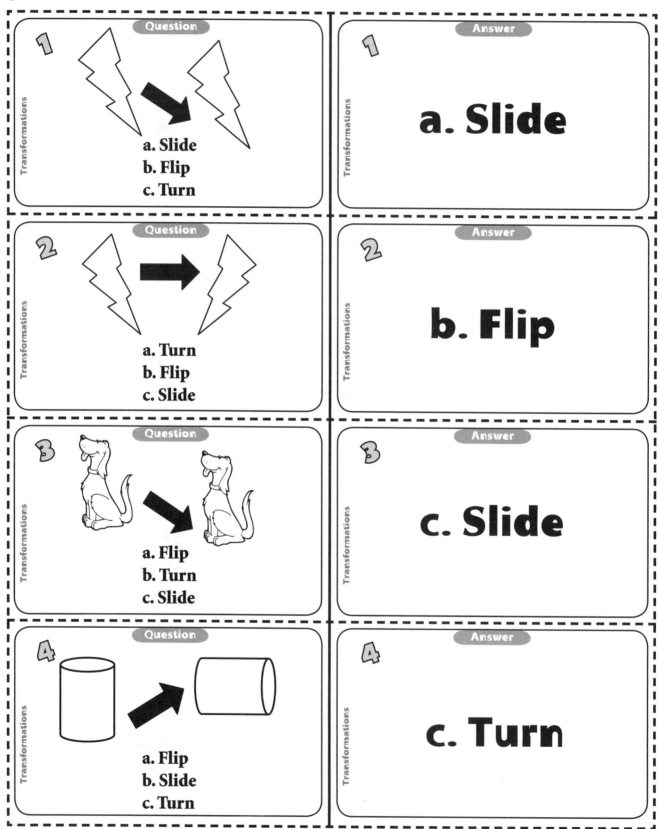

# Transformations

**Instructions:** Cut out each question and answer pair and fold along the line. Then, glue or tape card so each card will have the question on one side and answer on the other.

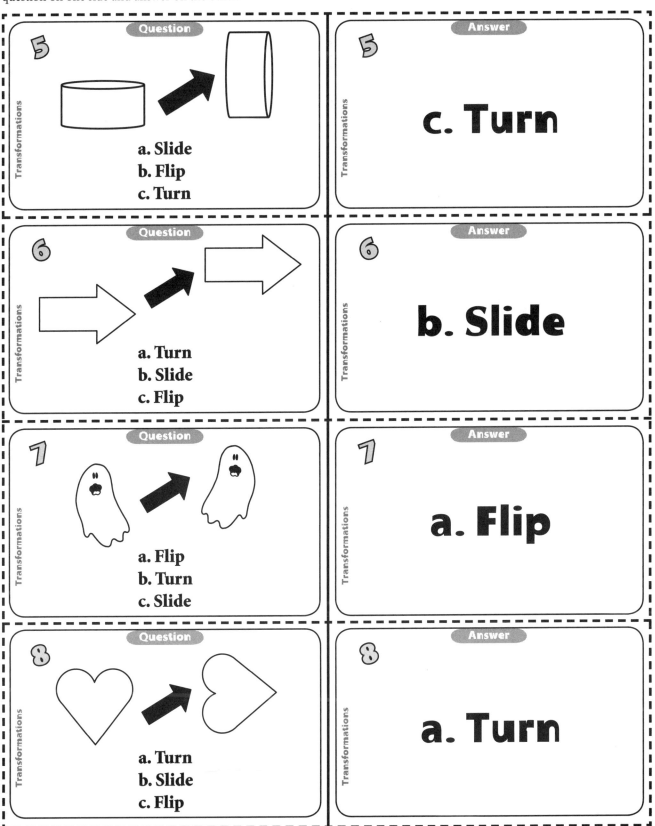

# Transformations

**Instructions:** Cut out each question and answer pair and fold along the line. Then, glue or tape card so each card will have the question on one side and answer on the other.

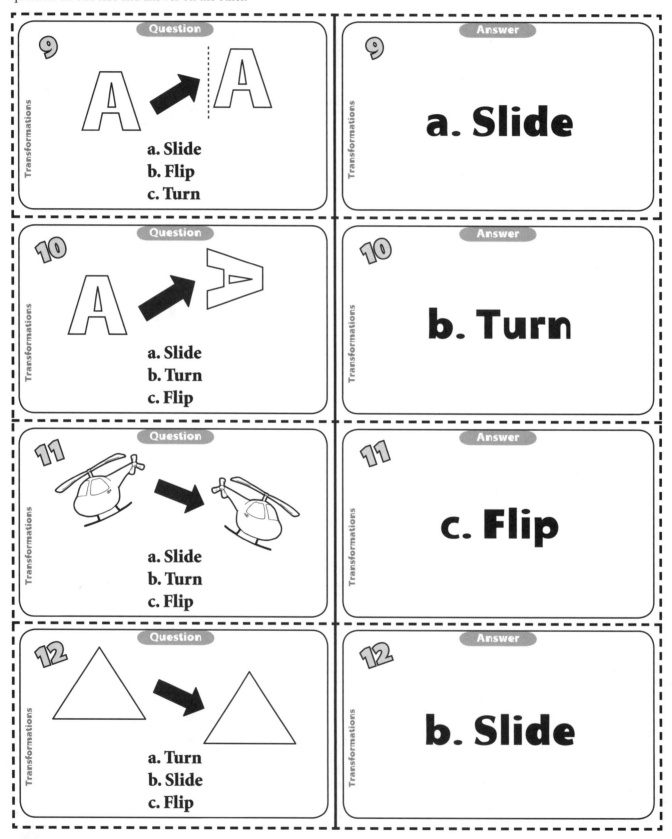

# Transformations

**Instructions:** Cut out each question and answer pair and fold along the line. Then, glue or tape card so each card will have the question on one side and answer on the other.

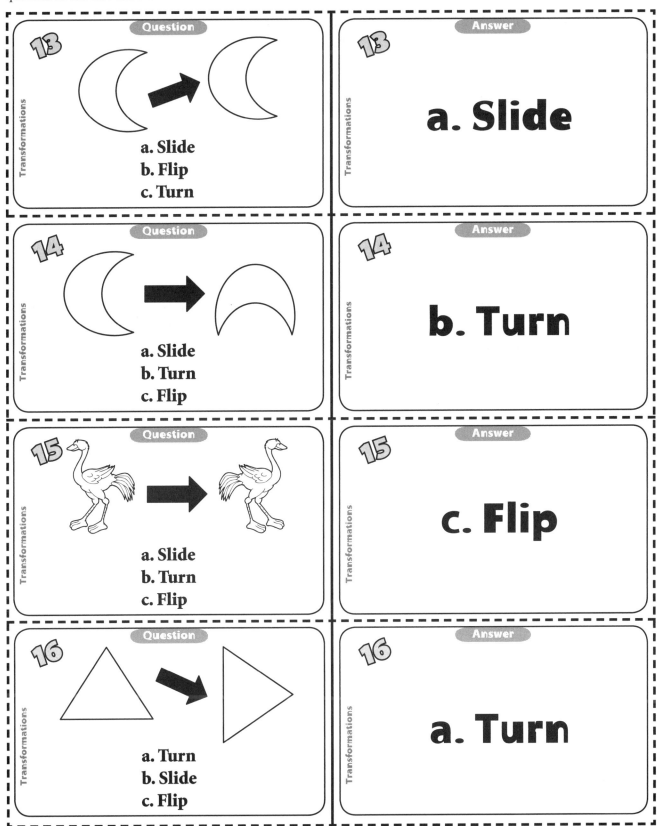

**Question 13** — Transformations

a. Slide
b. Flip
c. Turn

**Answer 13** — Transformations

## a. Slide

**Question 14** — Transformations

a. Slide
b. Turn
c. Flip

**Answer 14** — Transformations

## b. Turn

**Question 15** — Transformations

a. Slide
b. Turn
c. Flip

**Answer 15** — Transformations

## c. Flip

**Question 16** — Transformations

a. Turn
b. Slide
c. Flip

**Answer 16** — Transformations

## a. Turn

# Transformations

**Instructions:** Cut out each question and answer pair and fold along the line. Then, glue or tape card so each card will have the question on one side and answer on the other.

**17** Question

a. Slide
b. Flip
c. Turn

**17** Answer

**b. Flip**

**18** Question

a. Slide
b. Turn
c. Flip

**18** Answer

**a. Slide**

**19** Question

a. Slide
b. Flip
c. Turn

**19** Answer

**c. Turn**

**20** Question

a. Turn
b. Slide
c. Flip

**20** Answer

**a. Turn**

# Transformations

**Instructions:** Cut out each question and answer pair and fold along the line. Then, glue or tape card so each card will have the question on one side and answer on the other.

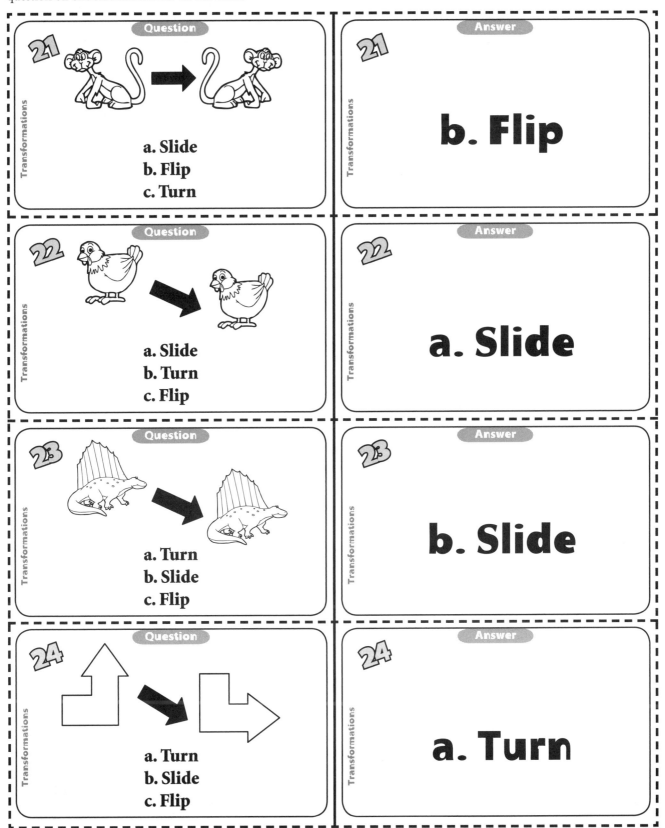

# Measurement

**Instructions:** Cut out each question and answer pair and fold along the line. Then, glue or tape card so each card will have the question on one side and answer on the other.

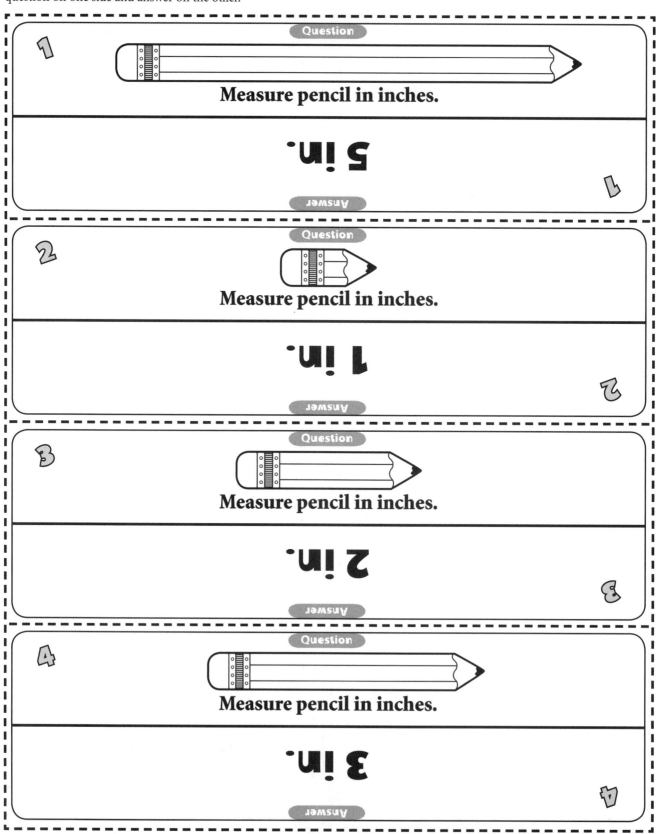

**1**

Question

Measure pencil in inches.

5 in.

Answer

**1**

**2**

Question

Measure pencil in inches.

1 in.

Answer

**2**

**3**

Question

Measure pencil in inches.

2 in.

Answer

**3**

**4**

Question

Measure pencil in inches.

3 in.

Answer

**4**

# Measurement

**Instructions:** Cut out each question and answer pair and fold along the line. Then, glue or tape card so each card will have the question on one side and answer on the other.

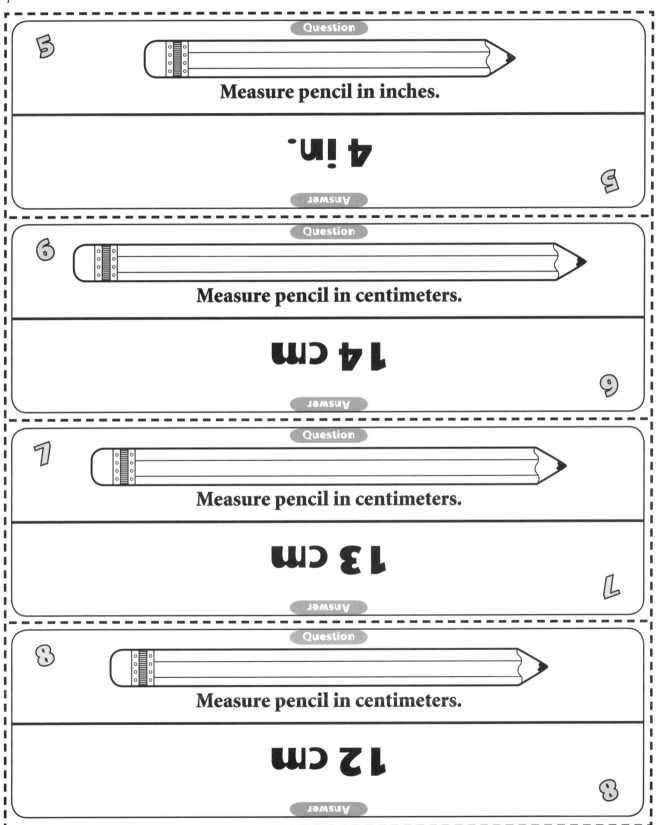

5

**Question**

Measure pencil in inches.

4 in.

**Answer**

5

6

**Question**

Measure pencil in centimeters.

14 cm

**Answer**

6

7

**Question**

Measure pencil in centimeters.

13 cm

**Answer**

7

8

**Question**

Measure pencil in centimeters.

12 cm

**Answer**

8

# Measurement

**Instructions:** Cut out each question and answer pair and fold along the line. Then, glue or tape card so each card will have the question on one side and answer on the other.

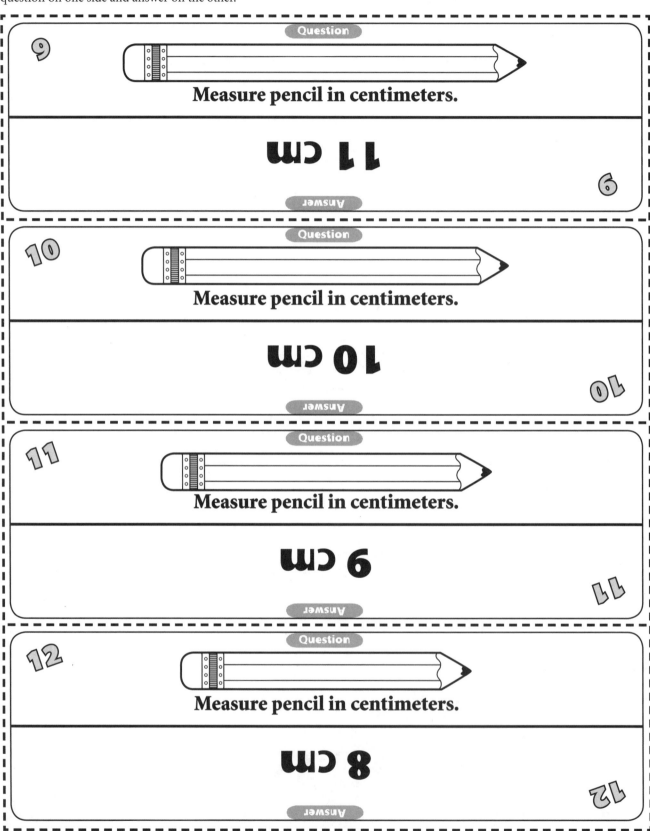

9

**Question**

Measure pencil in centimeters.

11 cm

**Answer**

6

10

**Question**

Measure pencil in centimeters.

10 cm

**Answer**

10

11

**Question**

Measure pencil in centimeters.

9 cm

**Answer**

11

12

**Question**

Measure pencil in centimeters.

8 cm

**Answer**

12

# Measurement

**Instructions:** Cut out each question and answer pair and fold along the line. Then, glue or tape card so each card will have the question on one side and answer on the other.

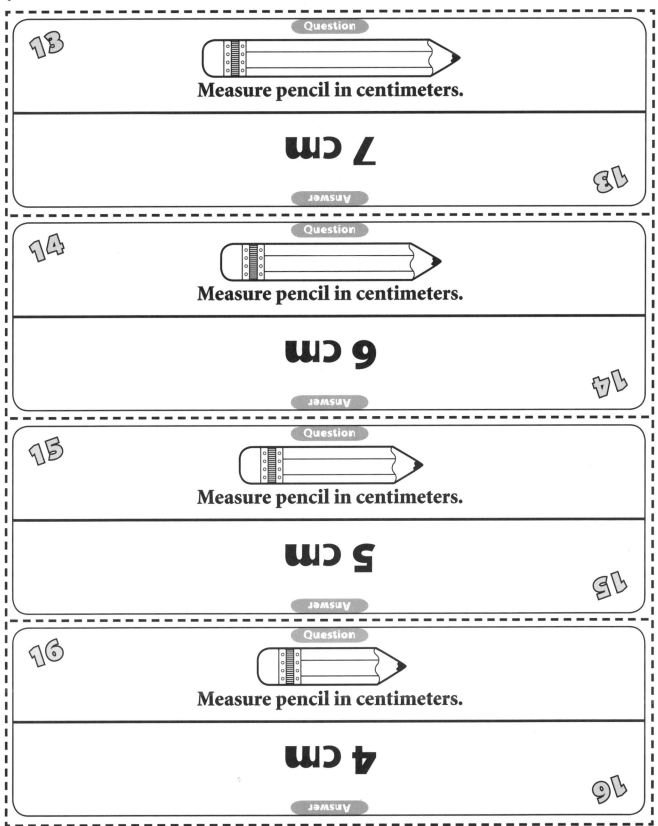

13
**Question**
Measure pencil in centimeters.
7 cm
13
**Answer**

14
**Question**
Measure pencil in centimeters.
6 cm
14
**Answer**

15
**Question**
Measure pencil in centimeters.
5 cm
15
**Answer**

16
**Question**
Measure pencil in centimeters.
4 cm
16
**Answer**

# Measurement

**Instructions:** Cut out each question and answer pair and fold along the line. Then, glue or tape card so each card will have the question on one side and answer on the other.

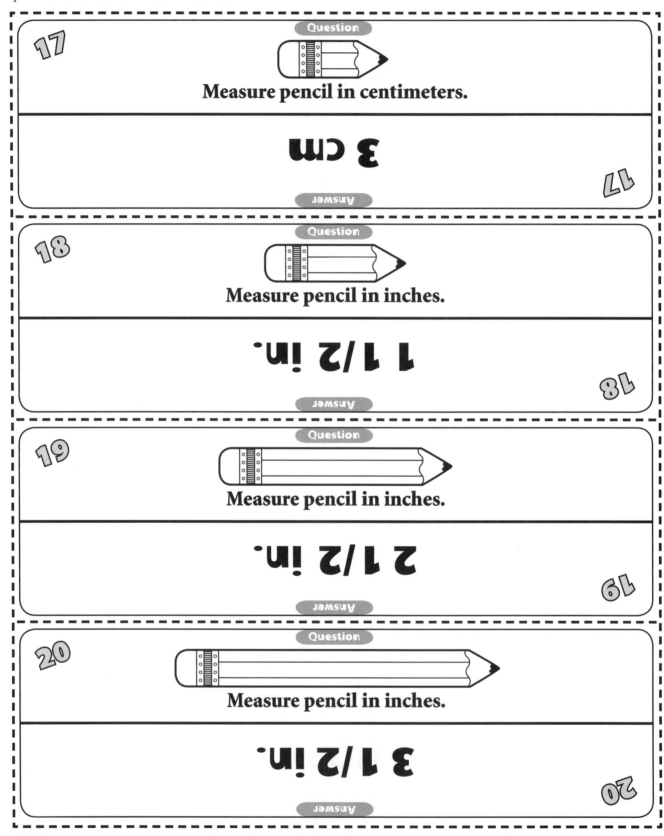

**17**

Question

Measure pencil in centimeters.

3 cm

17

Answer

**18**

Question

Measure pencil in inches.

1 1/2 in.

18

Answer

**19**

Question

Measure pencil in inches.

2 1/2 in.

19

Answer

**20**

Question

Measure pencil in inches.

3 1/2 in.

20

Answer

# Measurement

**Instructions:** Cut out each question and answer pair and fold along the line. Then, glue or tape card so each card will have the question on one side and answer on the other.

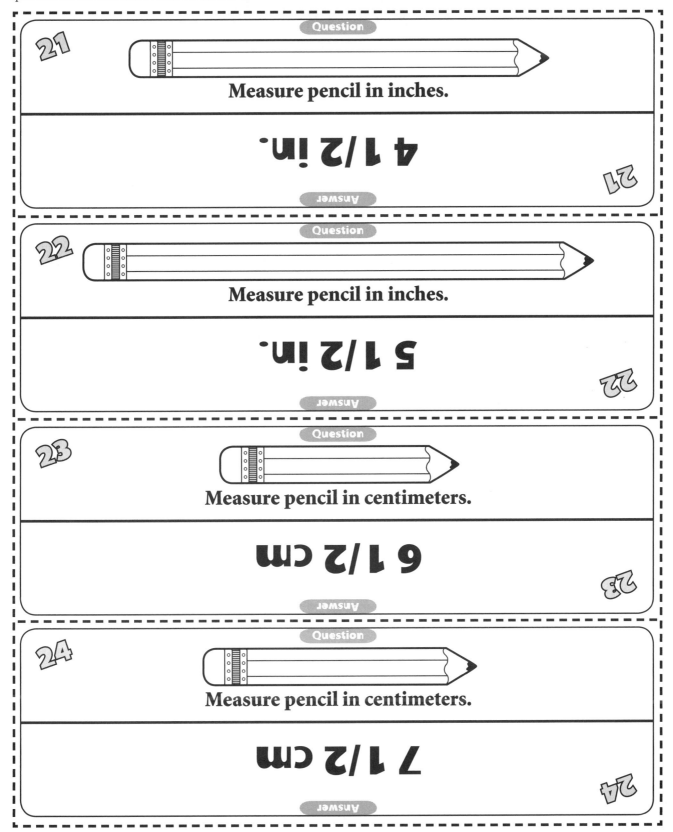

21

Question

Measure pencil in inches.

4 1/2 in.

Answer

21

22

Question

Measure pencil in inches.

5 1/2 in.

Answer

22

23

Question

Measure pencil in centimeters.

6 1/2 cm

Answer

23

24

Question

Measure pencil in centimeters.

7 1/2 cm

Answer

24

# Fan-N-Pick Answer Key

## 1.1 Base Ten Blocks

1. 3
2. 4
3. 5
4. 6
5. 7
6. 8
7. 9
8. 10
9. 20
10. 30
11. 40
12. 50
13. 60
14. 70
15. 80
16. 90
17. 12
18. 15
19. 17
20. 29
21. 37
22. 31
23. 43
24. 46
25. 55
26. 52
27. 68
28. 65
29. 23
30. 36
31. 34
32. 100

## 1.2 Ordinal Numbers

1. a. 1st
2. a. 3rd
3. b. 5th
4. c. 7th
5. c. 8th
6. b. 10th
7. b. 12th
8. b. 14th
9. a. 16th
10. a. 18th
11. c. 10th
12. a. 6th
13. c. 2nd
14. b. 4th
15. c. 6th
16. a. 2nd
17. b. 9th
18. c. 11th
19. a. 13th
20. c. 15th
21. b. 17th
22. b. 4th
23. a. 1st
24. b. 5th

# Fan-N-Pick Answer Key

## 1.3 Count the Coins

1. 2 cents
2. 4 cents
3. 6 cents
4. 8 cents
5. 5 cents
6. 25 cents
7. 35 cents
8. 55 cents
9. 10 cents
10. 30 cents
11. 70 cents
12. 90 cents
13. 25 cents
14. 50 cents
15. 75 cents
16. 100 cents (1 dollar)
17. 26 cents
18. 30 cents
19. 41 cents
20. 77 cents
21. 65 cents
22. 74 cents
23. 86 cents
24. 90 cents
25. 20 cents
26. 49 cents
27. 61 cents
28. 82 cents

## 1.4 Naming Patterns

1. a. AB
2. c. ABC
3. a. ABCD
4. c. ABBA
5. b. AABB
6. a. AB
7. c. AAB
8. a. ABCD
9. b. ABA
10. a. ABAA
11. c. AAAB
12. a. ABCC
13. b. ABBCD
14. a. ABC
15. b. AABB
16. c. ABCD
17. a. ABCC
18. b. AABC
19. c. ABAC
20. c. ABCC
21. b. ABBBB
22. a. ABAC
23. c. AAB
24. b. AABBC

# Fan-N-Pick Answer Key

## 1.5 Properties of Addition

1. b. 8 + 4 = 12
2. c. 3 + 9 = 12
3. b. 9 + 4 = 13
4. a. 2 + 3 = 5
5. b. 6 + 5 = 11
6. c. 5 + 4 = 9
7. a. 7 + 5 = 12
8. c. 10 + 2 = 12
9. a. 4
10. c. 1
11. a. 15
12. b. 12
13. c. 6 + 3 = 9
14. a. 4 + 5 = 9
15. b. 9 + 2 = 11
16. a. 5 + 7 = 12
17. c. 3 + 5 = 8
18. a. 6 + 4 = 10
19. b. 6 + 7 = 13
20. c. 2 + 8 = 10
21. a. 9
22. b. 6
23. c. 7
24. a. 9

## 1.6 Relative Position

1. c. Circle
2. a. Rectangle
3. c. Circle
4. a. Square
5. b. Cross
6. a. Triangle
7. b. Triangle
8. c. Circle
9. b. Circle
10. a. Octagon
11. c. Triangle
12. b. Triangle
13. b. Circle
14. a. Cube
15. b. Triangle
16. c. Circle
17. b. Diamond
18. a. Cylinder
19. c. Square
20. b. Triangle
21. a. Triangle
22. c. Triangle
23. a. Cylinder
24. b. Triangle

# Fan-N-Pick Answer Key

## 1.7 Transformations

1. a. Slide
2. b. Flip
3. c. Slide
4. c. Turn
5. c. Turn
6. b. Slide
7. a. Flip
8. a. Turn
9. a. Slide
10. b. Turn
11. c. Flip
12. b. Slide
13. a. Slide
14. b. Turn
15. c. Flip
16. a. Turn
17. b. Flip
18. a. Slide
19. c. Turn
20. a. Turn
21. b. Flip
22. a. Slide
23. b. Slide
24. a. Turn

## 1.8 Measurement

1. 5 in.
2. 1 in.
3. 2 in.
4. 3 in.
5. 4 in.
6. 14 cm
7. 13 cm
8. 12 cm
9. 11 cm
10. 10 cm
11. 9 cm
12. 8 cm
13. 7 cm
14. 6 cm
15. 5 cm
16. 4 cm
17. 3 cm
18. $1 \frac{1}{2}$ in.
19. $2 \frac{1}{2}$ in.
20. $3 \frac{1}{2}$ in.
21. $4 \frac{1}{2}$ in.
22. $5 \frac{1}{2}$ in.
23. $6 \frac{1}{2}$ cm
24. $7 \frac{1}{2}$ cm

COOPERATIVE MATH

Structure **2**

Find Someone Who

# Structure 2
# Find Someone Who

**Students circulate through the classroom, forming and reforming pairs, trying to "find someone who" knows the answer, then they become "someone who knows."**

## Instructions

*Each student receives a worksheet.*

**1** Students mix in the class, keeping a hand raised until they find a partner that is not a teammate.

**2** In pairs, Partner A asks a question from the worksheet; Partner B responds. Partner A records the answer on his or her own worksheet and expresses appreciation.

**3** Partner B checks and initials the answer.

**4** Partner B asks a question; Partner A responds. Partner B records the answer on his or her own worksheet and expresses appreciation.

**5** Partner A checks and initials the answer.

**6** Partners shake hands, part, and raise a hand as they search for a new partner.

**7** Students repeat Steps 1–6 until their worksheets are complete.

**8** When their worksheets are complete, students sit down; seated students may be approached by others as a resource.

**9** In teams, students compare answers; if there is disagreement or uncertainty, they raise four hands to ask a team question.

Students love playing Find Someone Who. They enjoy getting out of their seats and interacting with classmates. They feel a sense of pride when they can solve a math problem on someone else's worksheet. Students who may not have known an answer now become someone who knows and can help classmates.

# Find Someone Who Activities

## Number and Operations

## Algebra

## Geometry

## Measurement

## Answer Key ........................... 97

# Find Someone Who
# Primary Tips

## General Tips

- Limit number of concepts being reviewed. It is okay for primary students to practice concepts multiple times.
- Put the worksheet on clipboards for students to carry from partner to partner.
- Encourage students to get answers from as many different students as they can.
- Content should be a review of material previously taught.
- If you have students with special needs, prepare them with the answer to a couple of questions so they can participate by being the "expert" for those questions.

## Before
### Teaching the Structure

- Start with a visual of the structure. Use the visual to explain the steps.
- Model with students how to find a partner, ask the question, answer questions, coach, and praise their partners.
  - ★ **Tips on "How to find a partner"**
    - Model with four students. Demonstrate how to "pair up" with the closest person without passing someone.
    - Model with students how to keep their hands high until they find a partner. No bent elbows.
    - Once a partner is found, model with students how to give a quiet high five with no slapping.
    - Watch that students are not following friends.

## Before
### Teaching the Structure *(continued)*

★ **Tips on "Asking and Answering"**
- Model asking. Demonstrate how the first person asks a question from their worksheet.
- The listening student puts his or her hands behind his or her back and looks directly at his or her partner. Make sure their shoulders are "squared up."
- Model how to record the answer on his or her own worksheet.
- Model how and where to initial the answer.

★ **Tips on "Coaching"**
- Give students examples of coaching phrases without giving their partner the answer. For example: "Count with me." Coaching is always specific to the task so the teacher must model specific coaching phrases that match the content. Phrases like "keep trying" or "try again" are encouraging statements, not coaching.
- Student coaches could also use manipulatives to help show things such as addition/subtraction, counting, etc.

★ **Tips on "Praising"**
- Give specific praise or cheer that all students do when done quizzing/answering (examples: high five, a round of applause, thumbs up, "Great job!"). Watch to make sure the praising does not distract students from the content.

## During
### Doing the Structure

- Start with short amounts of time. If the structure continues for too long, students start to get loud and off task.
- Listen for good coaching and praising. Stop the group if appropriate and hold up a pair as models. Do this during the structure so that other students can practice what you have emphasized.

## After
### Processing the Structure

- Talk about what went well. Demonstrate if needed.
- Note any problems.
- Set goals for next time.

# Find Someone Who

# Activities

## Activity 2.1

### Cardinal Numbers

A *cardinal number* is a whole number that names how many objects are in a group. Give each student the "Cardinal Number" sheet and follow the Find Someone Who steps.

**NCTM Standard: Number and Operations Standard PreK–2**

★ Understand numbers, ways of representing numbers, relationships among numbers, and number systems.
  • Develop understanding of the relative position and magnitude of whole numbers and of ordinal and cardinal numbers and their connections.

**pp. 81–83**

## Activity 2.2

### Find the Missing Number

A *number in a pattern* is a sequence of numbers that repeat in a regular way. Students find the missing number in a pattern. Give each student the "Find the Missing Number" sheet and follow the Find Someone Who steps.

**NCTM Standard: Algebra Standard PreK–2**

★ Understand patterns, relations, and functions.
  • Recognize, describe, and extend patterns, such as sequences of sounds and shapes or simple numeric patterns, and translate from one representation to another.

**pp. 84–87**

## Activity 2.3

# Ordering Objects

*Ordering objects* is a sequence in which objects are placed. Students order objects according to the property given. Give each

student the "Ordering Objects" sheet and follow the Find Someone Who steps.

**NCTM Standard: Algebra Standard PreK–2**
★ Understand patterns, relations, and functions.
 • Sort, classify, and order objects by size, number, and other properties.

pp. 88–89

## Activity 2.4

# Shape Attributes

*Shape attributes* are areas on a shape that define the object. Students identify the number of faces, edges, and vertices on

a three-dimensional object. Give each student the "Shape Attributes" sheet and follow the Find Someone Who steps.

**NCTM Standard: Geometry Standard PreK–2**
★ Analyze characteristics and properties of two- and three-dimensional geometric shapes and develop mathematical arguments about geometric relationships.
 • Describe attributes and parts of two- and three-dimensional shapes.

p. 90–91

## Activity 2.5

# Environmental Shapes

*Environmental shapes* are three-dimensional objects. Students identify the three-dimensional shapes represented

by everyday objects. Give each student the "Environmental Shapes" sheet and follow the Find Someone Who steps.

**NCTM Standard: Geometry Standard PreK–2**
★ Analyze characteristics and properties of two- and three-dimensional geometric shapes and develop mathematical arguments about geometric relationships.
 • Recognize, name, build, draw, compare, and sort two- and three-dimensional shapes.

p. 92

## Activity 2.6

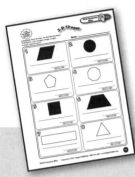

### 2-D Shapes

*Two-dimensional shapes* are objects that have length and width but no depth. Students identify the two-dimensional shapes. Give each student the "2-D Shapes" sheet and follow the Find Someone Who steps.

**NCTM Standard: Geometry Standard PreK–2**

★ Analyze characteristics and properties of two- and three-dimensional geometric shapes and develop mathematical arguments about geometric relationships
  • Recognize, name, build, draw, compare, and sort two- and three-dimensional shapes.

p. 93

## Activity 2.7

### Measurement

A *measurement* is a comparison to some other known unit. Students measure to the nearest inch. Give each student the "Measurement" sheet and follow the Find Someone Who steps.

**NCTM Standard: Measurement Standard PreK–2**

★ Understand measurable attributes of objects and the units, systems, and processes of measurement.
  • Understand how to measure using nonstandard and standard units.

p. 94

## Activity 2.8

### Repetition Measuring

*Repetition measuring* is measuring the same unit in different increments. Students use one unit (a dinosaur) to measure a given line. Students measure to the nearest dinosaur. Give each student the "Repetition Measuring" sheet and follow the Find Someone Who steps.

**NCTM Standard: Measurement Standard PreK–2**

★ Apply appropriate techniques, tools, and formulas to determine measurements.
  • Use repetition of a single unit to measure something larger than the unit.

pp. 95–96

"I ask.
You answer.
I record.
You sign."

# Cardinal Numbers #1

**Instructions:** Write the number of objects.

Name _____

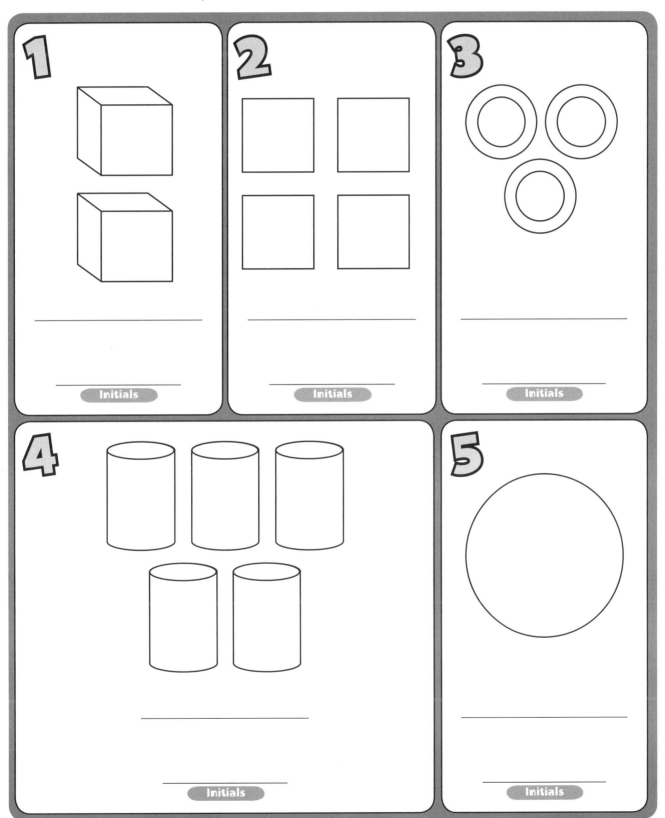

# Cardinal Numbers #2

**Instructions:** Write the number of objects.

**Name** _____

1 ☆☆☆☆ ☆☆☆☆
_____ Initials

2 😀😀😀 😀😀😀
_____ Initials

3 ♡♡♡♡♡ ♡♡♡♡♡
_____ Initials

4 ✦✦✦ ✦✦✦✦
_____ Initials

5 ⬤⬤⬤ ⬤⬤
_____ Initials

6 ✚
_____ Initials

7 ☀☀
_____ Initials

"I ask. You answer. I record. You sign."

# Cardinal Numbers #3

**Instructions:** Write the number of objects.

Name _____

**1**

_____ Initials

**2**

_____ Initials

**3**

_____ Initials

**4**

_____ Initials

**5**

_____ Initials

**6**

_____ Initials

**7**

_____ Initials

**Find Someone Who**

# Find the Missing Number #1

"I ask.
You answer.
I record.
You sign."

**Instructions:** Find the missing number(s) and write them in the blank(s).

**Name** _____

**1**

____, 8

_____ Initials

**2**

1, ____

_____ Initials

**3**

5, ____

_____ Initials

**4**

____, 3

_____ Initials

**5**

9, ____

_____ Initials

**6**

6, ____

_____ Initials

Cooperative Math • Kagan Publishing • (800) 933-2667 • www.KaganOnline.com     **Structure 2**

"I ask. You answer. I record. You sign."

# Find the Missing Number #2

**Instructions:** Find the missing number(s) and write them in the blank(s).

Name _____

**1**

_____, 10, _____

Initials

**2**

_____, 22, _____

Initials

**3**

_____, 15, _____

Initials

**4**

_____, 26, _____

Initials

**5**

_____, 13, _____

Initials

**6**

_____, 19, _____

Initials

**Find Someone Who**

# Find the Missing Number #3

"I ask.
You answer.
I record.
You sign."

**Instructions:** Find the missing number(s) and
write them in the blank(s).

**Name** _____

**1**

\_\_\_\_, 5, \_\_\_\_

Initials

**2**

\_\_\_\_, 8, \_\_\_\_

Initials

**3**

\_\_\_\_, 10, \_\_\_\_

Initials

**4**

\_\_\_\_, 4, \_\_\_\_

Initials

**5**

\_\_\_\_, 12, \_\_\_\_

Initials

**6**

\_\_\_\_, 7, \_\_\_\_

Initials

"I ask. You answer. I record. You sign."

# Find the Missing Number #4

**Instructions:** Find the missing number(s) and write them in the blank(s).

Name _____

**1**

____, 9, ____

Initials

**2**

____, 13, ____

Initials

**3**

____, 30, ____

Initials

**4**

____, 25, ____

Initials

**5**

____, 98, ____

Initials

**6**

____, 17, ____

Initials

# Ordering Objects #1

"I ask. You answer. I record. You sign."

**Instructions:** Circle the correct answer.     **Name** _____

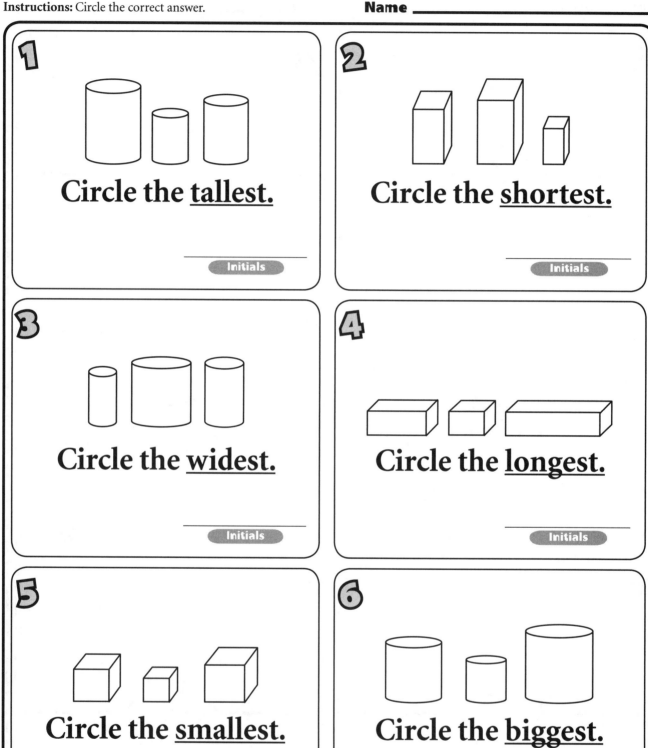

**1**

Circle the **tallest**.

_____ Initials

**2**

Circle the **shortest**.

_____ Initials

**3**

Circle the **widest**.

_____ Initials

**4**

Circle the **longest**.

_____ Initials

**5**

Circle the **smallest**.

_____ Initials

**6**

Circle the **biggest**.

_____ Initials

"I ask. You answer. I record. You sign."

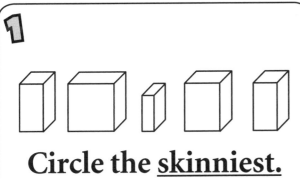
## Ordering Objects #2

**Instructions:** Circle the correct answer.

**Name** _____

**1**

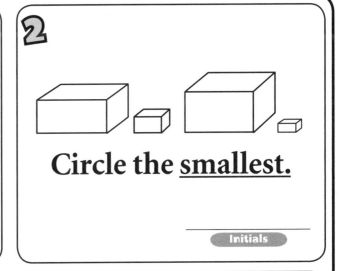

Circle the **skinniest.**

_____
Initials

**2**

Circle the **smallest.**

_____
Initials

**3**

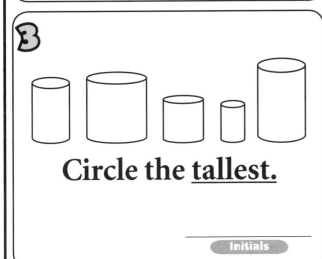

Circle the **tallest.**

_____
Initials

**4**

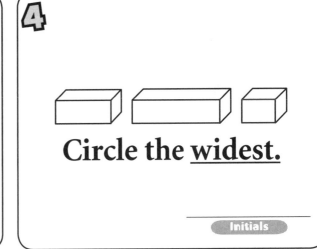

Circle the **widest.**

_____
Initials

**5**

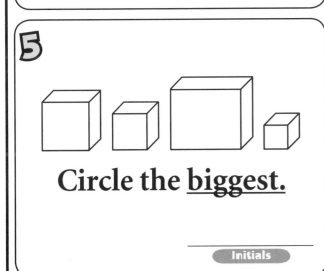

Circle the **biggest.**

_____
Initials

**6**

Circle the **tiniest.**

_____
Initials

# Shape Attributes #1

**Instructions:** Write the number of edges, or vertices.

**Name** _____

**1**

Write the number of <u>edges.</u>

_____ Initials

**2**

Write the number of <u>edges.</u>

_____ Initials

**3**

Write the number of <u>vertices.</u>

_____ Initials

**4**

Write the number of <u>edges.</u>

_____ Initials

**5**

Write the number of <u>edges.</u>

_____ Initials

**6**

Write the number of <u>vertices.</u>

_____ Initials

"I ask. You answer. I record. You sign."

# Shape Attributes #2

**Instructions:** Write the number of edges, faces, or vertices.        **Name** _____

**1**

Write the number of <u>edges.</u>

_____
Initials

**2**
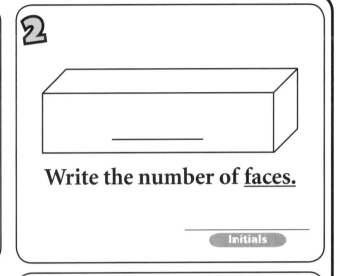

Write the number of <u>faces.</u>

_____
Initials

**3**
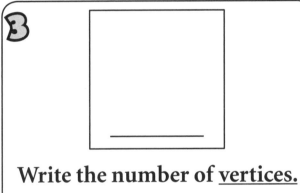

Write the number of <u>vertices.</u>

_____
Initials

**4**
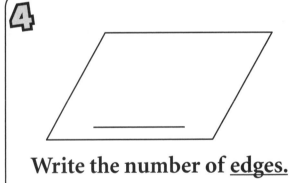

Write the number of <u>edges.</u>

_____
Initials

**5**
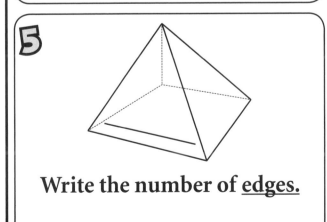

Write the number of <u>edges.</u>

_____
Initials

**6**
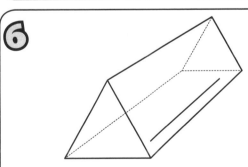

Write the number of <u>vertices.</u>

_____
Initials

# Enviornmental Shapes

**Instructions:** Determine which shape the object is most like:
rectangular prism, sphere, cone, triangular prism, cube, or cylinder.   **Name** _____

**1**

_____

Initials

**2**

_____

Initials

**3**

_____

Initials

**4**

_____

Initials

**5**

_____

Initials

**6**

_____

Initials

"I ask.
You answer.
I record.
You sign."

Find Someone
Who

2.6

# 2-D Shapes

**Instructions:** Name the shape. Use the following shapes:
parallelogram, circle, pentagon, triangle, octagon,
rectangle, trapezoid, or square.

Name _____

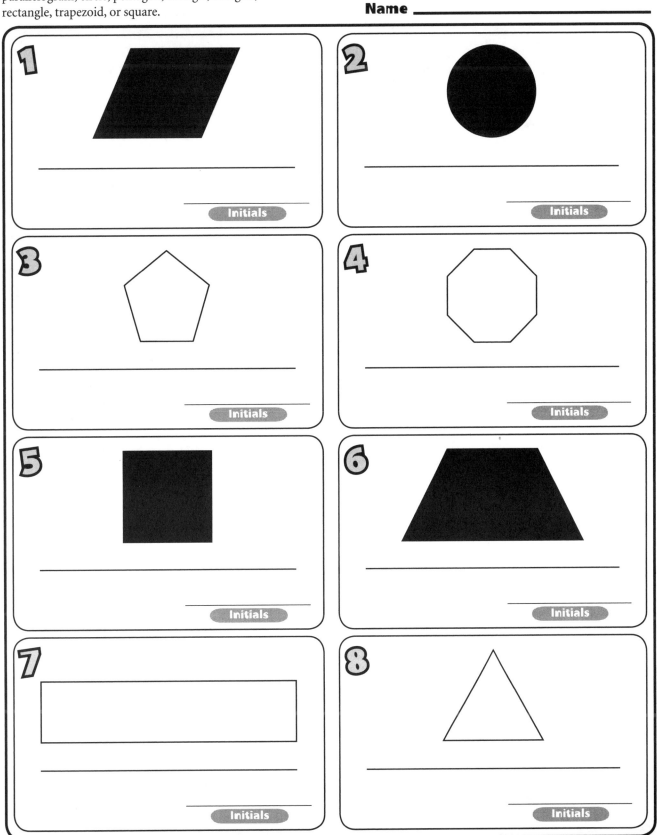

**1**

_____

Initials

**2**

_____

Initials

**3**

_____

Initials

**4**

_____

Initials

**5**

_____

Initials

**6**

_____

Initials

**7**

_____

Initials

**8**

_____

Initials

# Measurement

"I ask.
You answer.
I record.
You sign."

**Instructions:**
Answer the measurement questions.
Measure all items to the nearest inch.

**Name** _____

---

**1** ## How many inches?

_____  _____ inches

Initials

---

**2** ## How many inches?

_____  _____ inches

Initials

---

**3** ## How many inches?

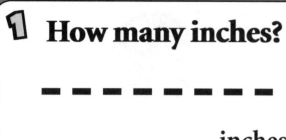

_____  _____ inch

Initials

---

**4** ## How many inches?

_____  _____ inches

Initials

---

**5** ## Which picture is the longest?
a. the line        b. the snake
c. the dog         d. the present        _____

Initials

---

**6**
a. What is the length of this
   paper? _____ inches

b. What is the length of your
   pencil? _____ inches

c. What is the length of
   your shoe? _____ inches

d. What is the length of your
   arm from elbow to wrist?
   _____ inches

_____
Initials

---

"I ask. You answer. I record. You sign."

# Repetition Measuring #1

**Instructions:** Cut out the dinosaur along the dotted line.
Measure each line to the nearest half dinosaur.

**Name** _____

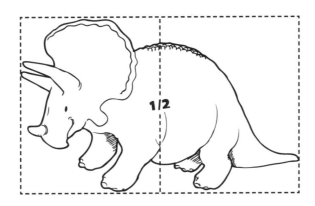

1/2

**1**

— — — — — — — — — — — — —

_____ dinosaurs long  _____
Initials

**2**

▬▬▬▬▬▬▬▬▬▬

_____ dinosaur long  _____
Initials

**3**

• • • • • • • • • • • • • • • • • • • • • •

_____ dinosaurs long  _____
Initials

**4**

◇◇◇◇◇◇◇◇◇

_____ dinosaur long  _____
Initials

# Repetition Measuring #2

"I ask. You answer. I record. You sign."

**Instructions:** Cut out the dinosaur along the dotted line.
Measure each line to the nearest dinosaur.

**Name** _____

**1/2**

**1**

— — — — — — —

_____ dinosaurs long _____
**Initials**

**2**

_____

_____ dinosaurs long _____
**Initials**

**3**

● ● ● ● ● ● ● ●

_____ dinosaur long _____
**Initials**

**4**

■ ■ ■ ■ ■ ■ ■ ■ ■ ■ ■ ■ ■

_____ dinosaurs long _____
**Initials**

**5**

◇◇◇◇◇◇◇◇◇◇◇◇◇◇◇

_____ dinosaurs long _____
**Initials**

# Find Someone Who Answer Key

## 2.1 Cardinal Numbers

**Worksheet #1**
1.  2
2.  4
3.  3
4.  5
5.  1

**Worksheet #2**
1.  8
2.  6
3.  10
4.  7
5.  5
6.  1
7.  2

**Worksheet #3**
1.  17
2.  15
3.  13
4.  10
5.  4
6.  5
7.  18

## 2.2 Find the Missing Number

**Worksheet #1**
1.  <u>7</u>, 8
2.  1, <u>2</u>
3.  5, <u>6</u>
4.  <u>2</u>, 3
5.  9, <u>10</u>
6.  6, <u>7</u>

**Worksheet #2**
1.  <u>9</u>, 10, <u>11</u>
2.  <u>21</u>, 22, <u>23</u>
3.  <u>14</u>, 15, <u>16</u>
4.  <u>25</u>, 26, <u>27</u>
5.  <u>12</u>, 13, <u>14</u>
6.  <u>18</u>, 19, <u>20</u>

**Worksheet #3**
1.  <u>4</u>, 5, <u>6</u>
2.  <u>7</u>, 8, <u>9</u>
3.  <u>9</u>, 10, <u>11</u>
4.  <u>3</u>, 4, <u>5</u>
5.  <u>11</u>, 12, <u>13</u>
6.  <u>6</u>, 7, <u>8</u>

**Worksheet #4**
1.  <u>8</u>, 9, <u>10</u>
2.  <u>12</u>, 13, <u>14</u>
3.  <u>29</u>, 30, <u>31</u>
4.  <u>24</u>, 25, <u>26</u>
5.  <u>97</u>, 98, <u>99</u>
6.  <u>16</u>, 17, <u>18</u>

## 2.3 Ordering Objects

**Worksheet #1**
1.
2.
3.
4.
5.
6.

**Worksheet #2**
1.
2.
3.
4.
5.
6.

## 2.4 Shape Attributes

**Worksheet #1**
1. 4 edges
2. 3 edges
3. 4 vertices
4. 3 edges
5. 6 edges
6. 5 vertices

**Worksheet #2**
1. 12 edges
2. 6 faces
3. 4 vertices
4. 4 edges
5. 8 edges
6. 6 vertices

## 2.5 Enviornmental Shapes

1. Triangular Prism
2. Rectangular Prism
3. Cone
4. Sphere
5. Cube
6. Cylinder

## 2.6 2-D Shapes

1. Parallelogram
2. Circle
3. Pentagon
4. Octagon
5. Square
6. Trapezoid
7. Rectangle
8. Triangle

## 2.7 Measurement

1. 2.5 inches
2. 3 inches
3. 1 inch
4. 2 inches
5. b. the snake

6a. 11 inches
6b. Answers will vary in inches.
6c. Answers will vary in inches.
6d. Answer will vary in inches.

## 2.8 Repetition Measuring

**Worksheet #1**
1. 2 dinosaurs long
2. 1 dinosaur long
3. 1 ½ dinosaurs long
4. ½ dinosaur long

**Worksheet #2**
1. 2 dinosaurs long
2. 3 dinosaurs long
3. 1 dinosaur long
4. 2 ½ dinosaurs long
5. 1 ½ dinosaurs long

COOPERATIVE MATH

Structure **3**

## Match Mine

# 3
**Structure**

# Match Mine

**Partners on opposite sides of a barrier communicate with precision, attempting to match the other's arrangement of game pieces on a game board.**

## Instructions

*Partners sit on opposite sides of a barrier with identical game boards and game pieces. One is designated to be the Sender, the other the Receiver.*

**1** Sender arranges game pieces on game board while Receiver waits quietly.

**2** Sender gives the Receiver directions to match the Sender's arrangement of game pieces on the game board.

**3** When finished, partners set game boards side by side to check for accuracy.

**4** Receiver praises Sender, and they develop improvement strategies.

**5** Roles are switched, and the game is played again.

*Hints: Teacher instructs students in communication skills: asking for clarification, checking for understanding, giving unambiguous directions.*

Match Mine boosts mathematical vocabulary and communication skills. Since partners cannot see each other's work, they need to communicate about math with precision. As they communicate, they learn mathematical terms associated with the activity, as well as how to coordinate efforts to make a match.

# Match Mine Activities

## Numbers & Operations

## Measurement

## Geometry

# Match Mine
# Primary Tips

## General Tips

- Limit number of concepts being reviewed. It is okay for primary students to practice concepts multiple times.
- Laminate pieces for durability.
- Put "game boards" inside sheet protectors to use with wet-erase markers.
- Content should be a review of material previously taught.
- Create folders to place in between students.
- Simplify game board. Limit number of pieces.

## Before
### Teaching the Structure

- Start with a visual of the structure. Use the visual to explain the steps.
- Show how to set up the folders to create a barrier between the students.
  - ★ **Tips on "Giving Instructions"**
    - Model giving instructions. Give specific instruction examples that coordinate with the activity.
      - Give specific vocabulary to be used.

## Before
### Teaching the Structure *(continued)*

★ **Tips on "Checking Answers"**
  - Model how the game boards should be checked. Have students remove the folders while checking. Discuss ways to improve.

★ **Tips on "Praising"**
  - Give specific praise or cheer that all students do when finished (examples: high five, a round of applause, thumbs up, "Great job!"). Watch to make sure the praising does not distract students from the content.

## During
### Doing the Structure

- Start with short amounts of time. If the structure continues for too long, students start to get loud and off task.
- Listen for good questions and correct vocabulary.
- Keep class together.
  - Round 1: A's Send, B's Receive. Stop. Check boards.
  - Round 2: B's Send, A's Receive. Stop. Check boards.

## After
### Processing the Structure

- Talk about what went well. Demonstrate if needed.
- Note any problems.
- Set goals for next time.

# Match Mine
# Activities

## Activity 3.1

### Match My Number Sentence

The Sender creates number sentences on the game board. The Sender then gives the Receiver clues, such as "The addend is greater than four but less than six" or "The two numbers added together equal 7," to match the Sender's number sentence. When finished with the designated number of sentences, partners check the game boards. The Receiver praises the Sender for his or her instructions, they develop improvement strategies, and then switch roles.

**NCTM Standard: Numbers and Operations Standard PreK–2**
★ Understand meanings of operations and how they relate to one another.
  • Understand the effects of adding and subtracting whole numbers.

**pp. 108–110**

## Activity 3.2

### Match My Shape Design

The Sender creates a picture using the geometric shapes. The Sender then gives the Receiver directions to match the Sender's arrangement of shapes. When finished, partners check the game boards. The Receiver praises the Sender for his or her instructions, they develop improvement strategies, and then switch roles.

**NCTM Standard: Geometry Standard PreK–2**
★ Analyze characteristics and properties of two- and three dimensional geometric shapes and develop mathematical arguments about geometric relationships.
  • Recognize, name, build, draw, compare, and sort two- and three-dimensional shapes.

**pp. 111–113**

## Activity 3.3

# Match My Coordinate Grid

The Sender places animals on the coordinate grid. The Sender then gives the Receiver directions to match the Sender's arrangement of animals.

When finished, partners check the game boards. The Receiver praises the Sender for his or her instructions, they develop improvement strategies, and then switch roles.

**NCTM Standard: Geometry Standard PreK–2**
★ Specify locations and describe spatial relationships using coordinate geometry and other representational systems.
  • Find and name locations with simple relationships such as "near to" and in coordinate systems such as maps.

**pp. 114–116**

## Activity 3.4

# Match My Location

The Sender arranges the pictures on the game board. The Sender then gives the Receiver directions to match the Sender's arrangement of pictures. For example, "Place the sun in the upper right hand corner." Or "Place the heart below the sun." When finished, partners check the game boards. The Receiver praises the Sender for his or her instructions, they develop improvement strategies, and then switch roles.

**NCTM Standard: Geometry Standard PreK–2**
★ Specify locations and describe spatial relationships using coordinate geometry and other representational systems.
  • Find and name locations with simple relationships such as "near to and in coordinate systems such as maps."

**pp. 117–119**

## Activity 3.5

# Match My Time

The sender writes a time under each clock and draws the appropriate clock hands. The Sender then gives the Receiver directions to match the Sender's clocks.

When finished, partners check the clocks. The Receiver praises the Sender for his or her instructions, they develop improvement strategies, and then switch roles.

**NCTM Standard: Measurement Standard PreK–2**
★ Understand measurable attributes of objects and the units, systems, and processes of measurement.
  • Recognize the attributes of length, volume, weight, area, and time.

**pp. 120–121**

# Match My Number Sentence

**Instructions:** The Sender creates a number sentence in each space, then describes it for the Receiver to match it.

## Game Board

<br>

<br>

<br>

<br>

<br>

<br>

# Match My Number Sentence

Cut out each piece.

| 1 | 1 | 1 | 2 | 2 | 2 | 3 | 3 | 3 |
| 4 | 4 | 4 | 5 | 5 | 5 | 6 | 6 | 6 |
| 7 | 7 | 7 | 8 | 8 | 8 | 9 | 9 | 9 |
| 10 | 10 | 10 | 11 | 11 | 11 | 12 | 12 | 12 |
| 13 | 13 | 13 | 14 | 14 | 14 | 15 | 15 | 15 |
| 16 | 16 | 16 | 17 | 17 | 17 | 18 | 18 | 18 |
| − | − | − | − | − | − | = | = | = |
| + | + | + | + | + | + | = | = | = |

# Match My Number Sentence

**Game Pieces – Partner B**    Cut out each piece.

| | | | | | | | | |
|---|---|---|---|---|---|---|---|---|
| **1** | **1** | **1** | **2** | **2** | **2** | **3** | **3** | **3** |
| **4** | **4** | **4** | **5** | **5** | **5** | **6** | **6** | **6** |
| **7** | **7** | **7** | **8** | **8** | **8** | **9** | **9** | **9** |
| **10** | **10** | **10** | **11** | **11** | **11** | **12** | **12** | **12** |
| **13** | **13** | **13** | **14** | **14** | **14** | **15** | **15** | **15** |
| **16** | **16** | **16** | **17** | **17** | **17** | **18** | **18** | **18** |
| **–** | **–** | **–** | **–** | **–** | **–** | **=** | **=** | **=** |
| **+** | **+** | **+** | **+** | **+** | **+** | **=** | **=** | **=** |

# Match My Shape Design

**Instructions:** The Sender creates a design using shapes, then describes it for the Reciever to match it.

**Game Board**

# Match My Shape Design

**Game Pieces – Partner A**   **Cut out each shape.**

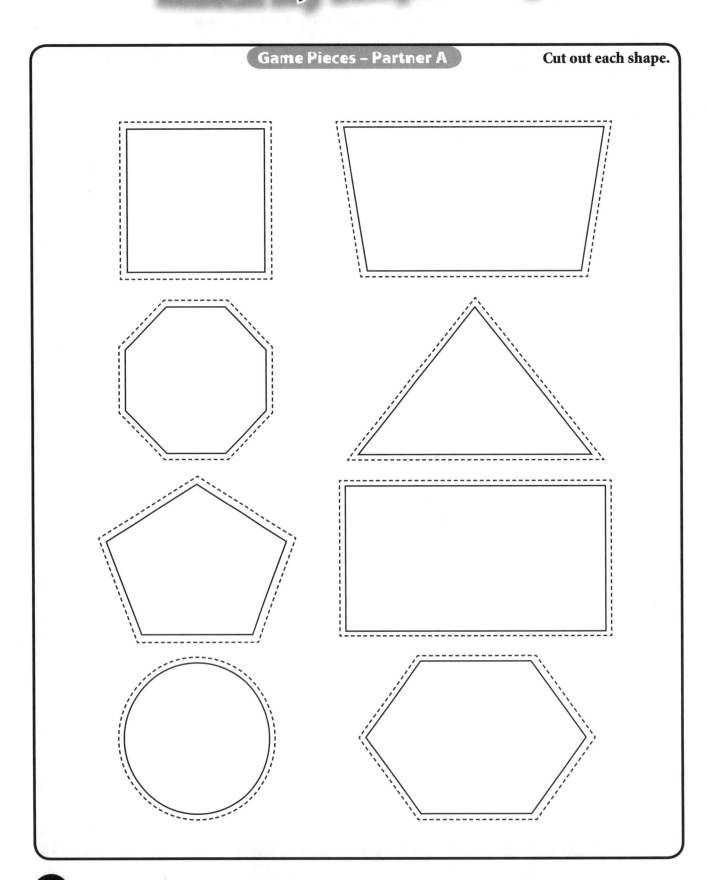

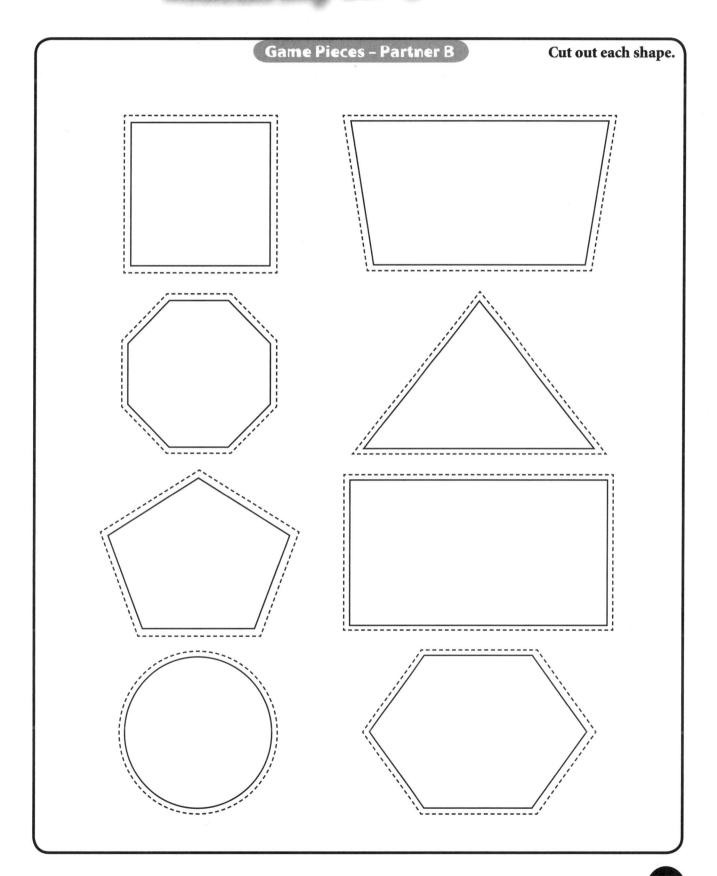

# Match My Shape Design

**Game Pieces – Partner B**   Cut out each shape.

# Match My Coordinate Grid

**Instructions:** The Sender places animal pieces on the grid, then describes it to the Reciever to match it.

**Game Board**

|  |  |  |  |  | |
|---|---|---|---|---|---|
|  |  |  |  |  | **F** |
|  |  |  |  |  | **E** |
|  |  |  |  |  | **D** |
|  |  |  |  |  | **C** |
|  |  |  |  |  | **B** |
|  |  |  |  |  | **A** |
| **5** | **4** | **3** | **2** | **1** | |

# Match My Coordinate Grid

Cut out each animal.

# Match My Coordinate Grid

Game Pieces – Partner B

Cut out each animal.

# Match My Location

**Instructions:** The Sender places pictures on the board, then describes the arrangement to the Receiver to match it.

## Game Board

# Match My Location

Game Pieces – Partner A          Cut out each picture.

# Match My Location

# Match My Time

**Instructions:** The Sender writes a time under each clock and draws in the appropriate clock hands. Then, the Sender describes each clock for the Receiver to match.

## Partner A

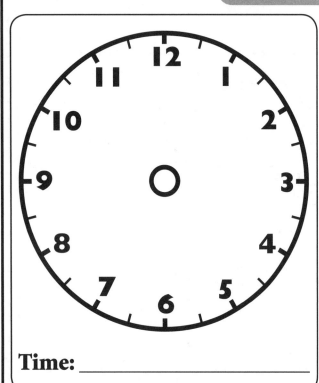

Time: _____

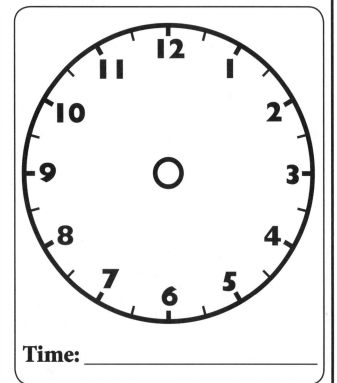

Time: _____

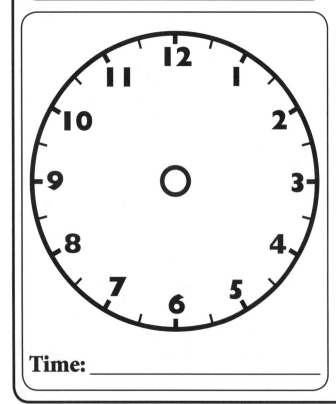

Time: _____

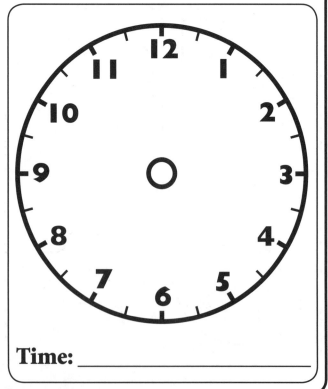

Time: _____

# Match My Time

**Instructions:** The Sender writes a time under each clock and draws in the appropriate clock hands. Then, the Sender describes each clock for the Receiver to match.

## Partner B

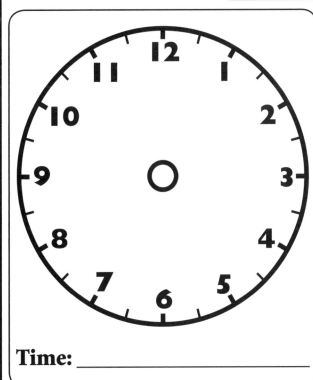

Time: _____

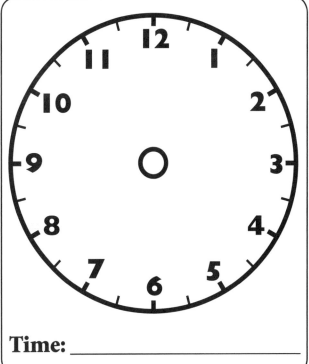

Time: _____

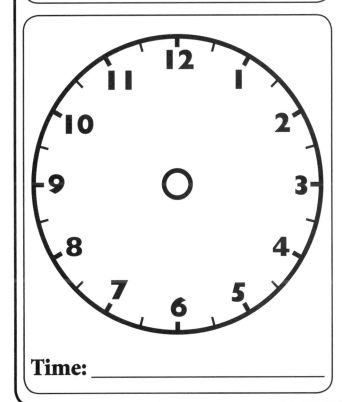

Time: _____

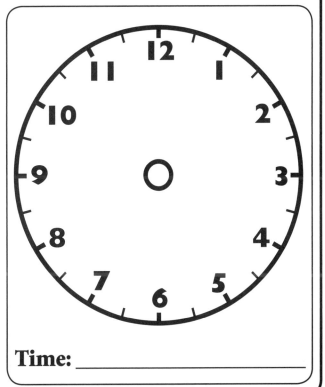

Time: _____

COOPERATIVE MATH

# Structure **4**
## Mix-Freeze-Group

**Structure**

# Mix-Freeze-Group

**Students rush to form groups of a specific size, hoping not to land in "Lost and Found."**

## Instructions

*The teacher prepares questions to which the answers are numbers or correspond to a key.*

**1** Students "mix" around the room.

**2** Teacher calls, "Freeze," and students freeze.

**3** Teacher asks a question to which the answer is a number or which corresponds to a key with a number. Teacher gives think time. (Examples: What is five take away three? Which shape has three faces? Key: Triangle = 2, Circle = 3, Square = 4, Pentagon = 5)

**4** Teacher calls, "Show Me," and students show their answer with fingers on their chests.

**5** Students group according to the number, and kneel down.

**6** Students in their groups discuss a question provided by the teacher. *Show five take away three using your fingers. What other properties does a triangle have?*

**7** Students not in groups go to the "Lost and Found."

*Optional: Once students know the game, students in Lost and Found may be the ones to generate and ask the next question. After they ask the question, they rush to join a group.*

## ★★Boosting Engagement★★

Mix-Freeze-Group transforms basic math practice into a whole-body game. Students group with classmates to form groups that represent the answer. The movement makes math learning active and fun. Plus, everyone needs to stay alert if they want to avoid the Lost and Found.

# Mix-Freeze-Group Activities

## Numbers & Operations

## Geometry

## Answer Key.................... 172

# Mix-Freeze-Group
# Primary Tips

## General Tips

- Limit number of concepts being reviewed. It is okay for primary students to practice concepts multiple times.
- Music can be used to start and stop "mixing."
- Content should be a review of material previously taught.
- Use visual aids (e.g., board, overhead, interactive whiteboard).

## Before
### Teaching the Structure

- Start with a visual of the structure. Use the visual to explain the steps.
- Model with students how to mix, freeze, show their answer, and group.
  - ★ **Tips on "How to mix"**
    - Model with four students how to mix around the room. Demonstrate the parameters of their mixing area. Model how they are to walk and where to put their hands (high fives, in pockets, behind backs).
    - Model when to start and stop "mixing."
  - ★ **Tips on "How to freeze"**
    - Demonstrate how and when to "freeze." When students freeze, they should end up with their eyes toward the teacher. For younger students, model how both feet should also be on the floor when they are in their "freeze" position.
  - ★ **Tips on "How to show your answer"**
    - Model how students can show their answer using their fingers placed on their chest. For younger students, have them cover their answer with their other hand until the teacher asks for it.

## Before
### Teaching the Structure (continued)

★ **Tips on "How to group"**
- Model with four students. Demonstrate how to group with the same number of people as they had for their answer. For example: If their answer was 3, they need to get into groups of 3. Model how to group with the closest people without passing someone.
- Model with students how to keep their hands high until they find a partner. No bent elbows.
- Once a group is found, model with students how to show the teacher they are ready by kneeling on the floor with their eyes on the teacher.
- Watch out for students following friends.

★ **Tips on "Lost and Found"**
- Demonstrate how to go to "lost and found" if there are "extra" students after grouping. The students in this area will form their own group. If there is only one student, this student can join the nearest group or discuss with the teacher.
- Make a rule where students can't be in "lost and found" twice in a row. Example: Before you start the next question tell the students, "Look who is in Lost and Found; make sure they have a group next time around."

★ **Tips on "Answering discussion questions"**
- If the teacher chooses to give a discussion question to answer once students have formed groups, demonstrate how and when students should answer the questions. Students could answer to the whole group or in pairs.
- If answering to the entire group, demonstrate how the answering student should stand and face the group,
- In pairs, listening students put their hands behind their back and look directly at the speaker. Make sure their shoulders are "squared up."

## During
### Doing the Structure

- Start with short amounts of time. If the structure continues for too long, students start to get loud and off task.

## After
### Processing the Structure

- Talk about what went well. Demonstrate if needed.
- Note any problems.
- Set goals for next time.

# Mix-Freeze-Group Activities

## Activity 4.1

### Subtraction Situations

Students answer the *subtraction* word problem. Students mix around the room. The teacher calls, "Freeze," and students freeze. The teacher asks a question from the question sheet and gives think time. The teacher calls, "Show me," and students show their answer with fingers on their chest or on paper. Students group according to the number, and kneel down. Students in their groups discuss a question provided by the teacher. Students not in groups go to the "Lost and Found."

**NCTM Standard: Numbers and Operations Standard PreK–2**

★ Understand meanings of operations and how they relate to one another.
• Understand various meanings of addition and subtraction of whole numbers and the relationship between the two operations.

**pp. 131–132**

## Activity 4.2

### Fractions

Students identify the *fraction* on the card. Students mix around the room. The teacher calls, "Freeze," and students freeze. The teacher asks a question from the question sheet and gives think time. The teacher calls, "Show me," and students show their answer with fingers on their chest or on paper. Students group according to the number, and kneel down. Students in their groups discuss a question provided by the teacher. Students not in groups go to the "Lost and Found."

**NCTM Standard: Numbers and Operations Standard PreK–2**

★ Understand numbers, ways of representing numbers, relationships among numbers, and number systems.
• Understand and represent commonly used fractions.

**pp. 133–140**

# Activity 4.3

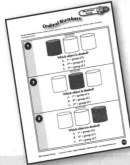

## Ordinal Numbers

Students identify the *ordinal number*. Students mix around the room. The teacher calls, "Freeze," and students freeze. The teacher asks a question from the question sheet and gives think time. The teacher calls, "Show me," and students show their answer with fingers on their chest or on paper. Students group according to the number, and kneel down. Students in their groups discuss a question provided by the teacher. Students not in groups go to the "Lost and Found."

**NCTM Standard: Numbers and Operations Standard PreK–2**
★ Understand numbers, ways of representing numbers, relationships among numbers, and number systems.
• Develop understanding of the relative position and magnitude of whole numbers and of ordinal and cardinal numbers and their connections.

**pp. 141–148**

# Activity 4.4

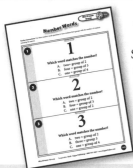

## Number Words

Students identify the *number that matches the word*. Students mix around the room. The teacher calls, "Freeze," and students freeze. The teacher asks a question from the question sheet and gives think time. The teacher calls, "Show me," and students show their answer with fingers on their chest or on paper. Students group according to the number, and kneel down. Students in their groups discuss a question provided by the teacher. Students not in groups go to the "Lost and Found."

**NCTM Standard: Numbers and Operations Standard PreK–2**
★ Understand numbers, ways of representing numbers, relationships among numbers, and number systems.
• Develop understanding of the relative position and magnitude of whole numbers and of ordinal and cardinal numbers and their connections.

**pp. 149–156**

# Activity 4.5

## Money

Students identify the coin *money* value. Students mix around the room. The teacher calls, "Freeze," and students freeze. The teacher asks a question from the question sheet and gives think time. The teacher calls, "Show me," and students show their answer with fingers on their chest or on paper. Students group according to the number, and kneel down. Students in their groups discuss a question provided by the teacher. Students not in groups go to the "Lost and Found."

**NCTM Standard: Numbers and Operations Standard PreK–2**
★ Compute fluently and make reasonable estimates.
• Develop fluency with basic number combinations for addition and subtraction.

**pp. 157–164**

# Mix-Freeze-Group
## Activities continued

## Activity 4.6

### Shapes #1

Students identify the *number of sides of the shape* on the card and get into groups accordingly. Students mix around the room. The teacher calls, "Freeze," and students freeze. The teacher asks a question from the question sheet and gives think time. The teacher calls, "Show me," and students show their answer with fingers on their chest or on paper. Students group according to the number, and kneel down. Students in their groups discuss a question provided by the teacher. Students not in groups go to the "Lost and Found."

**NCTM Standard: Geometry Standard PreK–2**
★ Analyze characteristics and properties of two- and three-dimensional geometric shapes and develop mathematical arguments about geometric relationships.
• Describe attributes and parts of two- and three-dimensional shapes.

**pp. 165–166**

## Activity 4.7

### Shapes #2

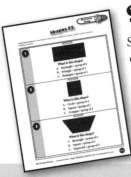

Students identify the *shape* shown on the card and get into groups accordingly. Students mix around the room. The teacher calls, "Freeze," and students freeze. The teacher asks a question from the question sheet and gives think time. The teacher calls, "Show me," and students show their answer with fingers on their chest or on paper. Students group according to the number, and kneel down. Students in their groups discuss a question provided by the teacher. Students not in groups go to the "Lost and Found."

**NCTM Standard: Geometry Standard Pre–K–2**
★ Analyze characteristics and properties of two- and three-dimensional geometric shapes and develop mathematical arguments about geometric relationships.
• Recognize, name, build, draw, compare, and sort two- and three-dimensional shapes.

**pp. 167-171**

# Subtraction Situations

**Teacher instructions:** Use these subtraction questions to have students form groups with the number of students matching the answer.

**1**

**Question**
*The dog has 3 bones. He ate 1 of them.*
*How many does he have left?*

**Answer**
**The dog has 2 bones.**

**2**

**Question**
*The boy has a bag of 10 marbles.*
*He lost 5 marbles. How many does he have left?*

**Answer**
**The boy has 5 marbles.**

**3**

**Question**
*The girl has 9 cookies. She gave 3 away.*
*How many does she have left?*

**Answer**
**The girl has 6 cookies.**

**4**

**Question**
*The elephant has 7 peanuts. He ate 4.*
*How many peanuts does he have left?*

**Answer**
**The elephant has 3 peanuts.**

**5**

**Question**
*The cat has 4 play toys. One was lost.*
*How many does he have left?*

**Answer**
**The cat has 3 toys.**

**6**

**Question**
*The boy has 6 candies. He gave 3 away.*
*How many does he have left?*

**Answer**
**The boy has 3 candies.**

**7**

**Question**
*Brady has 10 blocks. His brother took 3 of them.*
*How many does Brady have left?*

**Answer**
**Brady has 7 blocks.**

**8**

**Question**
*Amanda has 8 dolls. Her sister took 2 of them.*
*How many does she have left?*

**Answer**
**Amanda has 6 dolls.**

**9**

**Question**
*Bruce has 9 toy cars. One car is lost.*
*How many cars does he have left?*

**Answer**
**Bruce has 8 cars.**

**10**

**Question**
*Matt has 7 pencils. He gives 2 away.*
*How many does he have left?*

**Answer**
**Matt has 5 pencils.**

# Subtraction Situations

**Teacher instructions:** Use these subtraction questions to have students form groups with the number of students matching the answer.

| | | |
|---|---|---|
| **11** | Question | *The girl had 3 brothers and 1 sister. How many more brothers than sisters does she have?* |
| | Answer | **The girl has 2 more brothers than sisters.** |
| **12** | Question | *Erin is 9 years old and her brother is 3 years old. How many more years older is Erin than her brother?* |
| | Answer | **Erin is 6 years older than her brother.** |
| **13** | Question | *Sara has 10 pens. Joe has 2. How many more pens does Sara have than Joe?* |
| | Answer | **Sara has 8 more pens than Joe.** |
| **14** | Question | *Lindsey is 8 years old. Jan is 7 years old. How many years older is Lindsey than Jan?* |
| | Answer | **Lindsey is one year older than Jan.** |
| **15** | Question | *Beth has 5 candies. Jennie has 3 candies. How many more candies does Beth have than Jennie?* |
| | Answer | **Beth has 2 more candies than Jennie.** |
| **16** | Question | *The garden has 12 ears of corn. The rabbit ate 8 of them. How many ears are left?* |
| | Answer | **There are 4 ears of corn left in the garden.** |
| **17** | Question | *Bo has 12 blocks. He lost 9 of them. How many blocks does he have left?* |
| | Answer | **Bo has 3 blocks left.** |
| **18** | Question | *Jake has 12 jacks. He picked up 5 of them. How many are left?* |
| | Answer | **Jake has 7 jacks left.** |
| **19** | Question | *Kristin has 11 balls. She gives 3 away. How many does she have left?* |
| | Answer | **Kristin has 8 balls left.** |
| **20** | Question | *Teresa has 11 CDs. Eight are lost. How many does she have left?* |
| | Answer | **Teresa has 3 CDs left.** |

# Fractions

**Teacher instructions:** Use these fraction questions to have students form groups with the number of students matching the answer.

**1**

Question

**How much is shaded?**

A.   ½ = group of 6
B.   ²⁄₂ = group of 2
C.   ⅓ = group of 5

**2**

Question

**How much is shaded?**

A.   ⅔ = group of 4
B.   ⅓ = group of 2
C.   ³⁄₃ = group of 5

**3**

Question

**How much is shaded?**

A.   ⅓ = group of 6
B.   ²⁄₂ = group of 2
C.   ⅔ = group of 5

# Fractions

**Teacher instructions:** Use these fraction questions to have students form groups with the number of students matching the answer.

**Question**

**4**

**How much is shaded?**

A. ⅔ = group of 4

B. ⅓ = group of 2

C. ⅗ = group of 6

**Question**

**5**

**How much is shaded?**

A. ⅓ = group of 3

B. ¼ = group of 4

C. ²⁄₄ = group of 5

**Question**

**6**

**How much is shaded?**

A. ²⁄₄ = group of 4

B. ⅓ = group of 2

C. ⅗ = group of 6

# Fractions

**Teacher instructions:** Use these fraction questions to have students form groups with the number of students matching the answer.

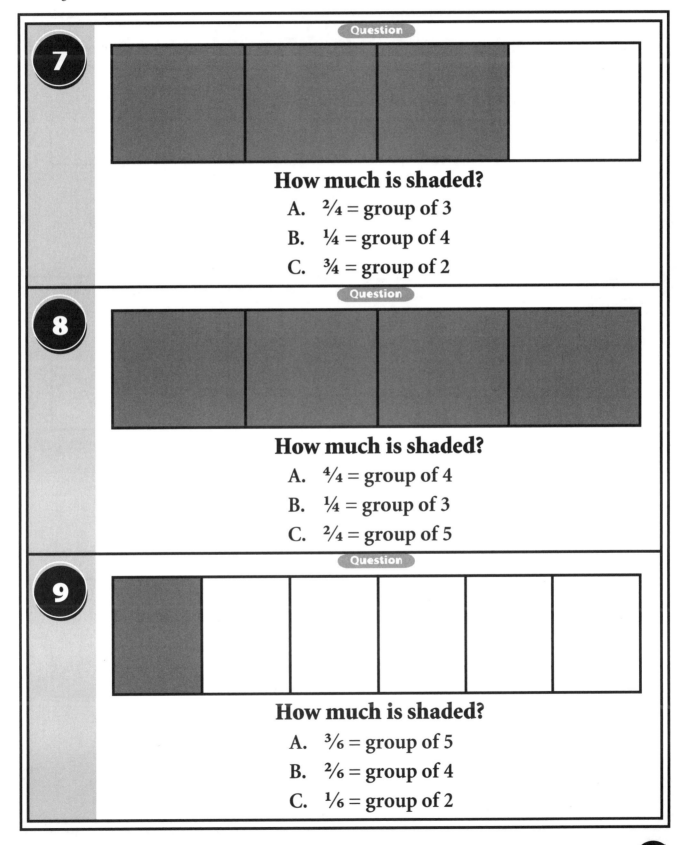

**Question**

**7**

**How much is shaded?**

A. ²/₄ = group of 3

B. ¼ = group of 4

C. ¾ = group of 2

**Question**

**8**

**How much is shaded?**

A. ⁴/₄ = group of 4

B. ¼ = group of 3

C. ²/₄ = group of 5

**Question**

**9**

**How much is shaded?**

A. ³/₆ = group of 5

B. ²/₆ = group of 4

C. ¹/₆ = group of 2

# Fractions

**Teacher instructions:** Use these fraction questions to have students form groups with the number of students matching the answer.

### 10

**Question**

## How much is shaded?

A. $\frac{1}{6}$ = group of 6

B. $\frac{2}{6}$ = group of 5

C. $\frac{4}{6}$ = group of 2

### 11

**Question**

## How much is shaded?

A. $\frac{3}{6}$ = group of 5

B. $\frac{2}{6}$ = group of 4

C. $\frac{1}{6}$ = group of 2

### 12

**Question**

## How much is shaded?

A. $\frac{1}{6}$ = group of 6

B. $\frac{2}{6}$ = group of 5

C. $\frac{4}{6}$ = group of 2

**Structure 4**

# Fractions

**Teacher instructions:** Use these fraction questions to have students form groups with the number of students matching the answer.

**13**

**Question**

### How much is shaded?

A. ⁵⁄₆ = group of 3

B. ²⁄₆ = group of 4

C. ¹⁄₆ = group of 2

**14**

**Question**

### How much is shaded?

A. ¹⁄₆ = group of 6

B. ⁶⁄₆ = group of 5

C. ⁴⁄₆ = group of 2

**15**

**Question**

### How much is shaded?

A. ¹⁄₈ = group of 3

B. ¹⁄₆ = group of 4

C. ¹⁄₅ = group of 2

# Fractions

**Teacher instructions:** Use these fraction questions to have students form groups with the number of students matching the answer.

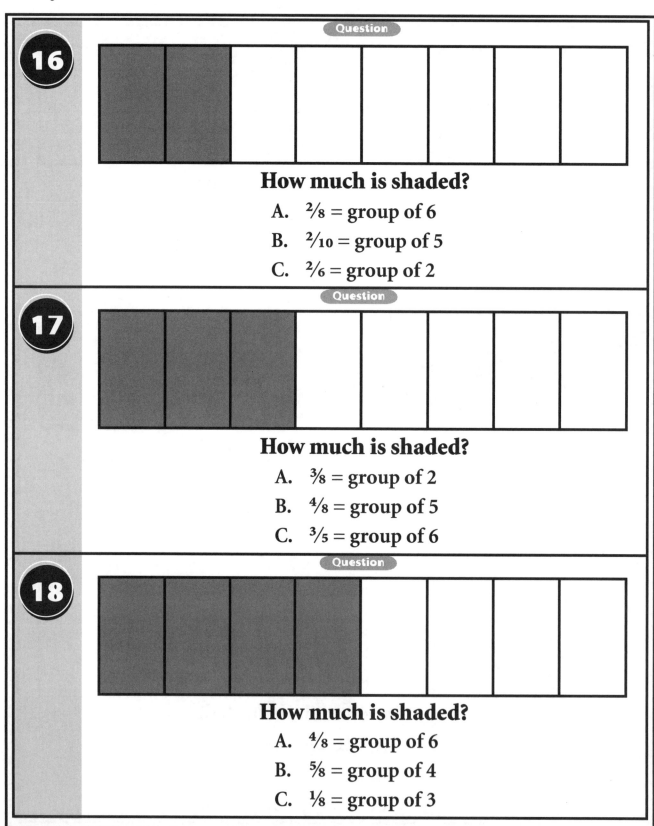

**Question**

**16**

## How much is shaded?

A.   $^2/_8$ = group of 6

B.   $^2/_{10}$ = group of 5

C.   $^2/_6$ = group of 2

**Question**

**17**

## How much is shaded?

A.   $^3/_8$ = group of 2

B.   $^4/_8$ = group of 5

C.   $^3/_5$ = group of 6

**Question**

**18**

## How much is shaded?

A.   $^4/_8$ = group of 6

B.   $^5/_8$ = group of 4

C.   $^1/_8$ = group of 3

# Fractions

**Teacher instructions:** Use these fraction questions to have students form groups with the number of students matching the answer.

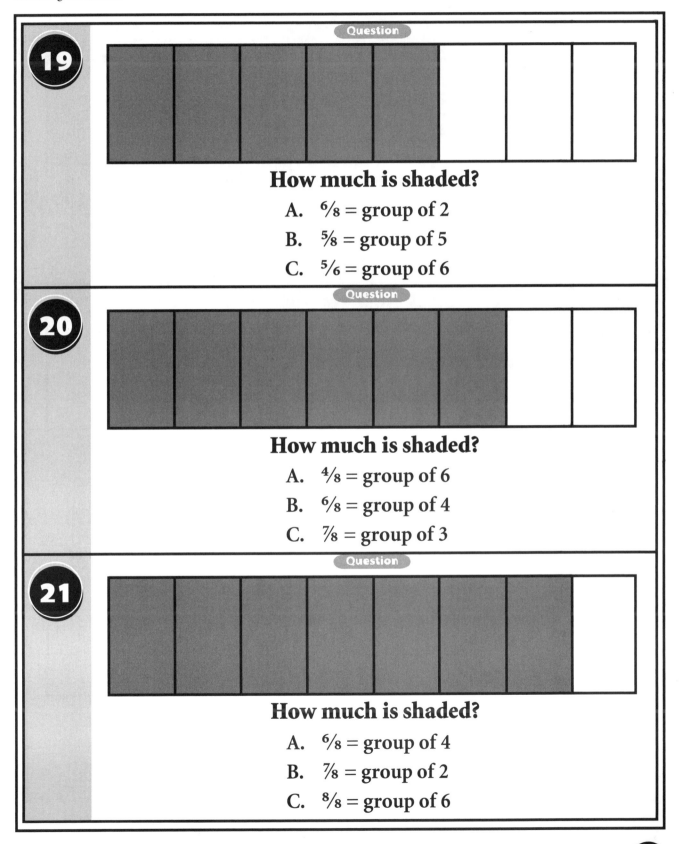

**Question**

**19**

### How much is shaded?

- A.   $6/8$ = group of 2
- B.   $5/8$ = group of 5
- C.   $5/6$ = group of 6

**Question**

**20**

### How much is shaded?

- A.   $4/8$ = group of 6
- B.   $6/8$ = group of 4
- C.   $7/8$ = group of 3

**Question**

**21**

### How much is shaded?

- A.   $6/8$ = group of 4
- B.   $7/8$ = group of 2
- C.   $8/8$ = group of 6

# Fractions

**Teacher instructions:** Use these fraction questions to have students form groups with the number of students matching the answer.

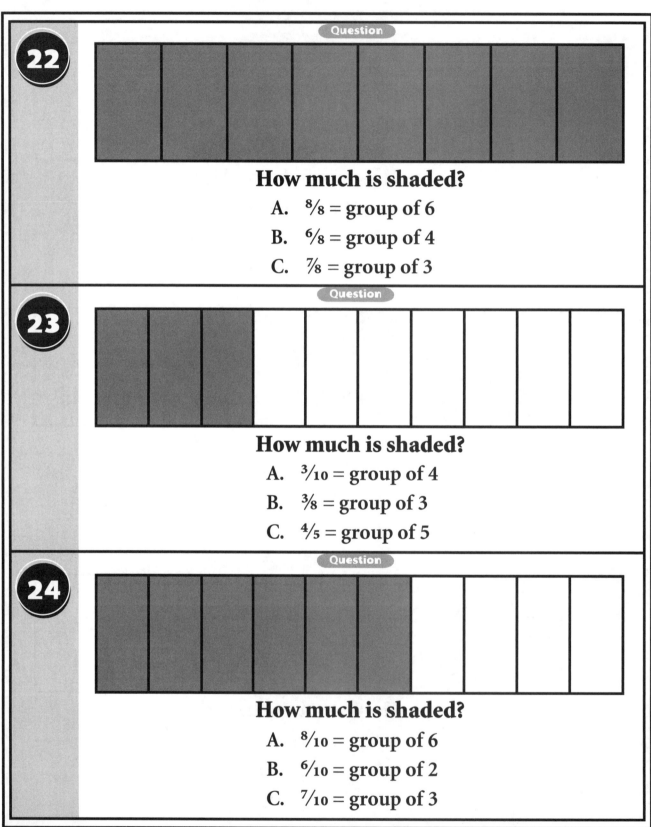

**Question**

**22**

## How much is shaded?

A. $\frac{8}{8}$ = group of 6

B. $\frac{6}{8}$ = group of 4

C. $\frac{7}{8}$ = group of 3

**Question**

**23**

## How much is shaded?

A. $\frac{3}{10}$ = group of 4

B. $\frac{3}{8}$ = group of 3

C. $\frac{4}{5}$ = group of 5

**Question**

**24**

## How much is shaded?

A. $\frac{8}{10}$ = group of 6

B. $\frac{6}{10}$ = group of 2

C. $\frac{7}{10}$ = group of 3

# Ordinal Numbers

**Teacher instructions:** Use these ordinal numbers questions to have students form groups with the number of students matching the answer.

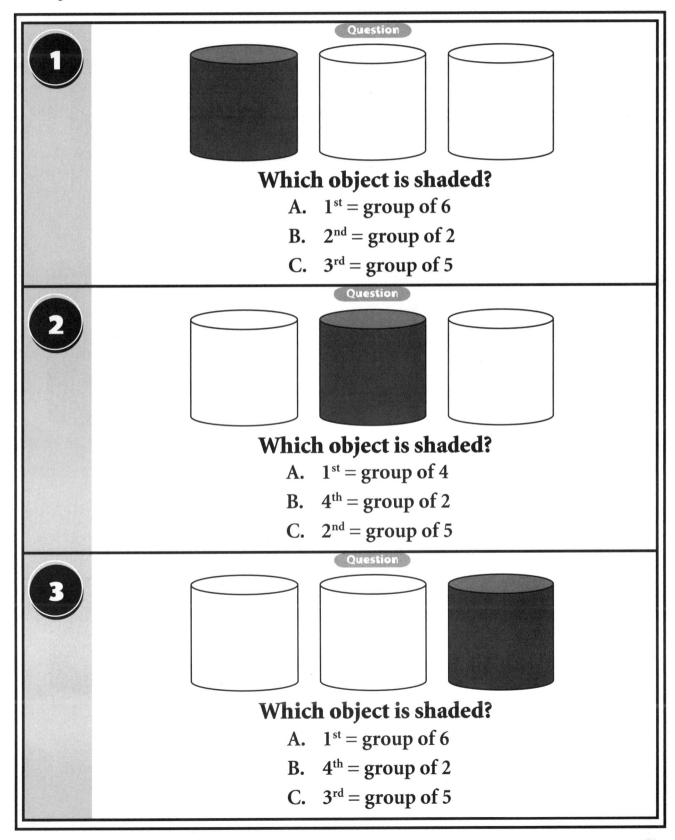

**Question**

## Which object is shaded?

A. 1$^{st}$ = group of 6

B. 2$^{nd}$ = group of 2

C. 3$^{rd}$ = group of 5

**Question**

## Which object is shaded?

A. 1$^{st}$ = group of 4

B. 4$^{th}$ = group of 2

C. 2$^{nd}$ = group of 5

**Question**

## Which object is shaded?

A. 1$^{st}$ = group of 6

B. 4$^{th}$ = group of 2

C. 3$^{rd}$ = group of 5

# Ordinal Numbers

**Teacher instructions:** Use these ordinal numbers questions to have students form groups with the number of students matching the answer.students matching the answer.

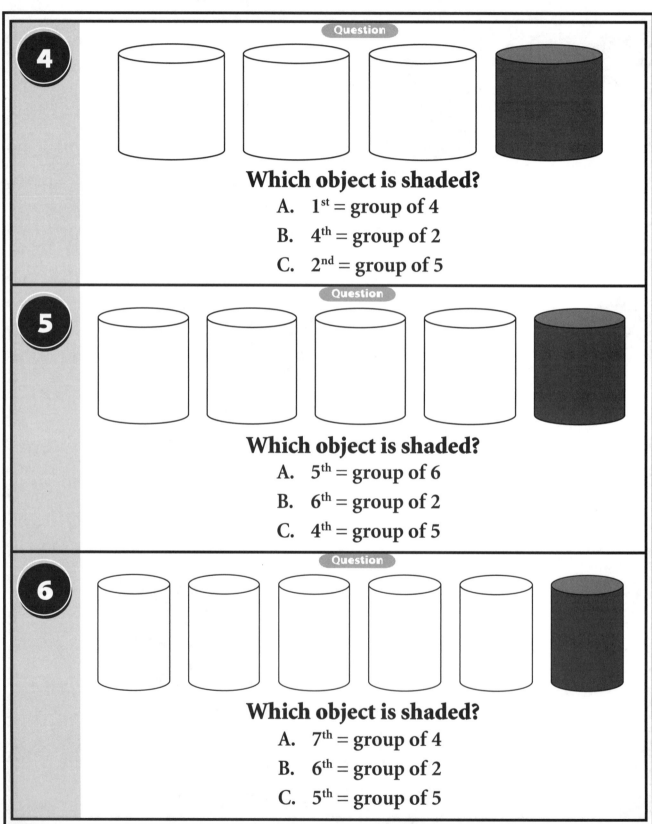

**4**

**Question**

## Which object is shaded?

A.   $1^{st}$ = group of 4

B.   $4^{th}$ = group of 2

C.   $2^{nd}$ = group of 5

**5**

**Question**

## Which object is shaded?

A.   $5^{th}$ = group of 6

B.   $6^{th}$ = group of 2

C.   $4^{th}$ = group of 5

**6**

**Question**

## Which object is shaded?

A.   $7^{th}$ = group of 4

B.   $6^{th}$ = group of 2

C.   $5^{th}$ = group of 5

# Ordinal Numbers

**Teacher instructions:** Use these ordinal numbers questions to have students form groups with the number of students matching the answer.

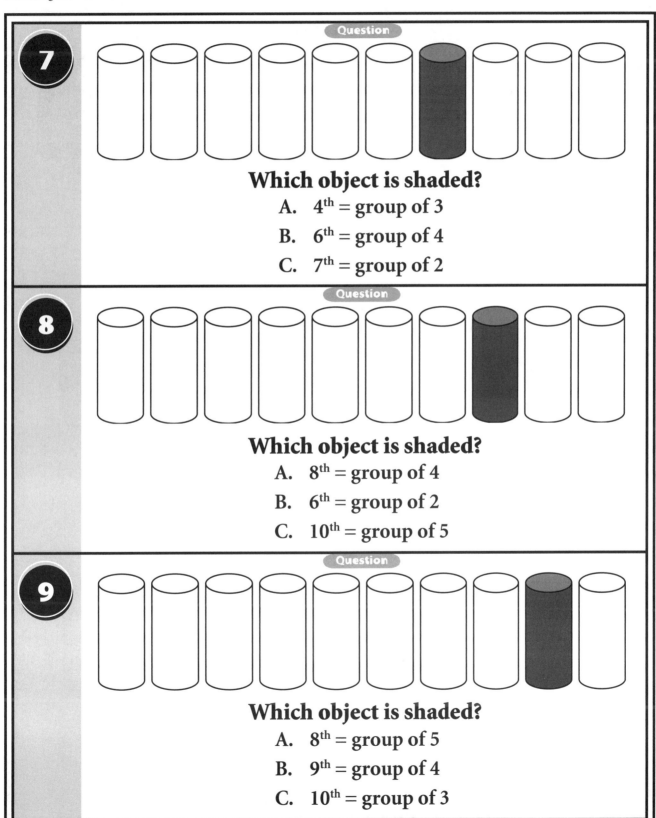

**Question**

**7**

## Which object is shaded?

A. 4th = group of 3

B. 6th = group of 4

C. 7th = group of 2

**Question**

**8**

## Which object is shaded?

A. 8th = group of 4

B. 6th = group of 2

C. 10th = group of 5

**Question**

**9**

## Which object is shaded?

A. 8th = group of 5

B. 9th = group of 4

C. 10th = group of 3

# Ordinal Numbers

**Teacher instructions:** Use these ordinal numbers questions to have students form groups with the number of students matching the answer.

**10**

Question

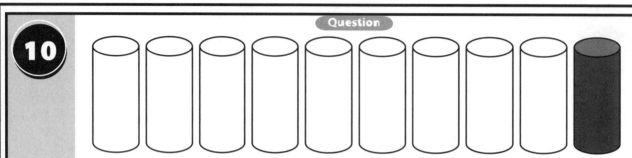

## Which object is shaded?

A. $8^{th}$ = group of 3

B. $6^{th}$ = group of 2

C. $10^{th}$ = group of 4

**11**

Question

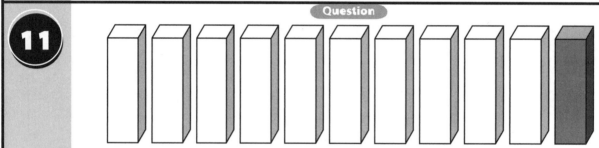

## Which object is shaded?

A. $11^{th}$ = group of 2

B. $12^{th}$ = group of 4

C. $10^{th}$ = group of 6

**12**

Question

## Which object is shaded?

A. $8^{th}$ = group of 3

B. $3^{rd}$ = group of 2

C. $4^{th}$ = group of 4

# Ordinal Numbers

**Teacher instructions:** Use these ordinal numbers questions to have students form groups with the number of students matching the answer.

**Question**

**13**

T.J.   Parker   Troy   Anson   Tyson   Taylor   Kayla

## What place is Troy?

A.   3$^{rd}$ = group of 2

B.   2$^{nd}$ = group of 4

C.   4$^{th}$ = group of 5

**Question**

**14**

## Which object is shaded?

A.   17$^{th}$ = group of 5

B.   15$^{th}$ = group of 6

C.   12$^{th}$ = group of 2

**Question**

**15**

## Which object is shaded?

A.   4$^{th}$ = group of 3

B.   6$^{th}$ = group of 4

C.   5$^{th}$ = group of 5

# Ordinal Numbers

**Teacher instructions:** Use these ordinal numbers questions to have students form groups with the number of students matching the answer.

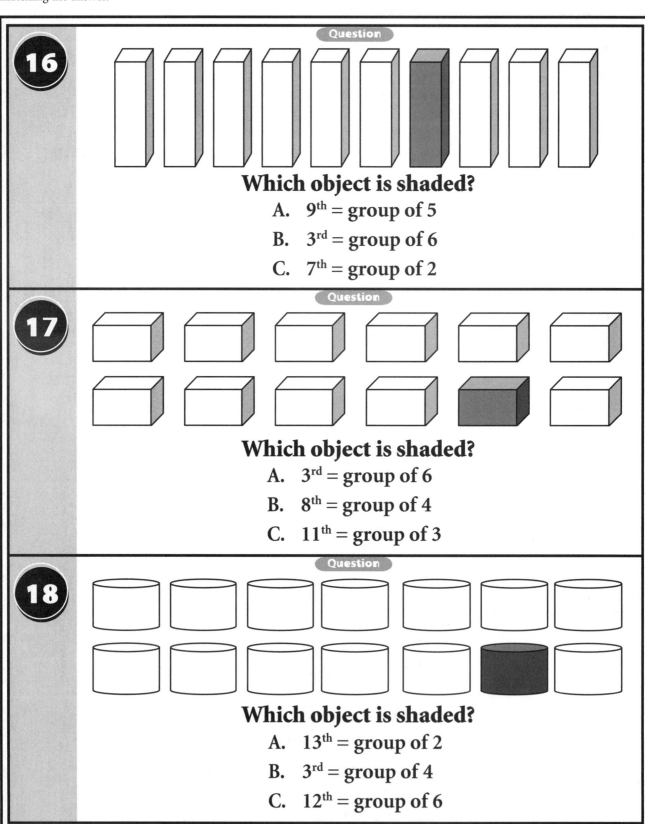

**16**

**Which object is shaded?**

A. $9^{th}$ = group of 5

B. $3^{rd}$ = group of 6

C. $7^{th}$ = group of 2

**17**

**Which object is shaded?**

A. $3^{rd}$ = group of 6

B. $8^{th}$ = group of 4

C. $11^{th}$ = group of 3

**18**

**Which object is shaded?**

A. $13^{th}$ = group of 2

B. $3^{rd}$ = group of 4

C. $12^{th}$ = group of 6

# Ordinal Numbers

**Teacher instructions:** Use these ordinal numbers questions to have students form groups with the number of students matching the answer.

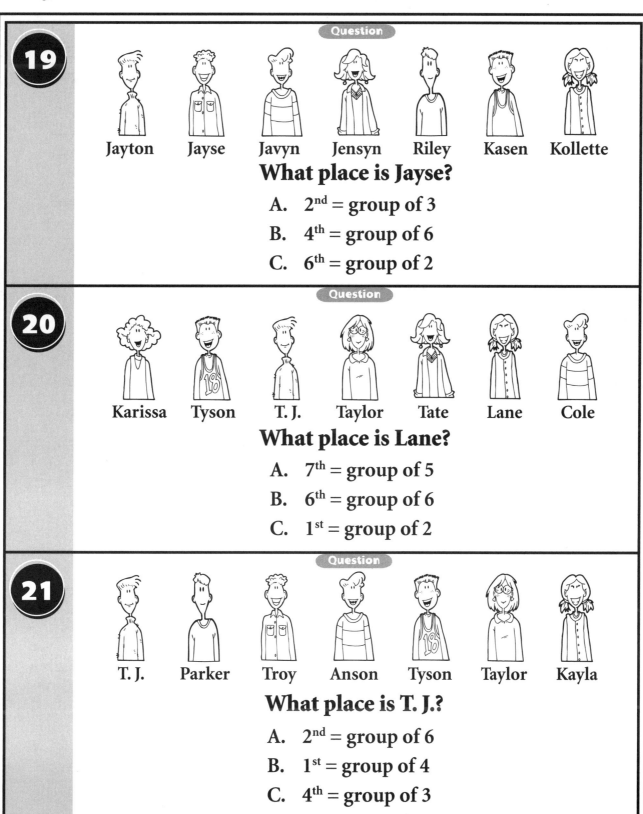

**Question**

**19**

Jayton　Jayse　Javyn　Jensyn　Riley　Kasen　Kollette

### What place is Jayse?

A. $2^{nd}$ = group of 3

B. $4^{th}$ = group of 6

C. $6^{th}$ = group of 2

**Question**

**20**

Karissa　Tyson　T. J.　Taylor　Tate　Lane　Cole

### What place is Lane?

A. $7^{th}$ = group of 5

B. $6^{th}$ = group of 6

C. $1^{st}$ = group of 2

**Question**

**21**

T. J.　Parker　Troy　Anson　Tyson　Taylor　Kayla

### What place is T. J.?

A. $2^{nd}$ = group of 6

B. $1^{st}$ = group of 4

C. $4^{th}$ = group of 3

# Ordinal Numbers

**Teacher instructions:** Use these ordinal numbers questions to have students form groups with the number of students matching the answer.

---

**22** *Question*

T. J.    Parker    Troy    Anson    Tyson    Taylor    Kayla

## What place is Tyson?

A.   5th = group of 5

B.   3rd = group of 6

C.   2nd = group of 2

---

**23** *Question*

T. J.    Parker    Troy    Anson    Tyson    Taylor    Kayla

## What place is Taylor?

A.   2nd = group of 3

B.   4th = group of 6

C.   6th = group of 2

---

**24** *Question*

Colby    Tyler    Trent    Annalise    Winter    Abby    Drayton

## What place is Drayton?

A.   7th = group of 5

B.   6th = group of 6

C.   1st = group of 2

---

# Number Words

**Teacher instructions:** Use these number word questions to have students form groups with the number of students matching the answer.

---

**1**

Question

# 1

### Which word matches this number?

A. two = group of 2
B. four = group of 3
C. one = group of 4

---

**2**

Question

# 2

### Which word matches this number?

A. two = group of 2
B. four = group of 3
C. one = group of 4

---

**3**

Question

# 3

### Which word matches this number?

A. two = group of 2
B. three = group 3
C. one = group of 4

---

# Number Words

**Teacher instructions:** Use these number word questions to have students form groups with the number of students matching the answer.

---

**Question**

# 4

**4**

## Which word matches this number?

- A. two = group of 2
- B. four = group of 3
- C. one = group of 4

---

**Question**

# 5

**5**

## Which word matches this number?

- A. five = group of 2
- B. seven = group of 3
- C. six = group of 4

---

**Question**

# 6

**6**

## Which word matches this number?

- A. five = group of 2
- B. seven = group of 3
- C. six = group of 4

---

# Number Words

**Teacher instructions:** Use these number word questions to have students form groups with the number of students matching the answer.

**Question**

# 7

## Which word matches this number?

A. seven = group of 2
B. three = group of 3
C. six = group of 4

**Question**

# 8

## Which word matches this number?

A. four = group of 2
B. eight = group of 3
C. twelve = group of 4

**Question**

# 9

## Which word matches this number?

A. one = group of 2
B. twelve = group of 3
C. nine = group of 4

# Number Words

**Teacher instructions:** Use these number word questions to have students form groups with the number of students matching the answer.

**Question**

## 10

### Which word matches this number?

A.   ten = group of 2
B.   two = group of 3
C.   eleven = group of 4

**Question**

## 11

### Which word matches this number?

A.   eight = group of 2
B.   seven = group of 3
C.   eleven = group of 4

**Question**

## 12

### Which word matches this number?

A.   twelve = group of 2
B.   two = group of 3
C.   six = group of 4

# Number Words

**Teacher instructions:** Use these number word questions to have students form groups with the number of students matching the answer.

---

**13**

Question

# two

## Which number matches this word?

A. 3 = group of 6
B. 2 = group of 4
C. 4 = group of 5

---

**14**

Question

# three

## Which number matches this word?

A. 5 = group of 3
B. 6 = group of 4
C. 3 = group of 2

---

**15**

Question

# four

## Which number matches this word?

A. 4 = group of 3
B. 5 = group of 4
C. 2 = group of 5

---

# Number Words

**Teacher instructions:** Use these number word questions to have students form groups with the number of students matching the answer.

**16**

# five

**Which number matches this word?**

A. 3 = group of 2
B. 2 = group of 3
C. 5 = group of 6

**17**

# six

**Which number matches this word?**

A. 5 = group of 3
B. 6 = group of 4
C. 2 = group of 5

**18**

# seven

**Which number matches this word?**

A. 8 = group of 2
B. 4 = group of 3
C. 7 = group of 5

# Number Words

**Teacher instructions:** Use these number word questions to have students form groups with the number of students matching the answer.

---

**19**

Question

# eight

**Which number matches this word?**

A. 9 = group of 3
B. 4 = group of 2
C. 8 = group of 4

---

**20**

Question

# nine

**Which number matches this word?**

A. 8 = group of 2
B. 9 = group of 5
C. 2 = group of 6

---

**21**

Question

# ten

**Which number matches this word?**

A. 10 = group of 4
B. 4 = group of 5
C. 7 = group of 2

---

# Number Words

**Teacher instructions:** Use these number word questions to have students form groups with the number of students matching the answer.

---

**Question**

### 22

# eleven

**Which number matches this word?**

    A.   6 = group of 8
    B.   11 = group of 6
    C.   5 = group of 2

---

**Question**

### 23

# twelve

**Which number matches this word?**

    A.   10 = group of 4
    B.   8 = group of 3
    C.   12 = group of 2

---

**Question**

### 24

# thirteen

**Which number matches this word?**

    A.   9 = group of 3
    B.   7 = group of 2
    C.   13 = group of 4

---

# Money

**Teacher instructions:** Use these money questions to have students form groups with the number of students matching the answer.

Question

**1**

## What is the total?

A.   7 cents = group of 2
B.   3 cents = group of 4
C.   12 cents = group of 6

Question

**2**

## What is the total?

A.   5 cents = group of 2
B.   13 cents = group of 4
C.   23 cents = group of 6

Question

**3**

## What is the total?

A.   6 cents = group of 2
B.   24 cents = group of 4
C.   19 cents = group of 6

# Money

**Teacher instructions:** Use these money questions to have students form groups with the number of students matching the answer.

**Question**

## 4

## What is the total?

A. 60 cents = group of 2
B. 45 cents = group of 4
C. 5 cents = group of 6

**Question**

## 5

## What is the total?

A. 73 cents = group of 2
B. 63 cents = group of 4
C. 43 cents = group of 6

**Question**

## 6

## What is the total?

A. 34 cents = group of 2
B. 59 cents = group of 4
C. 64 cents = group of 6

**Teacher instructions:** Use these money questions to have students form groups with the number of students matching the answer.

**7**

**Question**

## What is the total?

A.   24 cents = group of 2
B.   14 cents = group of 4
C.   6 cents = group of 6

**8**

**Question**

## What is the total?

A.   4 cents = group of 2
B.   26 cents = group of 4
C.   31 cents = group of 6

**9**

**Question**

## What is the total?

A.   4 cents = group of 2
B.   40 cents = group of 4
C.   20 cents = group of 6

# Money

**Teacher instructions:** Use these money questions to have students form groups with the number of students matching the answer.

**10**

Question

## What is the total?

- A. 71 cents = group of 2
- B. 69 cents = group of 4
- C. 91 cents = group of 6

**11**

Question

## What is the total?

- A. 70 cents = group of 2
- B. 72 cents = group of 4
- C. 82 cents = group of 6

**12**

Question

## What is the total?

- A. 95 cents = group of 2
- B. 85 cents = group of 4
- C. 75 cents = group of 6

# Money

**Teacher instructions:** Use these money questions to have students form groups with the number of students matching the answer.

**13**

## What is the total?

A.   93 cents = group of 2
B.   95 cents = group of 4
C.   98 cents = group of 6

**14**

## What is the total?

A.   35 cents = group of 2
B.   95 cents = group of 4
C.   90 cents = group of 6

**15**

## What is the total?

A.   32 cents = group of 2
B.   92 cents = group of 4
C.   97 cents = group of 6

# Money

**Teacher instructions:** Use these money questions to have students form groups with the number of students matching the answer.

**16**

Question

## What is the total?

A. 34 cents = group of 2
B. 36 cents = group of 4
C. 30 cents = group of 6

**17**

Question

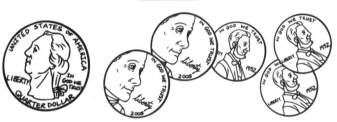

## What is the total?

A. 33 cents = group of 2
B. 38 cents = group of 4
C. 43 cents = group of 6

**18**

Question

## What is the total?

A. 20 cents = group of 2
B. 35 cents = group of 4
C. 30 cents = group of 6

# Money

**Teacher instructions:** Use these money questions to have students form groups with the number of students matching the answer.

**Question**

## What is the total?

A.   50 cents = group of 2
B.   51 cents = group of 4
C.   60 cents = group of 6

**Question**

## What is the total?

A.   25 cents = group of 2
B.   55 cents = group of 4
C.   65 cents = group of 6

**Question**

## What is the total?

A.   44 cents = group of 2
B.   55 cents = group of 4
C.   59 cents = group of 6

# Money

**Teacher instructions:** Use these money questions to have students form groups with the number of students matching the answer.

**22** Question

## What is the total?

A. 41 cents = group of 2
B. 51 cents = group of 4
C. 47 cents = group of 6

**23** Question

## What is the total?

A. 30 cents = group of 2
B. 40 cents = group of 4
C. 50 cents = group of 6

**24** Question

## What is the total?

A. 41 cents = group of 2
B. 51 cents = group of 4
C. 47 cents = group of 6

# Shapes #1

**Teacher instructions:** Use these shape questions to have students form groups with the number of students matching the answer.

**1**

**Question**
*How many sides does a triangle have?*

**Answer**
**A triangle has 3 sides.**

**2**

**Question**
*How many sides does a square have?*

**Answer**
**A square has 4 sides.**

**3**

**Question**
*How many sides does a rectangle have?*

**Answer**
**A rectangle has 4 sides.**

**4**

**Question**
*How many sides does a pentagon have?*

**Answer**
**A pentagon has 5 sides.**

**5**

**Question**
*How many sides does a hexagon have?*

**Answer**
**A hexagon has 6 sides.**

**6**

**Question**
*How many sides does an octagon have?*

**Answer**
**An octagon has 8 sides.**

# Shapes #1

**Teacher instructions:** Use these shape questions to have students form groups with the number of students matching the answer.

**7**

**Question**
How many sides does a decagon have?

**Answer**
A decagon has 10 sides.

**8**

**Question**
How many sides does a parallelogram have?

**Answer**
A parallelogram has 4 sides.

**9**

**Question**
How many sides does a trapezoid have?

**Answer**
A trapezoid has 4 sides.

**10**

**Question**
How many parallel lines does a square have?

**Answer**
A square has 2 pairs of parallel lines.

**11**

**Question**
How many pairs of parallel lines does a trapezoid have?

**Answer**
A trapezoid has 1 pair of parallel lines.

**12**

**Question**
How many pairs of parallel lines does a rectangle have?

**Answer**
A rectangle has 2 pairs of parallel lines.

# Shapes #2

**Teacher instructions:** Use these shape questions to have students form groups with the number of students matching the answer.

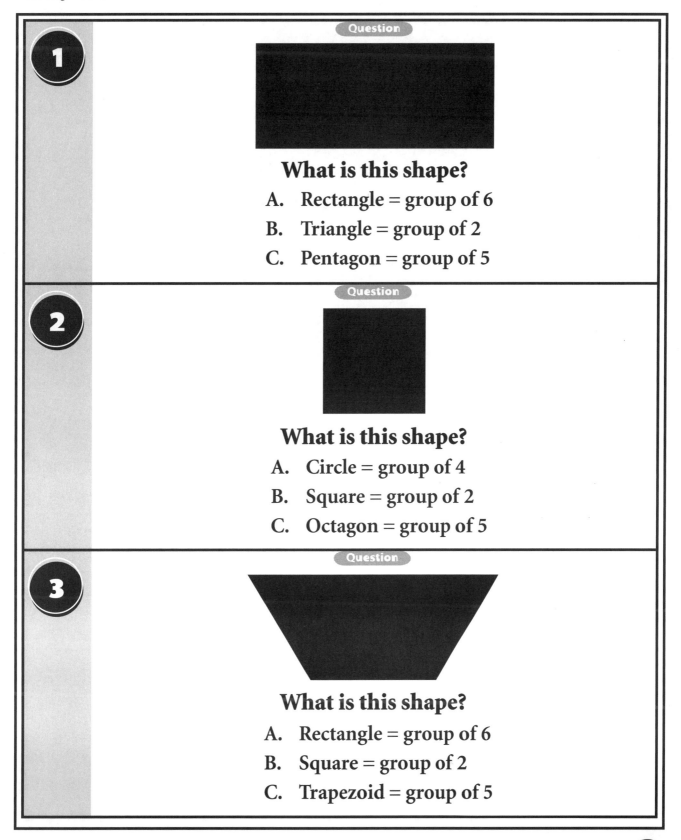

**Question**

## What is this shape?

A. Rectangle = group of 6
B. Triangle = group of 2
C. Pentagon = group of 5

**Question**

## What is this shape?

A. Circle = group of 4
B. Square = group of 2
C. Octagon = group of 5

**Question**

## What is this shape?

A. Rectangle = group of 6
B. Square = group of 2
C. Trapezoid = group of 5

# Shapes #2

**Teacher instructions:** Use these shape questions to have students form groups with the number of students matching the answer.

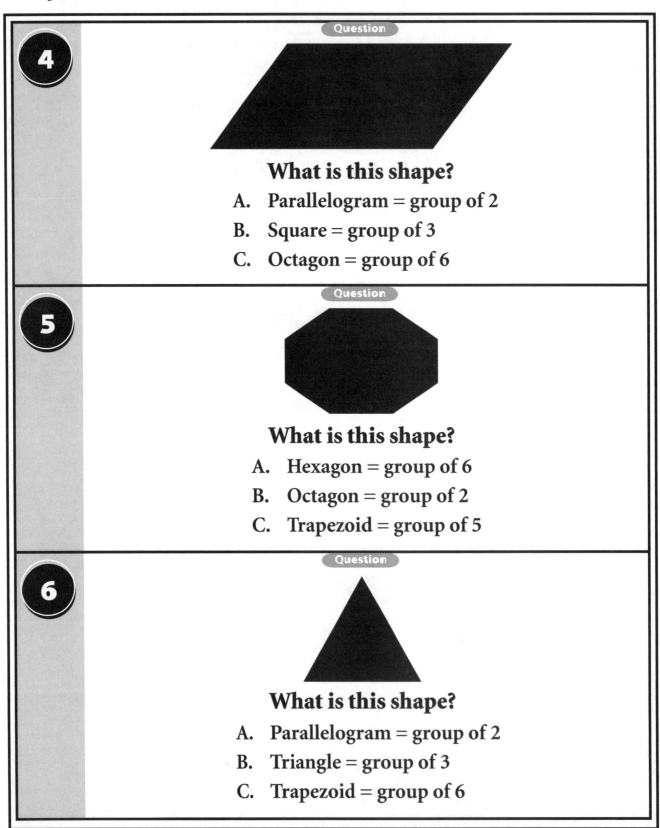

**Question**

### What is this shape?

A. Parallelogram = group of 2

B. Square = group of 3

C. Octagon = group of 6

**Question**

### What is this shape?

A. Hexagon = group of 6

B. Octagon = group of 2

C. Trapezoid = group of 5

**Question**

### What is this shape?

A. Parallelogram = group of 2

B. Triangle = group of 3

C. Trapezoid = group of 6

# Shapes #2

**Teacher instructions:** Use these shape questions to have students form groups with the number of students matching the answer.

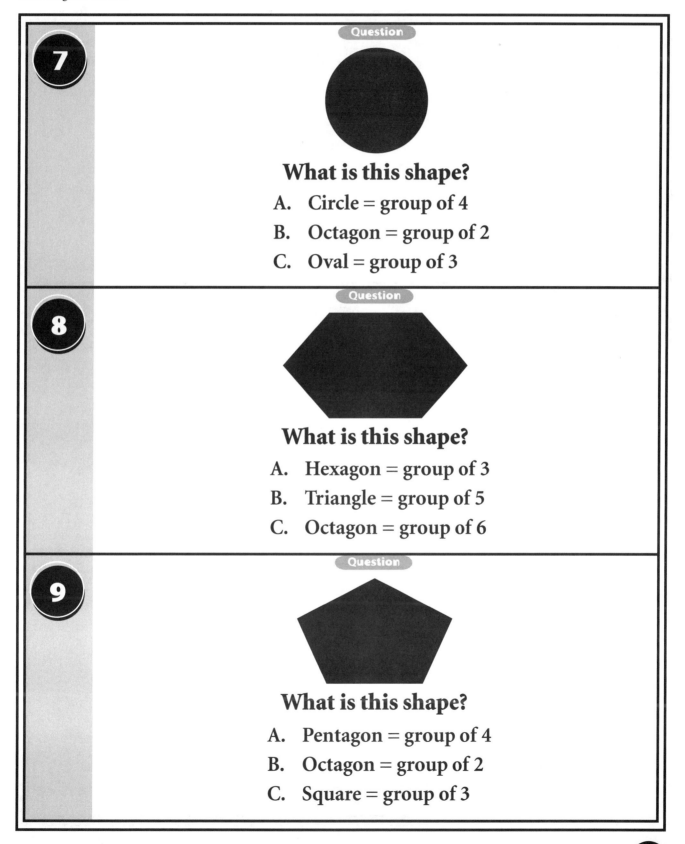

**Question**

**7**

**What is this shape?**

A. Circle = group of 4

B. Octagon = group of 2

C. Oval = group of 3

**Question**

**8**

**What is this shape?**

A. Hexagon = group of 3

B. Triangle = group of 5

C. Octagon = group of 6

**Question**

**9**

**What is this shape?**

A. Pentagon = group of 4

B. Octagon = group of 2

C. Square = group of 3

# Shapes #2

**Teacher instructions:** Use these shape questions to have students form groups with the number of students matching the answer.

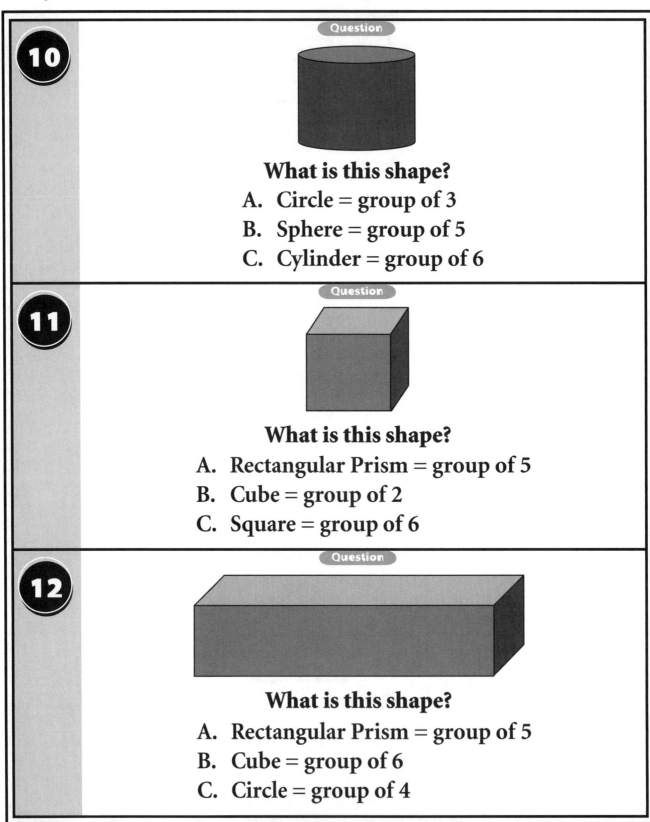

**10**

Question

**What is this shape?**

A. Circle = group of 3
B. Sphere = group of 5
C. Cylinder = group of 6

**11**

Question

**What is this shape?**

A. Rectangular Prism = group of 5
B. Cube = group of 2
C. Square = group of 6

**12**

Question

**What is this shape?**

A. Rectangular Prism = group of 5
B. Cube = group of 6
C. Circle = group of 4

# Shapes #2

**Teacher instructions:** Use these shape questions to have students form groups with the number of students matching the answer.

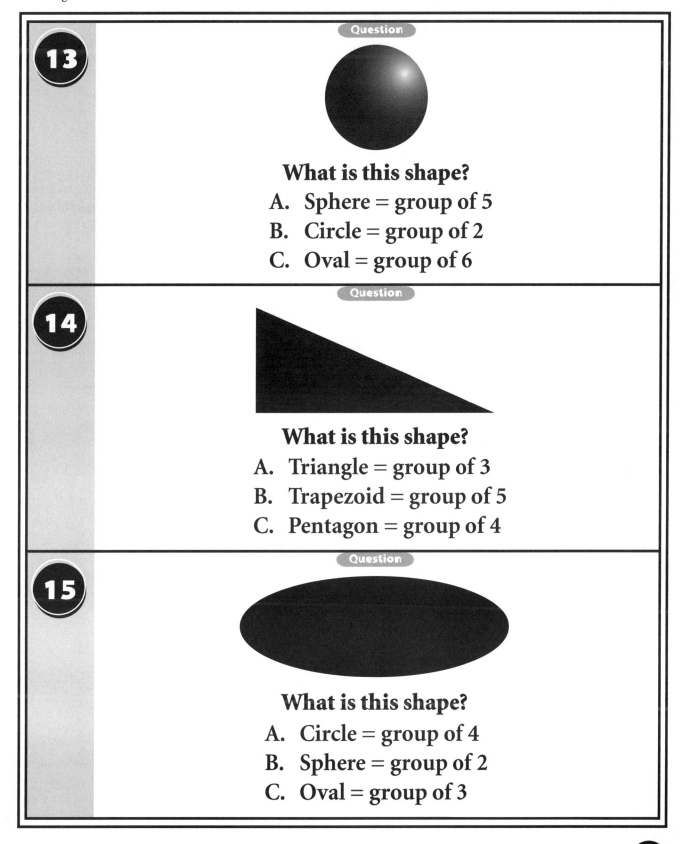

**13**

Question

**What is this shape?**

A. Sphere = group of 5
B. Circle = group of 2
C. Oval = group of 6

**14**

Question

**What is this shape?**

A. Triangle = group of 3
B. Trapezoid = group of 5
C. Pentagon = group of 4

**15**

Question

**What is this shape?**

A. Circle = group of 4
B. Sphere = group of 2
C. Oval = group of 3

# Mix-Freeze-Group Answer Key

## 4.1 Subtraction Situations

1. The dog has 2 bones.
2. The boy has 5 marbles.
3. The girl has 6 cookies.
4. The elephant has 3 peanuts.
5. The cat has 3 toys.
6. The boy has 3 candies.
7. Brady has 7 blocks.
8. Amanda has 6 dolls.
9. Bruce has 8 cars.
10. Matt has 5 pencils.
11. The girl has 2 more brothers than sisters.

12. Erin is 6 years older than her brother.
13. Sara has 8 more pens than Joe.
14. Lindsey is one year older than Jan.
15. Beth has 2 more candies than Jennie.
16. There are 4 ears of corn left in the garden.
17. Bo has 3 blocks left.
18. Jake has 7 jacks left.
19. Kristin has 8 balls left.
20. Teresa has 3 CDs left.

## 4.2 Fractions

1. A. ½ = 6 students per group
2. B. ⅓ = 2 students per group
3. C. ⅔ = 5 students per group
4. C. ³⁄₃ = 6 students per group
5. B. ¼ = 4 students per group
6. A. ²⁄₄ = 4 students per group
7. C. ¾ = 2 students per group
8. A. ⁴⁄₄ = 4 students per group
9. C. ⅙ = 2 students per group
10. B. ²⁄₆ = 5 students per group
11. A. ³⁄₆ = 5 students per group
12. C. ⁴⁄₆ = 2 students per group

13. A. ⁵⁄₆ = 3 students per group
14. B. ⁶⁄₆ = 5 students per group
15. A. ⅛ = 3 students per group
16. A. ²⁄₈ = 6 students per group
17. A. ⅜ = 2 students per group
18. A. ⁴⁄₈ = 6 students per group
19. B. ⅝ = 5 students per group
20. B. ⁶⁄₈ = 4 students per group
21. B. ⅞ = 2 students per group
22. A. ⁸⁄₈ = 6 students per group
23. A. ³⁄₁₀ = 4 students per group
24. B. ⁶⁄₁₀ = 2 students per group

# Mix-Freeze-Group Answer Key

## 4.3 Ordinal Numbers

1. A. 1st = 6 students per group
2. C. 2nd = 5 students per group
3. C. 3rd = 5 students per group
4. B. 4th = 2 students per group
5. A. 5th = 6 students per group
6. B. 6th = 2 students per group
7. C. 7th = 2 students per group
8. A. 8th = 4 students per group
9. B. 9th = 4 students per group
10. C. 10th = 4 students per group
11. A. 11th = 2 students per group
12. B. 3rd = 2 students per group
13. A. 3rd = 2 students per group
14. B. 15th = 6 students per group
15. B. 6th = 4 students per group
16. C. 7th = 2 students per group
17. C. 11th = 3 students per group
18. A. 13th = 2 students per group
19. A. 2nd = 3 students per group
20. B. 6th = 6 students per group
21. B. 1st = 4 students per group
22. A. 5th = 5 students per group
23. C. 6th = 2 students per group
24. A. 7th = 5 students per group

## 4.4 Number Words

1. C. One = 4 students per group
2. A. Two = 2 students per group
3. B. Three = 3 students per group
4. B. Four = 3 students per group
5. A. Five = 2 students per group
6. C. Six = 4 students per group
7. A. Seven = 2 students per group
8. B. Eight = 3 students per group
9. C Nine = 4 students per group
10. A. Ten = 2 students per group
11. C. Eleven = 4 students per group
12. A. Twelve = 2 students per group
13. B. 2 = 4 students per group
14. C. 3 = 2 students per group
15. A. 4 = 3 students per group
16. C. 5 = 6 students per group
17. B. 6 = 4 students per group
18. C. 7 = 5 students per group
19. C. 8 = 4 students per group
20. B. 9 = 5 students per group
21. A. 10 = 4 students per group
22. B. 11 = 6 students per group
23. C. 12 = 2 students per group
24. C. 13 = 4 students per group

# Mix-Freeze-Group Answer Key

## 4.5 Money

1. A. 7 cents = 2 students per group
2. B. 13 cents = 4 students per group
3. C. 19 cents = 6 students per group
4. A. 60 cents = 2 students per group
5. B. 63 cents = 4 students per group
6. C. 64 cents = 6 students per group
7. A. 24 cents = 2 students per group
8. B. 26 cents = 4 students per group
9. C. 20 cents = 6 students per group
10. A. 71 cents = 2 students per group
11. B. 72 cents = 4 students per group
12. C. 75 cents = 6 students per group
13. A. 93 cents = 2 students per group
14. B. 95 cents = 4 students per group
15. C. 97 cents = 6 students per group
16. A. 34 cents = 2 students per group
17. B. 38 cents = 4 students per group
18. C. 30 cents = 6 students per group
19. A. 50 cents = 2 students per group
20. B. 55 cents = 4 students per group
21. C. 59 cents = 6 students per group
22. A. 41 cents = 2 students per group
23. B. 40 cents = 4 students per group
24. C. 47 cents = 6 students per group

## 4.6 Shapes #1

1. A triangle has 3 sides.
2. A square has 4 sides.
3. A rectangle has 4 sides.
4. A pentagon has 5 sides.
5. A hexagon has 6 sides.
6. An octagon has 8 sides.
7. A decagon has 10 sides.
8. A parallelogram has 4 sides.
9. A trapezoid has 4 sides.
10. A square has 2 pairs of parallel lines.
11. A trapezoid has 1 pair of parallel lines.
12. A rectangle has 2 pairs of parallel lines.

## 4.7 Shapes #2

1. A. Rectangle = 6 students per group
2. B. Square = 2 students per group
3. C. Trapezoid = 5 students per group
4. A. Parallelogram = 2 students per group
5. B. Octagon = 2 students per group
6. B. Triangle = 3 students per group
7. A. Circle = 4 students per group
8. A. Hexagon = 3 students per group
9. A. Pentagon = 4 students per group
10. C. Cylinder = 6 students per group
11. B. Cube = 2 students per group
12. A. Rectangular Prism = 5 students per group
13. A. Sphere = 5 students per group
14. A. Triangle = 3 students per group
15. C. Oval = 3 students per group

# COOPERATIVE MATH

# Structure 5

# Quiz-Quiz-Trade

# Structure 5

# Quiz-Quiz-Trade

**Students quiz a partner, get quizzed by a partner, and then trade cards to repeat the process with a new partner.**

## Instructions

*Students each get a Quiz-Quiz-Trade card.*

**1** Students stand up, put a hand up, and pair up with a classmate.

**2** Partner A uses his or her card to quiz Partner B.

**3** Partner B answers.

**4** Partner A praises Partner B if he or she answers correctly. If not, Partner A shows the correct answer and coaches Partner B.

**5** Students switch roles and Partner B quizzes Partner A.

**6** Partners trade cards.

**7** Repeat Steps 1–6 a number of times, each time with a new partner.

**⭐Boosting Engagement⭐**

Quiz-Quiz-Trade converts math drill and kill into an engaging social event. Students get the benefit of repeated practice, but it becomes fun and interactive when they get to pair up with a different classmate for every problem. Students are motivated to show their classmates what they know. And when they need help, they have a tutor right there to help.

# Quiz-Quiz-Trade Activities

## ✚ Number and Operations

## Geometry

## 🎲 Data Analysis & Probability

## 🔑 Answer Key

# Quiz-Quiz-Trade Primary Tips

## General Tips

- Limit number of concepts being reviewed. It is okay for primary students to practice concepts multiple times.
- Laminate cards for durability.
- Content should be a review of material previously taught.
- When making cards, label front of card "Q" for question. Label back of card "A" for answer.
- Establish a quiet signal to bring the class focus back to the teacher.

## Before
### Teaching the Structure

- Start with a visual of the structure. Use the visual to explain the steps.
- Model with students how to find a partner, quiz, coach, trade cards, and praise their partner.
  - ★ **Tips on "How to find a partner"**
    - Model with four students. Demonstrate how to "pair up" with the closest person without passing someone.
    - Model with students how to keep their hands high until they find a partner. No bent elbows.
      - Once a partner is found, model with students how to give a quiet high five with no slapping.
      - Watch out for students "following" friends.

## Before
### Teaching the Structure *(continued)*

★ **Tips on "Quizzing"**
- Model quizzing. Demonstrate how to hold the card and ask the question. If the answer is on the back, remind students to show the question side only to their partner.
- The listening student puts his or her hands behind their back and looks directly at his or her partner. Make sure their shoulders are "squared up."

★ **Tips on "Coaching"**
- Give students examples of coaching phrases without giving their partner the answer. For example: "Count with me." Coaching is always specific to the task so the teacher must model specific coaching phrases that match the content. Phrases like "keep trying" or "try again" are encouraging statements, not coaching.
- Student coaches could also use manipulatives to help show things such as addition/subtraction, counting, etc.

★ **Tips on "Praising"**
- Give specific praise or cheer that all students do when done quizzing/answering (Examples: high five, a round of applause, thumbs up, "Great job!"). Watch to make sure the praising does not distract students from the content.

## During
### Doing the Structure

- Start with short amounts of time. If the structure continues for too long, students start to get loud and off task.
- Do not use music.
- Listen for good coaching and praising. Stop the group if appropriate and hold up a pair as models. Do this during the structure so that other students can practice what you have emphasized.
- Make sure students do not get too close together.
- Listen for "partner voices." You should not hear individuals.

## After
### Processing the Structure

- Talk about what went well. Demonstrate if needed.
- Note any problems.
- Set goals for next time.

# Quiz-Quiz-Trade Activities

## Activity 5.1

### How Many?

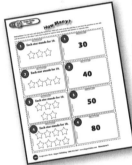

Students each receive a card with stars representing a number. Using Quiz-Quiz-Trade, partners stand up, put hand up, and pair up with a classmate. Partner A quizzes Partner B, asking the number of stars on the card. Partner B states the number that matches the number of stars. Partner A praises Partner B if he or she answers correctly or coaches if Partner B doesn't answer or answers incorrectly. Students switch roles so Partner B quizzes and Partner A answers. Partners trade cards. Repeat a number of times, each time with a new partner.

**NCTM Standard: Number and Operations Standard for Grades PreK–2**
★ Understand numbers, ways of representing numbers, relationships among numbers, and number systems.
• Connect number words and numerals to the quantities they represent, using various physical models and representations.  **pp. 184–193**

## Activity 5.2

### Addition Facts

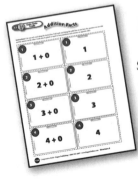

Students each receive a card with an addition problem. Using Quiz-Quiz-Trade, partners stand up, put hand up, and pair up with a classmate. Partner A quizzes Partner B with the addition sentence on the card. Partner B states the answer that matches the addition sentence. Partner A praises Partner B if he or she answers correctly or coaches if Partner B doesn't answer or answers incorrectly. Students switch roles so Partner B quizzes and Partner A answers. Partners trade cards. Repeat a number of times, each time with a new partner.

**NCTM Standard: Number and Operations Standard for Grades PreK–2**
★ Understand meanings of operations and how they relate to one another.
• Understand various meanings of addition and subtraction of whole numbers and the relationship between the two operations.  **pp. 194–226**

# Activity 5.3

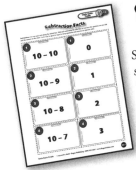

## Subtraction Facts

Students each receive a card with a subtraction problem. Using Quiz-Quiz-Trade, partners stand up, put hand up, and pair up with a classmate. Partner A quizzes Partner B with the subtraction sentence on the card. Partner B states the answer that matches the subtraction sentence.

Partner A praises Partner B if he or she answers correctly or coaches if Partner B doesn't answer or answers incorrectly. Students switch roles so Partner B quizzes and Partner A answers. Partners trade cards. Repeat a number of times, each time with a new partner.

**NCTM Standard: Number and Operations Standard for Grades PreK–2**
★ Understand meanings of operations and how they relate to one another.
  • Understand various meanings of addition and subtraction of whole numbers and the relationship between the two operations.

pp. 227–242

# Activity 5.4

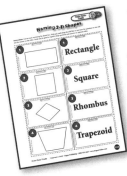

## Naming 2-D Shapes

*Two-dimensional shapes* relate to objects that have length and width, but no depth. Students explore plane shapes such as polygons and circles. Students each receive a 2-D shape or picture card. Using Quiz-Quiz-Trade, partners stand up, put hand up, and pair up with a classmate. Partner A quizzes Partner B with the shape on the card or shape of the shaded face. Partner B states the name of the shape. Partner A praises Partner B if he or she answers correctly or coaches if Partner B doesn't answer or answers incorrectly. Students switch roles so Partner B quizzes and Partner A answers. Partners trade cards. Repeat a number of times, each time with a new partner.

**NCTM Standard: Geometry Standard PreK–2**
★ Analyze characteristics and properties of two- and three-dimensional geometric shapes and develop mathematical arguments about geometric relationships.
  • Recognize, name, build, draw, compare, and sort two- and three-dimensional shapes.

pp. 243–247

# Quiz-Quiz-Trade
## Activities continued

---

## Activity 5.5

### Naming 3-D Shapes

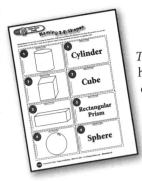

*Three-dimensional shapes* are objects that have length, width, and depth. Students explore shapes such as cones and spheres. Students each receive a 3-D shape or picture card. Using Quiz-Quiz-Trade, partners stand up, put hand up, and pair up with a classmate. Partner A quizzes Partner B with the shape on the card. Partner B states the name of the shape. Partner A praises Partner B if he or she answers correctly or coaches if Partner B doesn't answer or answers incorrectly. Students switch roles so Partner B quizzes and Partner A answers. Partners trade cards. Repeat a number of times, each time with a new partner.

**NCTM Standard: Geometry Standard PreK–2**
★ Analyze characteristics and properties of two- and three-dimensional geometric shapes and develop mathematical arguments about geometric relationships.
 • Recognize, name, build, draw, compare, and sort two- and three-dimensional shapes.

pp. 248–252

---

## Activity 5.6

### Coordinate Points

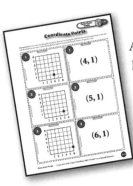

A *coordinate grid* is a system in which a point is described by its distance from two perpendicular lines called axes. In an ordered pair, the first number is the distance of the point from the *x*-axis (horizontal) and the second number is the distance of the point from the *y*-axis (vertical). Students each receive a card with a coordinate point. Using Quiz-Quiz-Trade, partners stand up, put hand up, and pair up with a classmate. Partner A quizzes Partner B with the coordinate grid on the card. Partner B states the ordered pair that matches the point. Partner A praises Partner B if he or she answers correctly or coaches if Partner B doesn't answer or answers incorrectly. Students switch roles so Partner B quizzes and Partner A answers. Partners trade cards. Repeat a number of times, each time with a new partner.

**NCTM Standard: Geometry Standard PreK–2**
★ Specify locations and describe spatial relationships using coordinate geometry and other representational systems.
 • Find and name locations with simple relationships such as "near to" and in coordinate systems such as maps.

pp. 253–264

# Activity 5.7

## Likely or Unlikely?

*Probability* is the chance of an event happening. Students each receive a card with a likely or unlikely event. Using Quiz-Quiz-Trade, partners stand up, put hand up, and pair up with a classmate. Partner A quizzes Partner B with the situation on the card. Partner B states whether the situation is likely or unlikely. Partner A praises Partner B if he or she answers correctly or coaches if Partner B doesn't answer or answers incorrectly. Students switch roles so Partner B quizzes and Partner A answers. Partners trade cards. Repeat steps a number of times, each time with a new partner.

**NCTM Standard: Data Analysis and Probability PreK–2**
★ Develop and evaluate inferences and predictions that are based on data.
• Discuss events related to students' experiences as likely or unlikely.

pp. 265–269

# How Many?

**Instructions:** Cut out each card along the dotted line. Fold each card along the solid line so you have the question on one side and the answer on the other. Cards may be glued or taped to keep questions and answers on opposite sides.

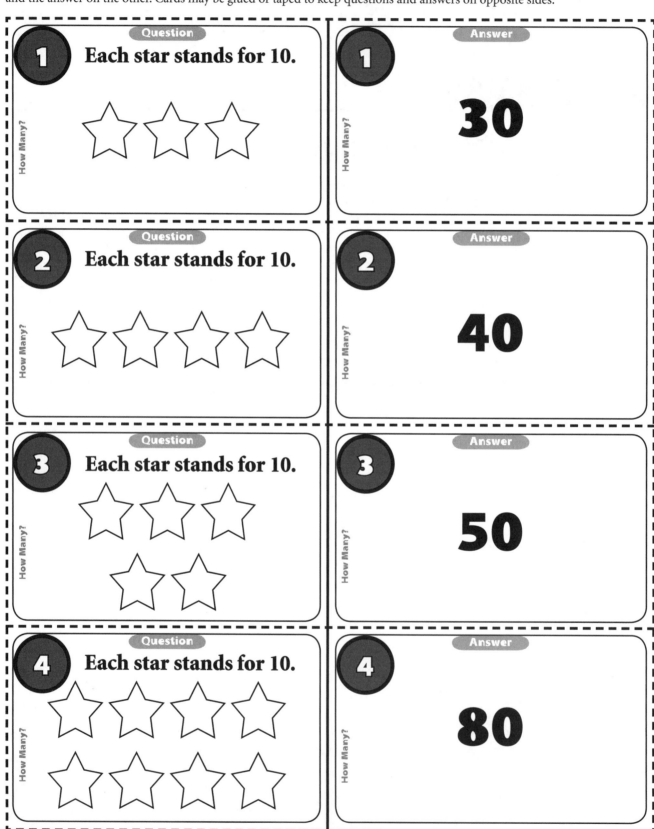

# How Many?

**Instructions:** Cut out each card along the dotted line. Fold each card along the solid line so you have the question on one side and the answer on the other. Cards may be glued or taped to keep questions and answers on opposite sides.

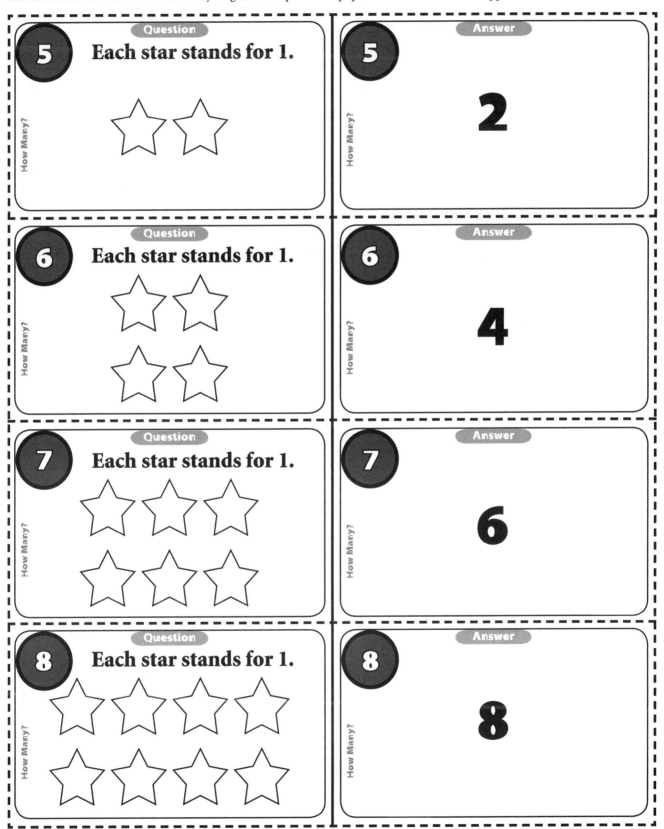

# How Many?

**Instructions:** Cut out each card along the dotted line. Fold each card along the solid line so you have the question on one side and the answer on the other. Cards may be glued or taped to keep questions and answers on opposite sides.

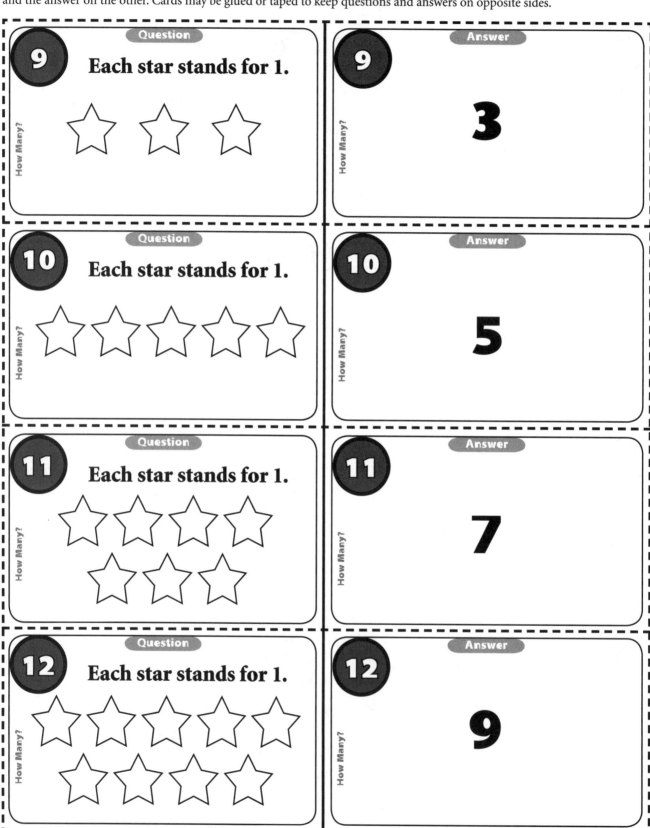

# How Many?

**Instructions:** Cut out each card along the dotted line. Fold each card along the solid line so you have the question on one side and the answer on the other. Cards may be glued or taped to keep questions and answers on opposite sides.

# How Many?

**Instructions:** Cut out each card along the dotted line. Fold each card along the solid line so you have the question on one side and the answer on the other. Cards may be glued or taped to keep questions and answers on opposite sides.

**17** Question — Each star stands for 1. How Many?

**17** Answer — **14** How Many?

**18** Question — Each star stands for 1. How Many?

**18** Answer — **15** How Many?

**19** Question — Each star stands for 1. How Many?

**19** Answer — **16** How Many?

**20** Question — Each star stands for 1. How Many?

**20** Answer — **17** How Many?

# How Many?

**Instructions:** Cut out each card along the dotted line. Fold each card along the solid line so you have the question on one side and the answer on the other. Cards may be glued or taped to keep questions and answers on opposite sides.

# How Many?

**Instructions:** Cut out each card along the dotted line. Fold each card along the solid line so you have the question on one side and the answer on the other. Cards may be glued or taped to keep questions and answers on opposite sides.

# How Many?

**Instructions:** Cut out each card along the dotted line. Fold each card along the solid line so you have the question on one side and the answer on the other. Cards may be glued or taped to keep questions and answers on opposite sides.

**29** **Question** Each star stands for 2. How Many?

**29** **Answer** **32** How Many?

**30** **Question** Each star stands for 2. How Many?

**30** **Answer** **24** How Many?

**31** **Question** Each star stands for 2. How Many?

**31** **Answer** **28** How Many?

**32** **Question** Each star stands for 2. How Many?

**32** **Answer** **36** How Many?

# How Many?

**Instructions:** Cut out each card along the dotted line. Fold each card along the solid line so you have the question on one side and the answer on the other. Cards may be glued or taped to keep questions and answers on opposite sides.

**33** Question — Each star stands for 5. How Many?

**33** Answer — 50

**34** Question — Each star stands for 5. How Many?

**34** Answer — 55

**35** Question — Each star stands for 5. How Many?

**35** Answer — 60

**36** Question — Each star stands for 5. How Many?

**36** Answer — 70

# How Many?

**Instructions:** Cut out each card along the dotted line. Fold each card along the solid line so you have the question on one side and the answer on the other. Cards may be glued or taped to keep questions and answers on opposite sides.

**37** Question — How Many? — Each star stands for 25. ☆

**37** Answer — How Many? — **25**

**38** Question — How Many? — Each star stands for 25. ☆ ☆

**38** Answer — How Many? — **50**

**39** Question — How Many? — Each star stands for 25. ☆ ☆ ☆

**39** Answer — How Many? — **75**

**40** Question — How Many? — Each star stands for 25. ☆ ☆ ☆ ☆

**40** Answer — How Many? — **100**

# Addition Facts

**Instructions:** Cut out each card along the dotted line. Fold each card along the solid line so you have the question on one side and the answer on the other. Cards may be glued or taped to keep questions and answers on opposite sides.

| | |
|---|---|
| **1** Question — Addition Facts — $1 + 0$ | **1** Answer — Addition Facts — $1$ |
| **2** Question — Addition Facts — $2 + 0$ | **2** Answer — Addition Facts — $2$ |
| **3** Question — Addition Facts — $3 + 0$ | **3** Answer — Addition Facts — $3$ |
| **4** Question — Addition Facts — $4 + 0$ | **4** Answer — Addition Facts — $4$ |

# Addition Facts

**Instructions:** Cut out each card along the dotted line. Fold each card along the solid line so you have the question on one side and the answer on the other. Cards may be glued or taped to keep questions and answers on opposite sides.

**5** Question

Addition Facts

$5 + 0$

**5** Answer

Addition Facts

$5$

**6** Question

Addition Facts

$6 + 0$

**6** Answer

Addition Facts

$6$

**7** Question

Addition Facts

$7 + 0$

**7** Answer

Addition Facts

$7$

**8** Question

Addition Facts

$8 + 0$

**8** Answer

Addition Facts

$8$

# Addition Facts

**Instructions:** Cut out each card along the dotted line. Fold each card along the solid line so you have the question on one side and the answer on the other. Cards may be glued or taped to keep questions and answers on opposite sides.

| | |
|---|---|
| **Question** **9** | **Answer** **9** |
| Addition Facts | Addition Facts |
| **9 + 0** | **9** |

| | |
|---|---|
| **Question** **10** | **Answer** **10** |
| Addition Facts | Addition Facts |
| **10 + 0** | **10** |

| | |
|---|---|
| **Question** **11** | **Answer** **11** |
| Addition Facts | Addition Facts |
| **11 + 0** | **11** |

| | |
|---|---|
| **Question** **12** | **Answer** **12** |
| Addition Facts | Addition Facts |
| **12 + 0** | **12** |

# Addition Facts

**Instructions:** Cut out each card along the dotted line. Fold each card along the solid line so you have the question on one side and the answer on the other. Cards may be glued or taped to keep questions and answers on opposite sides.

| | |
|---|---|
| **13** Question — Addition Facts — **1 + 1** | **13** Answer — Addition Facts — **2** |
| **14** Question — Addition Facts — **2 + 1** | **14** Answer — Addition Facts — **3** |
| **15** Question — Addition Facts — **3 + 1** | **15** Answer — Addition Facts — **4** |
| **16** Question — Addition Facts — **4 + 1** | **16** Answer — Addition Facts — **5** |

# Addition Facts

**Instructions:** Cut out each card along the dotted line. Fold each card along the solid line so you have the question on one side and the answer on the other. Cards may be glued or taped to keep questions and answers on opposite sides.

| | |
|---|---|
| **17** Question — Addition Facts — **5 + 1** | **17** Answer — Addition Facts — **6** |
| **18** Question — Addition Facts — **6 + 1** | **18** Answer — Addition Facts — **7** |
| **19** Question — Addition Facts — **7 + 1** | **19** Answer — Addition Facts — **8** |
| **20** Question — Addition Facts — **8 + 1** | **20** Answer — Addition Facts — **9** |

# Addition Facts

**Instructions:** Cut out each card along the dotted line. Fold each card along the solid line so you have the question on one side and the answer on the other. Cards may be glued or taped to keep questions and answers on opposite sides.

| | |
|---|---|
| **21** Question — Addition Facts — $9 + 1$ | **21** Answer — Addition Facts — $10$ |
| **22** Question — Addition Facts — $10 + 1$ | **22** Answer — Addition Facts — $11$ |
| **23** Question — Addition Facts — $11 + 1$ | **23** Answer — Addition Facts — $12$ |
| **24** Question — Addition Facts — $12 + 1$ | **24** Answer — Addition Facts — $13$ |

# Addition Facts

**Instructions:** Cut out each card along the dotted line. Fold each card along the solid line so you have the question on one side and the answer on the other. Cards may be glued or taped to keep questions and answers on opposite sides.

| | |
|---|---|
| **Question** **25** Addition Facts<br><br>**1 + 2** | **Answer** **25** Addition Facts<br><br>**3** |
| **Question** **26** Addition Facts<br><br>**2 + 2** | **Answer** **26** Addition Facts<br><br>**4** |
| **Question** **27** Addition Facts<br><br>**3 + 2** | **Answer** **27** Addition Facts<br><br>**5** |
| **Question** **28** Addition Facts<br><br>**4 + 2** | **Answer** **28** Addition Facts<br><br>**6** |

# Addition Facts

**Instructions:** Cut out each card along the dotted line. Fold each card along the solid line so you have the question on one side and the answer on the other. Cards may be glued or taped to keep questions and answers on opposite sides.

| | |
|---|---|
| **Question** 29 — Addition Facts — $5 + 2$ | **Answer** 29 — Addition Facts — $7$ |
| **Question** 30 — Addition Facts — $6 + 2$ | **Answer** 30 — Addition Facts — $8$ |
| **Question** 31 — Addition Facts — $7 + 2$ | **Answer** 31 — Addition Facts — $9$ |
| **Question** 32 — Addition Facts — $8 + 2$ | **Answer** 32 — Addition Facts — $10$ |

# Addition Facts

**Instructions:** Cut out each card along the dotted line. Fold each card along the solid line so you have the question on one side and the answer on the other. Cards may be glued or taped to keep questions and answers on opposite sides.

| | |
|---|---|
| **33** Question — Addition Facts — $9 + 2$ | **33** Answer — Addition Facts — $11$ |
| **34** Question — Addition Facts — $10 + 2$ | **34** Answer — Addition Facts — $12$ |
| **35** Question — Addition Facts — $11 + 2$ | **35** Answer — Addition Facts — $13$ |
| **36** Question — Addition Facts — $12 + 2$ | **36** Answer — Addition Facts — $14$ |

# Addition Facts

**Instructions:** Cut out each card along the dotted line. Fold each card along the solid line so you have the question on one side and the answer on the other. Cards may be glued or taped to keep questions and answers on opposite sides.

| | |
|---|---|
| **37** Question — Addition Facts<br><br>**1 + 3** | **37** Answer — Addition Facts<br><br>**4** |
| **38** Question — Addition Facts<br><br>**2 + 3** | **38** Answer — Addition Facts<br><br>**5** |
| **39** Question — Addition Facts<br><br>**3 + 3** | **39** Answer — Addition Facts<br><br>**6** |
| **40** Question — Addition Facts<br><br>**4 + 3** | **40** Answer — Addition Facts<br><br>**7** |

# Addition Facts

**Instructions:** Cut out each card along the dotted line. Fold each card along the solid line so you have the question on one side and the answer on the other. Cards may be glued or taped to keep questions and answers on opposite sides.

| Question 41 | Answer 41 |
|---|---|
| **5 + 3** | **8** |

Addition Facts | Addition Facts

| Question 42 | Answer 42 |
|---|---|
| **6 + 3** | **9** |

Addition Facts | Addition Facts

| Question 43 | Answer 43 |
|---|---|
| **7 + 3** | **10** |

Addition Facts | Addition Facts

| Question 44 | Answer 44 |
|---|---|
| **8 + 3** | **11** |

Addition Facts | Addition Facts

# Addition Facts

**Instructions:** Cut out each card along the dotted line. Fold each card along the solid line so you have the question on one side and the answer on the other. Cards may be glued or taped to keep questions and answers on opposite sides.

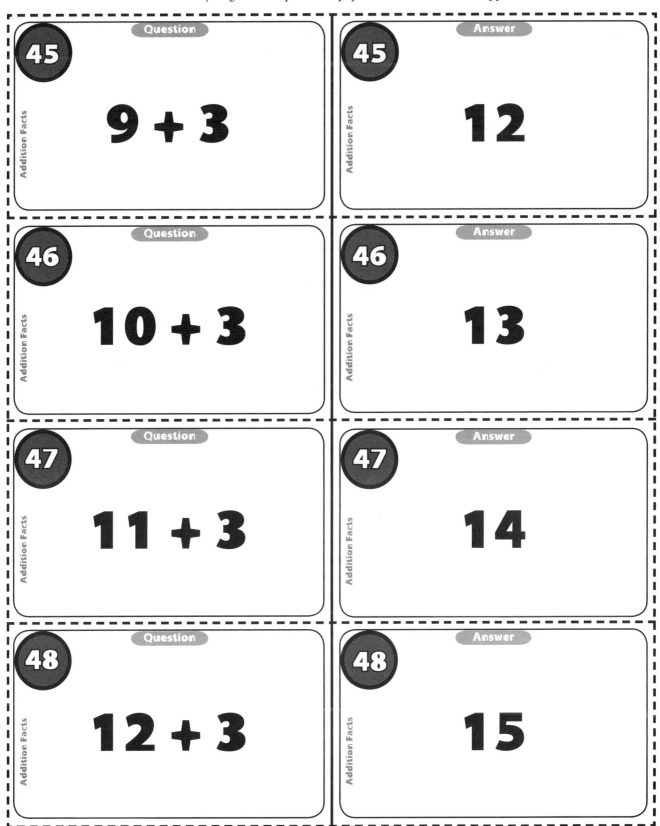

| Question 45 | Answer 45 |
|:---:|:---:|
| 9 + 3 | 12 |

| Question 46 | Answer 46 |
|:---:|:---:|
| 10 + 3 | 13 |

| Question 47 | Answer 47 |
|:---:|:---:|
| 11 + 3 | 14 |

| Question 48 | Answer 48 |
|:---:|:---:|
| 12 + 3 | 15 |

# Addition Facts

**Instructions:** Cut out each card along the dotted line. Fold each card along the solid line so you have the question on one side and the answer on the other. Cards may be glued or taped to keep questions and answers on opposite sides.

| **Question** | **Answer** |
|---|---|
| **49** Addition Facts **1 + 4** | **49** Addition Facts **5** |
| **50** Addition Facts **2 + 4** | **50** Addition Facts **6** |
| **51** Addition Facts **3 + 4** | **51** Addition Facts **7** |
| **52** Addition Facts **4 + 4** | **52** Addition Facts **8** |

# Addition Facts

**Instructions:** Cut out each card along the dotted line. Fold each card along the solid line so you have the question on one side and the answer on the other. Cards may be glued or taped to keep questions and answers on opposite sides.

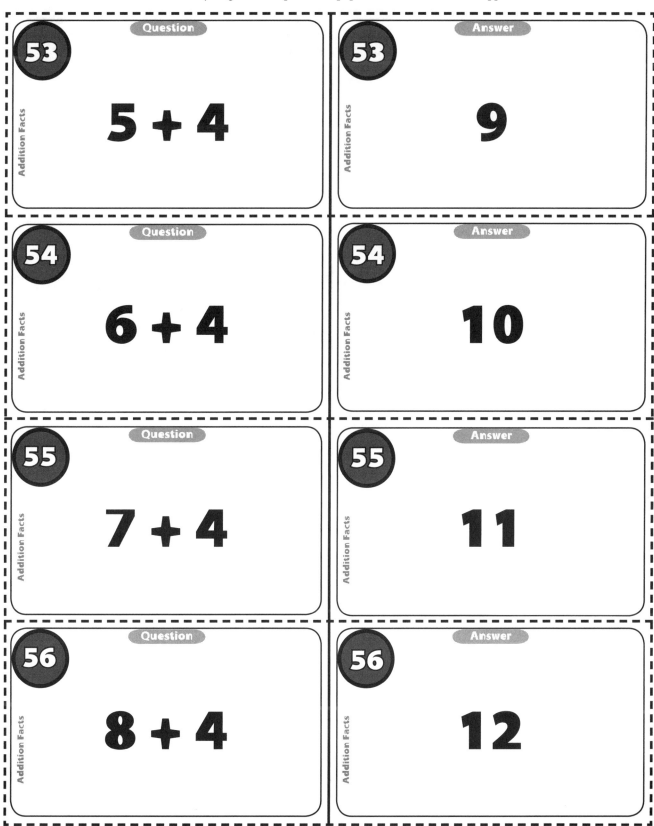

| Question | Answer |
|---|---|
| **53** Addition Facts | **53** Addition Facts |
| 5 + 4 | 9 |
| **54** Addition Facts | **54** Addition Facts |
| 6 + 4 | 10 |
| **55** Addition Facts | **55** Addition Facts |
| 7 + 4 | 11 |
| **56** Addition Facts | **56** Addition Facts |
| 8 + 4 | 12 |

**Instructions:** Cut out each card along the dotted line. Fold each card along the solid line so you have the question on one side and the answer on the other. Cards may be glued or taped to keep questions and answers on opposite sides.

| | |
|---|---|
| **57** Question — Addition Facts — **9 + 4** | **57** Answer — Addition Facts — **13** |
| **58** Question — Addition Facts — **10 + 4** | **58** Answer — Addition Facts — **14** |
| **59** Question — Addition Facts — **11 + 4** | **59** Answer — Addition Facts — **15** |
| **60** Question — Addition Facts — **12 + 4** | **60** Answer — Addition Facts — **16** |

# Addition Facts

**Instructions:** Cut out each card along the dotted line. Fold each card along the solid line so you have the question on one side and the answer on the other. Cards may be glued or taped to keep questions and answers on opposite sides.

| | |
|---|---|
| **61 Question** Addition Facts **1 + 5** | **61 Answer** Addition Facts **6** |
| **62 Question** Addition Facts **2 + 5** | **62 Answer** Addition Facts **7** |
| **63 Question** Addition Facts **3 + 5** | **63 Answer** Addition Facts **8** |
| **64 Question** Addition Facts **4 + 5** | **64 Answer** Addition Facts **9** |

# Addition Facts

**Instructions:** Cut out each card along the dotted line. Fold each card along the solid line so you have the question on one side and the answer on the other. Cards may be glued or taped to keep questions and answers on opposite sides.

| Question | Answer |
|---|---|
| **65** Addition Facts **5 + 5** | **65** Addition Facts **10** |
| **66** Addition Facts **6 + 5** | **66** Addition Facts **11** |
| **67** Addition Facts **7 + 5** | **67** Addition Facts **12** |
| **68** Addition Facts **8 + 5** | **68** Addition Facts **13** |

# Addition Facts

**Instructions:** Cut out each card along the dotted line. Fold each card along the solid line so you have the question on one side and the answer on the other. Cards may be glued or taped to keep questions and answers on opposite sides.

| | |
|---|---|
| **69** Question — Addition Facts<br><br>$9 + 5$ | **69** Answer — Addition Facts<br><br>**14** |
| **70** Question — Addition Facts<br><br>$10 + 5$ | **70** Answer — Addition Facts<br><br>**15** |
| **71** Question — Addition Facts<br><br>$11 + 5$ | **71** Answer — Addition Facts<br><br>**16** |
| **72** Question — Addition Facts<br><br>$12 + 5$ | **72** Answer — Addition Facts<br><br>**17** |

# Addition Facts

**Instructions:** Cut out each card along the dotted line. Fold each card along the solid line so you have the question on one side and the answer on the other. Cards may be glued or taped to keep questions and answers on opposite sides.

| | |
|---|---|
| **73** Question — Addition Facts — **1 + 6** | **73** Answer — Addition Facts — **7** |
| **74** Question — Addition Facts — **2 + 6** | **74** Answer — Addition Facts — **8** |
| **75** Question — Addition Facts — **3 + 6** | **75** Answer — Addition Facts — **9** |
| **76** Question — Addition Facts — **4 + 6** | **76** Answer — Addition Facts — **10** |

# Addition Facts

**Instructions:** Cut out each card along the dotted line. Fold each card along the solid line so you have the question on one side and the answer on the other. Cards may be glued or taped to keep questions and answers on opposite sides.

| | |
|---|---|
| **77** Question — Addition Facts<br><br>$5 + 6$ | **77** Answer — Addition Facts<br><br>**11** |
| **78** Question — Addition Facts<br><br>$6 + 6$ | **78** Answer — Addition Facts<br><br>**12** |
| **79** Question — Addition Facts<br><br>$7 + 6$ | **79** Answer — Addition Facts<br><br>**13** |
| **80** Question — Addition Facts<br><br>$8 + 6$ | **80** Answer — Addition Facts<br><br>**14** |

# Addition Facts

**Instructions:** Cut out each card along the dotted line. Fold each card along the solid line so you have the question on one side and the answer on the other. Cards may be glued or taped to keep questions and answers on opposite sides.

| | |
|---|---|
| **81** Question — Addition Facts<br>**9 + 6** | **81** Answer — Addition Facts<br>**15** |
| **82** Question — Addition Facts<br>**10 + 6** | **82** Answer — Addition Facts<br>**16** |
| **83** Question — Addition Facts<br>**11 + 6** | **83** Answer — Addition Facts<br>**17** |
| **84** Question — Addition Facts<br>**12 + 6** | **84** Answer — Addition Facts<br>**18** |

# Addition Facts

**Instructions:** Cut out each card along the dotted line. Fold each card along the solid line so you have the question on one side and the answer on the other. Cards may be glued or taped to keep questions and answers on opposite sides.

| | |
|---|---|
| **85** Question — Addition Facts **1 + 7** | **85** Answer — Addition Facts **8** |
| **86** Question — Addition Facts **2 + 7** | **86** Answer — Addition Facts **9** |
| **87** Question — Addition Facts **3 + 7** | **87** Answer — Addition Facts **10** |
| **88** Question — Addition Facts **4 + 7** | **88** Answer — Addition Facts **11** |

# Addition Facts

**Instructions:** Cut out each card along the dotted line. Fold each card along the solid line so you have the question on one side and the answer on the other. Cards may be glued or taped to keep questions and answers on opposite sides.

| Question | Answer |
|----------|--------|
| **89** Addition Facts **5 + 7** | **89** Addition Facts **12** |
| **90** Addition Facts **6 + 7** | **90** Addition Facts **13** |
| **91** Addition Facts **7 + 7** | **91** Addition Facts **14** |
| **92** Addition Facts **8 + 7** | **92** Addition Facts **15** |

# Addition Facts

**Instructions:** Cut out each card along the dotted line. Fold each card along the solid line so you have the question on one side and the answer on the other. Cards may be glued or taped to keep questions and answers on opposite sides.

| | |
|---|---|
| **Question** **93** Addition Facts $9 + 7$ | **Answer** **93** Addition Facts **16** |
| **Question** **94** Addition Facts $10 + 7$ | **Answer** **94** Addition Facts **17** |
| **Question** **95** Addition Facts $11 + 7$ | **Answer** **95** Addition Facts **18** |
| **Question** **96** Addition Facts $12 + 7$ | **Answer** **96** Addition Facts **19** |

# Addition Facts

**Instructions:** Cut out each card along the dotted line. Fold each card along the solid line so you have the question on one side and the answer on the other. Cards may be glued or taped to keep questions and answers on opposite sides.

| Question | Answer |
|---|---|
| **97** — Addition Facts — $1 + 8$ | **97** — Addition Facts — **9** |
| **98** — Addition Facts — $2 + 8$ | **98** — Addition Facts — **10** |
| **99** — Addition Facts — $3 + 8$ | **99** — Addition Facts — **11** |
| **100** — Addition Facts — $4 + 8$ | **100** — Addition Facts — **12** |

# Addition Facts

**Instructions:** Cut out each card along the dotted line. Fold each card along the solid line so you have the question on one side and the answer on the other. Cards may be glued or taped to keep questions and answers on opposite sides.

| | |
|---|---|
| **101** Question · Addition Facts<br><br>**5 + 8** | **101** Answer · Addition Facts<br><br>**13** |
| **102** Question · Addition Facts<br><br>**6 + 8** | **102** Answer · Addition Facts<br><br>**14** |
| **103** Question · Addition Facts<br><br>**7 + 8** | **103** Answer · Addition Facts<br><br>**15** |
| **104** Question · Addition Facts<br><br>**8 + 8** | **104** Answer · Addition Facts<br><br>**16** |

# Addition Facts

**Instructions:** Cut out each card along the dotted line. Fold each card along the solid line so you have the question on one side and the answer on the other. Cards may be glued or taped to keep questions and answers on opposite sides.

| | |
|---|---|
| **105** Question — Addition Facts — **9 + 8** | **105** Answer — Addition Facts — **17** |
| **106** Question — Addition Facts — **10 + 8** | **106** Answer — Addition Facts — **18** |
| **107** Question — Addition Facts — **11 + 8** | **107** Answer — Addition Facts — **19** |
| **108** Question — Addition Facts — **12 + 8** | **108** Answer — Addition Facts — **20** |

# Addition Facts

**Instructions:** Cut out each card along the dotted line. Fold each card along the solid line so you have the question on one side and the answer on the other. Cards may be glued or taped to keep questions and answers on opposite sides.

| | |
|---|---|
| **109** Question — Addition Facts — **1 + 9** | **109** Answer — Addition Facts — **10** |
| **110** Question — Addition Facts — **2 + 9** | **110** Answer — Addition Facts — **11** |
| **111** Question — Addition Facts — **3 + 9** | **111** Answer — Addition Facts — **12** |
| **112** Question — Addition Facts — **4 + 9** | **112** Answer — Addition Facts — **13** |

# Addition Facts

**Instructions:** Cut out each card along the dotted line. Fold each card along the solid line so you have the question on one side and the answer on the other. Cards may be glued or taped to keep questions and answers on opposite sides.

| | |
|---|---|
| **Question** **113** Addition Facts **5 + 9** | **Answer** **113** Addition Facts **14** |
| **Question** **114** Addition Facts **6 + 9** | **Answer** **114** Addition Facts **15** |
| **Question** **115** Addition Facts **7 + 9** | **Answer** **115** Addition Facts **16** |
| **Question** **116** Addition Facts **8 + 9** | **Answer** **116** Addition Facts **17** |

# Addition Facts

**Instructions:** Cut out each card along the dotted line. Fold each card along the solid line so you have the question on one side and the answer on the other. Cards may be glued or taped to keep questions and answers on opposite sides.

| Question | Answer |
|---|---|
| **117** Addition Facts $9 + 9$ | **117** Addition Facts $18$ |
| **118** Addition Facts $10 + 9$ | **118** Addition Facts $19$ |
| **119** Addition Facts $11 + 9$ | **119** Addition Facts $20$ |
| **120** Addition Facts $12 + 9$ | **120** Addition Facts $21$ |

# Addition Facts

**Instructions:** Cut out each card along the dotted line. Fold each card along the solid line so you have the question on one side and the answer on the other. Cards may be glued or taped to keep questions and answers on opposite sides.

| | |
|---|---|
| **Question** 121 — Addition Facts — **1 + 10** | **Answer** 121 — Addition Facts — **11** |
| **Question** 122 — Addition Facts — **2 + 10** | **Answer** 122 — Addition Facts — **12** |
| **Question** 123 — Addition Facts — **3 + 10** | **Answer** 123 — Addition Facts — **13** |
| **Question** 124 — Addition Facts — **4 + 10** | **Answer** 124 — Addition Facts — **14** |

# Addition Facts

**Instructions:** Cut out each card along the dotted line. Fold each card along the solid line so you have the question on one side and the answer on the other. Cards may be glued or taped to keep questions and answers on opposite sides.

| Question | Answer |
|---|---|
| **125** Addition Facts | **125** Addition Facts |
| $$5 + 10$$ | $$15$$ |
| **126** Addition Facts | **126** Addition Facts |
| $$6 + 10$$ | $$16$$ |
| **127** Addition Facts | **127** Addition Facts |
| $$7 + 10$$ | $$17$$ |
| **128** Addition Facts | **128** Addition Facts |
| $$8 + 10$$ | $$18$$ |

# Addition Facts

**Instructions:** Cut out each card along the dotted line. Fold each card along the solid line so you have the question on one side and the answer on the other. Cards may be glued or taped to keep questions and answers on opposite sides.

| | |
|---|---|
| **129** Question — Addition Facts | **129** Answer — Addition Facts |
| $9 + 10$ | $19$ |
| **130** Question — Addition Facts | **130** Answer — Addition Facts |
| $10 + 10$ | $20$ |
| **131** Question — Addition Facts | **131** Answer — Addition Facts |
| $10 + 11$ | $21$ |
| **132** Question — Addition Facts | **132** Answer — Addition Facts |
| $10 + 12$ | $22$ |

# Subtraction Facts

**Instructions:** Cut out each card along the dotted line. Fold each card along the solid line so you have the question on one side and the answer on the other. Cards may be glued or taped to keep questions and answers on opposite sides.

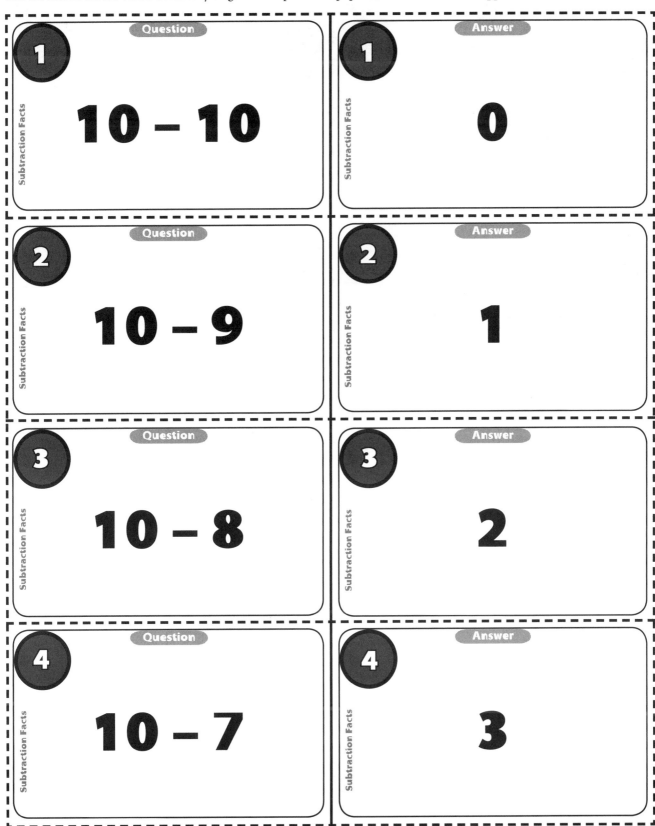

| Question | Answer |
|---|---|
| **1** Subtraction Facts $10 - 10$ | **1** Subtraction Facts $0$ |
| **2** Subtraction Facts $10 - 9$ | **2** Subtraction Facts $1$ |
| **3** Subtraction Facts $10 - 8$ | **3** Subtraction Facts $2$ |
| **4** Subtraction Facts $10 - 7$ | **4** Subtraction Facts $3$ |

# Subtraction Facts

**Instructions:** Cut out each card along the dotted line. Fold each card along the solid line so you have the question on one side and the answer on the other. Cards may be glued or taped to keep questions and answers on opposite sides.

| | |
|---|---|
| **5** Question<br>Subtraction Facts<br>**10 – 6** | **5** Answer<br>Subtraction Facts<br>**4** |
| **6** Question<br>Subtraction Facts<br>**10 – 5** | **6** Answer<br>Subtraction Facts<br>**5** |
| **7** Question<br>Subtraction Facts<br>**10 – 4** | **7** Answer<br>Subtraction Facts<br>**6** |
| **8** Question<br>Subtraction Facts<br>**10 – 3** | **8** Answer<br>Subtraction Facts<br>**7** |

# Subtraction Facts

**Instructions:** Cut out each card along the dotted line. Fold each card along the solid line so you have the question on one side and the answer on the other. Cards may be glued or taped to keep questions and answers on opposite sides.

| Question | Answer |
|---|---|
| **9** Subtraction Facts **10 – 2** | **9** Subtraction Facts **8** |
| **10** Subtraction Facts **10 – 1** | **10** Subtraction Facts **9** |
| **11** Subtraction Facts **10 – 0** | **11** Subtraction Facts **10** |
| **12** Subtraction Facts **9 – 9** | **12** Subtraction Facts **0** |

# Subtraction Facts

**Instructions:** Cut out each card along the dotted line. Fold each card along the solid line so you have the question on one side and the answer on the other. Cards may be glued or taped to keep questions and answers on opposite sides.

| | |
|---|---|
| **13** Question — Subtraction Facts<br><br>**9 – 8** | **13** Answer — Subtraction Facts<br><br>**1** |
| **14** Question — Subtraction Facts<br><br>**9 – 7** | **14** Answer — Subtraction Facts<br><br>**2** |
| **15** Question — Subtraction Facts<br><br>**9 – 6** | **15** Answer — Subtraction Facts<br><br>**3** |
| **16** Question — Subtraction Facts<br><br>**9 – 5** | **16** Answer — Subtraction Facts<br><br>**4** |

# Subtraction Facts

**Instructions:** Cut out each card along the dotted line. Fold each card along the solid line so you have the question on one side and the answer on the other. Cards may be glued or taped to keep questions and answers on opposite sides.

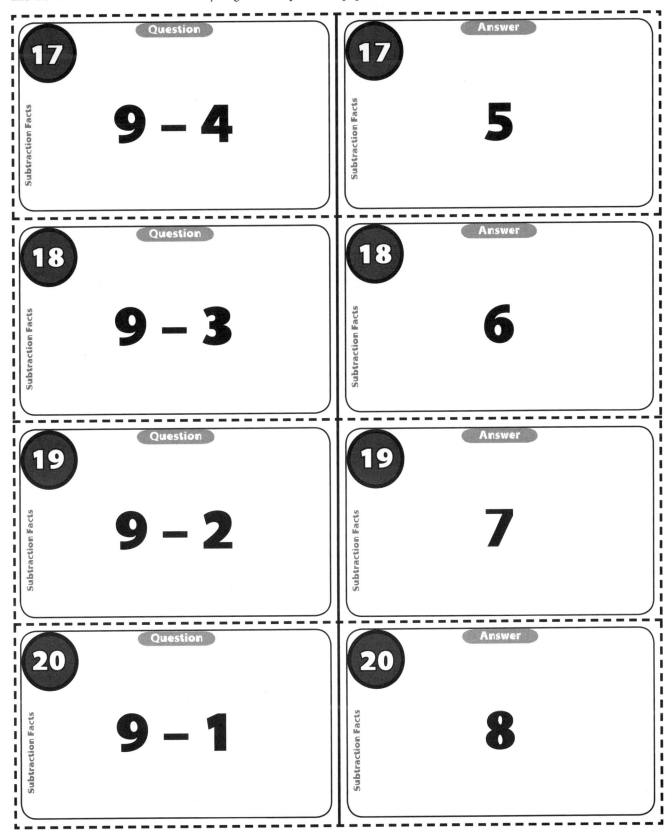

| Question 17 | Answer 17 |
| --- | --- |
| 9 – 4 | 5 |

| Question 18 | Answer 18 |
| --- | --- |
| 9 – 3 | 6 |

| Question 19 | Answer 19 |
| --- | --- |
| 9 – 2 | 7 |

| Question 20 | Answer 20 |
| --- | --- |
| 9 – 1 | 8 |

# Subtraction Facts

**Instructions:** Cut out each card along the dotted line. Fold each card along the solid line so you have the question on one side and the answer on the other. Cards may be glued or taped to keep questions and answers on opposite sides.

| Question | Answer |
|---|---|
| **21** Subtraction Facts<br><br>**9 – 0** | **21** Subtraction Facts<br><br>**9** |
| **22** Subtraction Facts<br><br>**8 – 8** | **22** Subtraction Facts<br><br>**0** |
| **23** Subtraction Facts<br><br>**8 – 7** | **23** Subtraction Facts<br><br>**1** |
| **24** Subtraction Facts<br><br>**8 – 6** | **24** Subtraction Facts<br><br>**2** |

# Subtraction Facts

**Instructions:** Cut out each card along the dotted line. Fold each card along the solid line so you have the question on one side and the answer on the other. Cards may be glued or taped to keep questions and answers on opposite sides.

| Question | Answer |
|---|---|
| **25** Subtraction Facts<br><br>**8 – 5** | **25** Subtraction Facts<br><br>**3** |
| **26** Subtraction Facts<br><br>**8 – 4** | **26** Subtraction Facts<br><br>**4** |
| **27** Subtraction Facts<br><br>**8 – 3** | **27** Subtraction Facts<br><br>**5** |
| **28** Subtraction Facts<br><br>**8 – 2** | **28** Subtraction Facts<br><br>**6** |

# Subtraction Facts

**Instructions:** Cut out each card along the dotted line. Fold each card along the solid line so you have the question on one side and the answer on the other. Cards may be glued or taped to keep questions and answers on opposite sides.

| | |
|---|---|
| **29** Question — Subtraction Facts<br><br>**8 – 1** | **29** Answer — Subtraction Facts<br><br>**7** |
| **30** Question — Subtraction Facts<br><br>**8 – 0** | **30** Answer — Subtraction Facts<br><br>**8** |
| **31** Question — Subtraction Facts<br><br>**7 – 7** | **31** Answer — Subtraction Facts<br><br>**0** |
| **32** Question — Subtraction Facts<br><br>**7 – 6** | **32** Answer — Subtraction Facts<br><br>**1** |

# Subtraction Facts

**Instructions:** Cut out each card along the dotted line. Fold each card along the solid line so you have the question on one side and the answer on the other. Cards may be glued or taped to keep questions and answers on opposite sides.

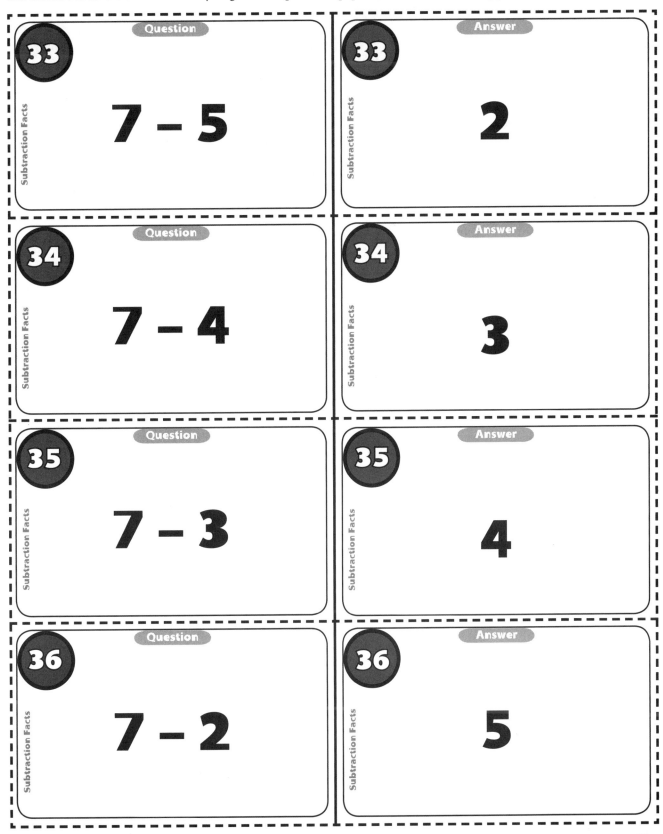

| | |
|---|---|
| **33** Question — Subtraction Facts — 7 – 5 | **33** Answer — Subtraction Facts — 2 |
| **34** Question — Subtraction Facts — 7 – 4 | **34** Answer — Subtraction Facts — 3 |
| **35** Question — Subtraction Facts — 7 – 3 | **35** Answer — Subtraction Facts — 4 |
| **36** Question — Subtraction Facts — 7 – 2 | **36** Answer — Subtraction Facts — 5 |

# Subtraction Facts

**Instructions:** Cut out each card along the dotted line. Fold each card along the solid line so you have the question on one side and the answer on the other. Cards may be glued or taped to keep questions and answers on opposite sides.

| | |
|---|---|
| **Question** 37 — Subtraction Facts — **7 – 1** | **Answer** 37 — Subtraction Facts — **6** |
| **Question** 38 — Subtraction Facts — **7 – 0** | **Answer** 38 — Subtraction Facts — **7** |
| **Question** 39 — Subtraction Facts — **6 – 6** | **Answer** 39 — Subtraction Facts — **0** |
| **Question** 40 — Subtraction Facts — **6 – 5** | **Answer** 40 — Subtraction Facts — **1** |

# Subtraction Facts

**Instructions:** Cut out each card along the dotted line. Fold each card along the solid line so you have the question on one side and the answer on the other. Cards may be glued or taped to keep questions and answers on opposite sides.

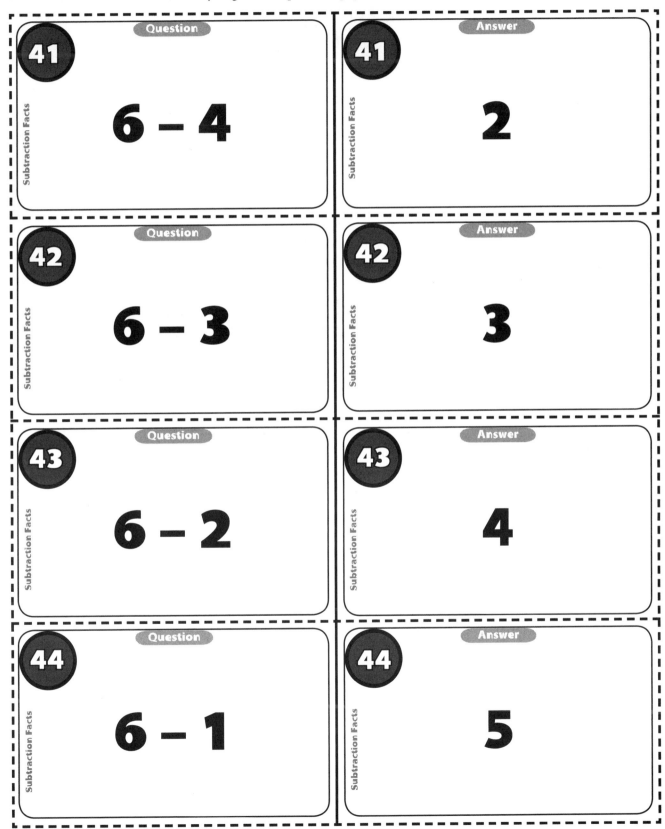

| Question | Answer |
|---|---|
| **41** Subtraction Facts **6 – 4** | **41** Subtraction Facts **2** |
| **42** Subtraction Facts **6 – 3** | **42** Subtraction Facts **3** |
| **43** Subtraction Facts **6 – 2** | **43** Subtraction Facts **4** |
| **44** Subtraction Facts **6 – 1** | **44** Subtraction Facts **5** |

# Subtraction Facts

**Instructions:** Cut out each card along the dotted line. Fold each card along the solid line so you have the question on one side and the answer on the other. Cards may be glued or taped to keep questions and answers on opposite sides.

| | |
|---|---|
| **45** Question — Subtraction Facts — $6 - 0$ | **45** Answer — Subtraction Facts — $6$ |
| **46** Question — Subtraction Facts — $5 - 5$ | **46** Answer — Subtraction Facts — $0$ |
| **47** Question — Subtraction Facts — $5 - 4$ | **47** Answer — Subtraction Facts — $1$ |
| **48** Question — Subtraction Facts — $5 - 3$ | **48** Answer — Subtraction Facts — $2$ |

# Subtraction Facts

**Instructions:** Cut out each card along the dotted line. Fold each card along the solid line so you have the question on one side and the answer on the other. Cards may be glued or taped to keep questions and answers on opposite sides.

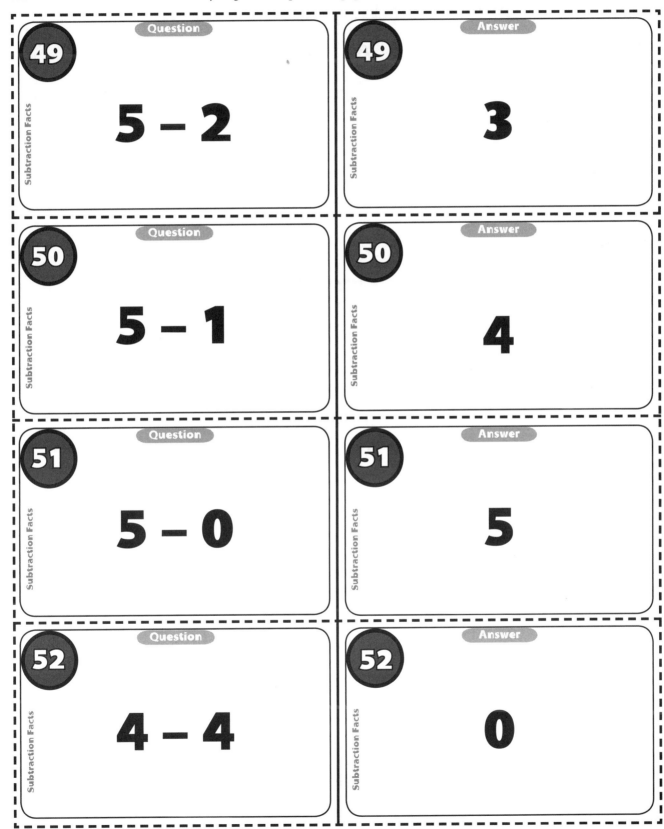

| Question 49 | Answer 49 |
|---|---|
| Subtraction Facts | Subtraction Facts |
| **5 – 2** | **3** |

| Question 50 | Answer 50 |
|---|---|
| Subtraction Facts | Subtraction Facts |
| **5 – 1** | **4** |

| Question 51 | Answer 51 |
|---|---|
| Subtraction Facts | Subtraction Facts |
| **5 – 0** | **5** |

| Question 52 | Answer 52 |
|---|---|
| Subtraction Facts | Subtraction Facts |
| **4 – 4** | **0** |

# Subtraction Facts

**Instructions:** Cut out each card along the dotted line. Fold each card along the solid line so you have the question on one side and the answer on the other. Cards may be glued or taped to keep questions and answers on opposite sides.

| | |
|---|---|
| **53** Question — Subtraction Facts — **4 – 3** | **53** Answer — Subtraction Facts — **1** |
| **54** Question — Subtraction Facts — **4 – 2** | **54** Answer — Subtraction Facts — **2** |
| **55** Question — Subtraction Facts — **4 – 1** | **55** Answer — Subtraction Facts — **3** |
| **56** Question — Subtraction Facts — **4 – 0** | **56** Answer — Subtraction Facts — **4** |

# Subtraction Facts

**Instructions:** Cut out each card along the dotted line. Fold each card along the solid line so you have the question on one side and the answer on the other. Cards may be glued or taped to keep questions and answers on opposite sides.

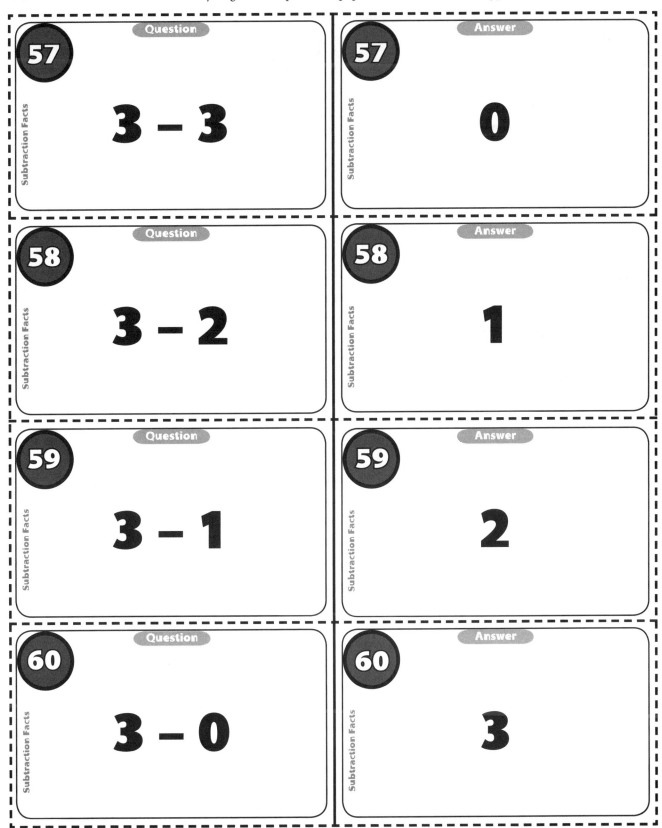

| Question | Answer |
|---|---|
| **57** Subtraction Facts $3 - 3$ | **57** Subtraction Facts $0$ |
| **58** Subtraction Facts $3 - 2$ | **58** Subtraction Facts $1$ |
| **59** Subtraction Facts $3 - 1$ | **59** Subtraction Facts $2$ |
| **60** Subtraction Facts $3 - 0$ | **60** Subtraction Facts $3$ |

# Subtraction Facts

**Instructions:** Cut out each card along the dotted line. Fold each card along the solid line so you have the question on one side and the answer on the other. Cards may be glued or taped to keep questions and answers on opposite sides.

| | |
|---|---|
| **61** Question — Subtraction Facts — **2 – 2** | **61** Answer — Subtraction Facts — **0** |
| **62** Question — Subtraction Facts — **2 – 1** | **62** Answer — Subtraction Facts — **1** |
| **63** Question — Subtraction Facts — **2 – 0** | **63** Answer — Subtraction Facts — **2** |
| **64** Question — Subtraction Facts — **1 – 1** | **64** Answer — Subtraction Facts — **0** |

# Naming 2-D Shapes

**Instructions:** Cut out each card along the dotted line. Fold each card along the solid line so you have the question on one side and the answer on the other. Cards may be glued or taped to keep questions and answers on opposite sides.

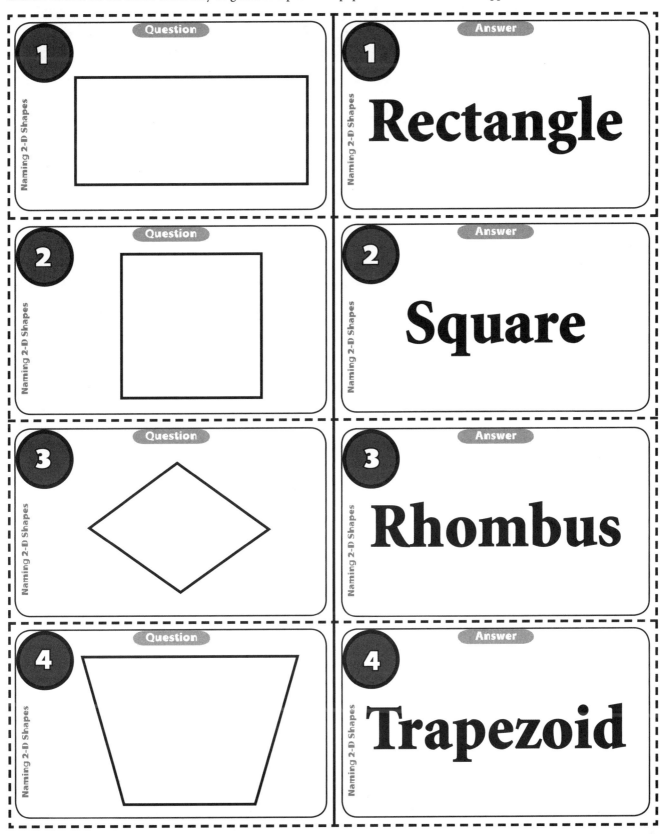

**Question**

1

Naming 2-D Shapes

**Answer**

1

Naming 2-D Shapes

# Rectangle

**Question**

2

Naming 2-D Shapes

**Answer**

2

Naming 2-D Shapes

# Square

**Question**

3

Naming 2-D Shapes

**Answer**

3

Naming 2-D Shapes

# Rhombus

**Question**

4

Naming 2-D Shapes

**Answer**

4

Naming 2-D Shapes

# Trapezoid

# Naming 2-D Shapes

**Instructions:** Cut out each card along the dotted line. Fold each card along the solid line so you have the question on one side and the answer on the other. Cards may be glued or taped to keep questions and answers on opposite sides.

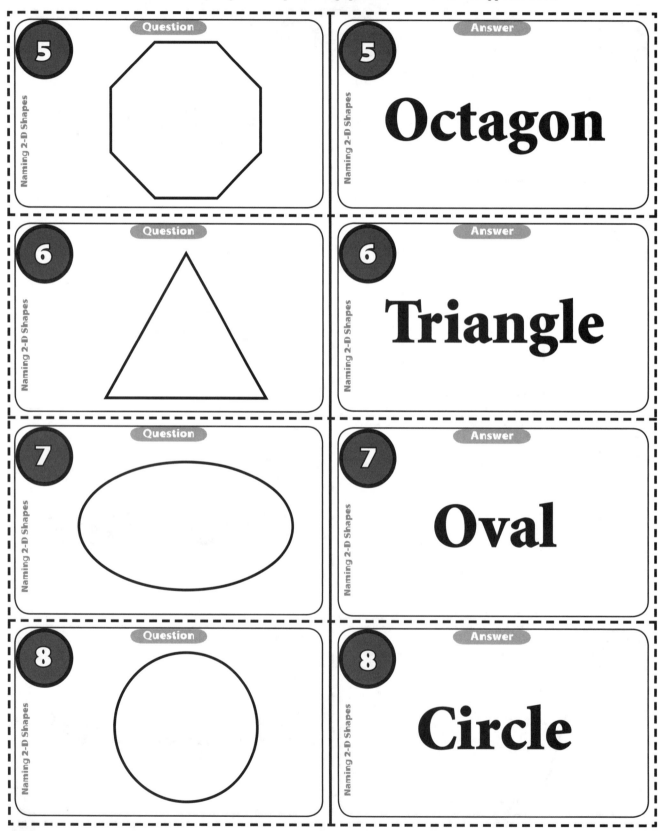

| Question | Answer |
|---|---|
| **5** | **5** Octagon |
| **6** | **6** Triangle |
| **7** | **7** Oval |
| **8** | **8** Circle |

# Naming 2-D Shapes

**Instructions:** Cut out each card along the dotted line. Fold each card along the solid line so you have the question on one side and the answer on the other. Cards may be glued or taped to keep questions and answers on opposite sides.

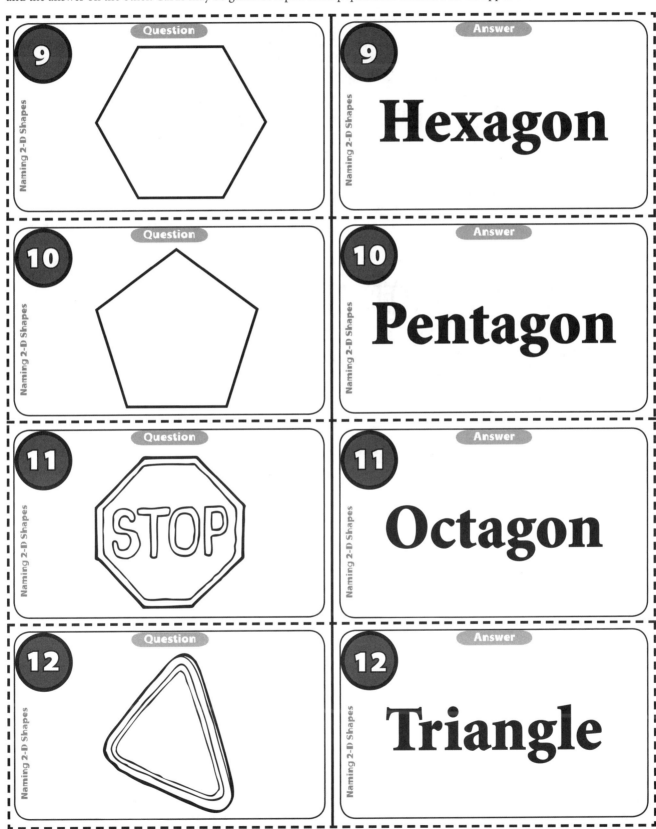

**Question**

9

Naming 2-D Shapes

**Answer**

9

Naming 2-D Shapes

# Hexagon

**Question**

10

Naming 2-D Shapes

**Answer**

10

Naming 2-D Shapes

# Pentagon

**Question**

11

Naming 2-D Shapes

STOP

**Answer**

11

Naming 2-D Shapes

# Octagon

**Question**

12

Naming 2-D Shapes

**Answer**

12

Naming 2-D Shapes

# Triangle

# Naming 2-D Shapes

**Instructions:** Cut out each card along the dotted line. Fold each card along the solid line so you have the question on one side and the answer on the other. Cards may be glued or taped to keep questions and answers on opposite sides.

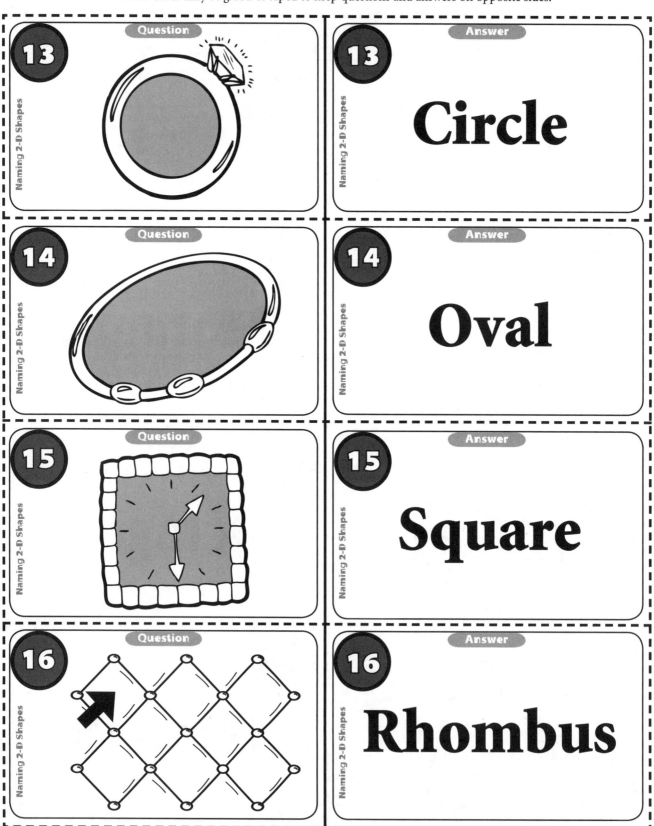

| | |
|---|---|
| **13** Question | **13** Answer — **Circle** |
| **14** Question | **14** Answer — **Oval** |
| **15** Question | **15** Answer — **Square** |
| **16** Question | **16** Answer — **Rhombus** |

# Naming 2-D Shapes

**Instructions:** Cut out each card along the dotted line. Fold each card along the solid line so you have the question on one side and the answer on the other. Cards may be glued or taped to keep questions and answers on opposite sides.

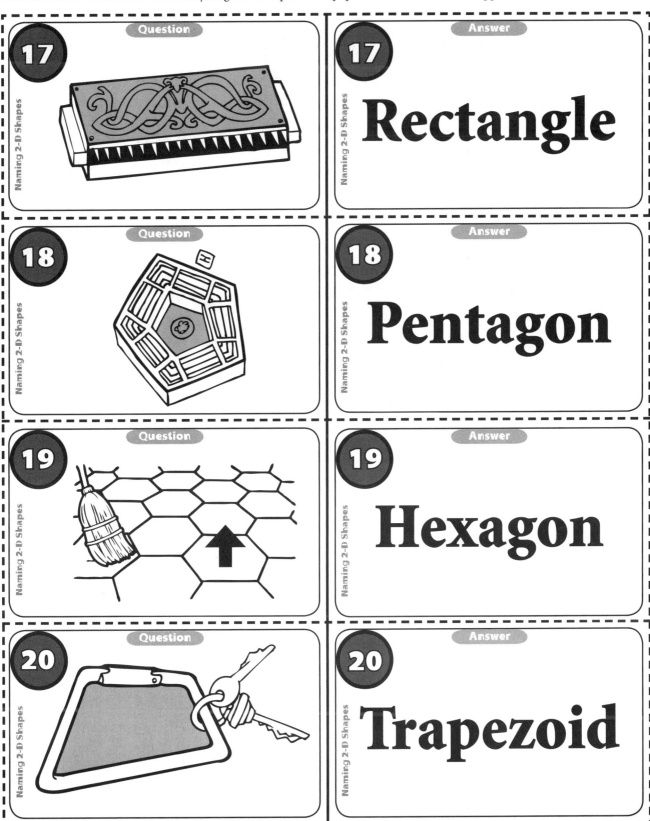

**Question 17** — Naming 2-D Shapes

**Answer 17** — Naming 2-D Shapes

## Rectangle

**Question 18** — Naming 2-D Shapes

**Answer 18** — Naming 2-D Shapes

## Pentagon

**Question 19** — Naming 2-D Shapes

**Answer 19** — Naming 2-D Shapes

## Hexagon

**Question 20** — Naming 2-D Shapes

**Answer 20** — Naming 2-D Shapes

## Trapezoid

# Naming 3-D Shapes

**Instructions:** Cut out each card along the dotted line. Fold each card along the solid line so you have the question on one side and the answer on the other. Cards may be glued or taped to keep questions and answers on opposite sides.

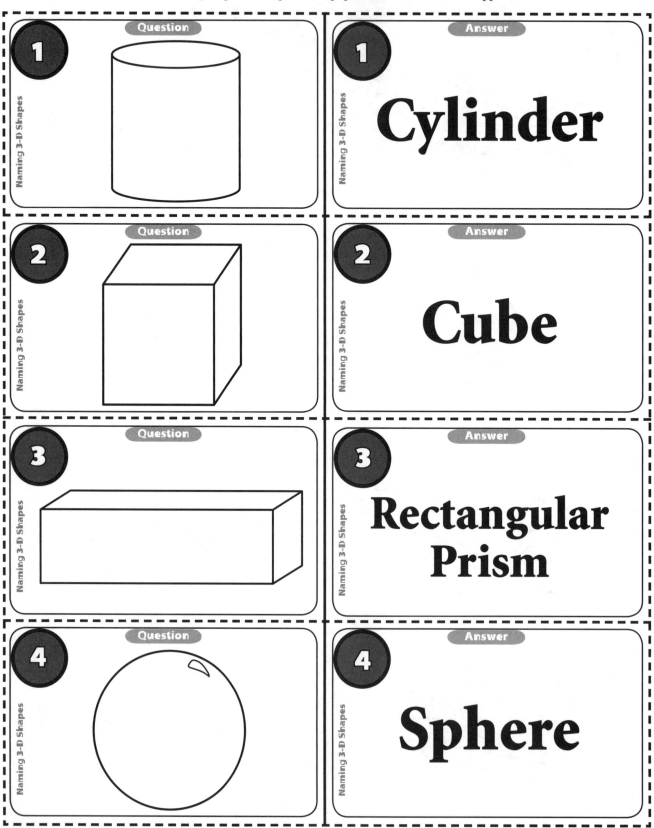

Question 1 — Naming 3-D Shapes

Answer 1 — Naming 3-D Shapes: **Cylinder**

Question 2 — Naming 3-D Shapes

Answer 2 — Naming 3-D Shapes: **Cube**

Question 3 — Naming 3-D Shapes

Answer 3 — Naming 3-D Shapes: **Rectangular Prism**

Question 4 — Naming 3-D Shapes

Answer 4 — Naming 3-D Shapes: **Sphere**

# Naming 3-D Shapes

**Instructions:** Cut out each card along the dotted line. Fold each card along the solid line so you have the question on one side and the answer on the other. Cards may be glued or taped to keep questions and answers on opposite sides.

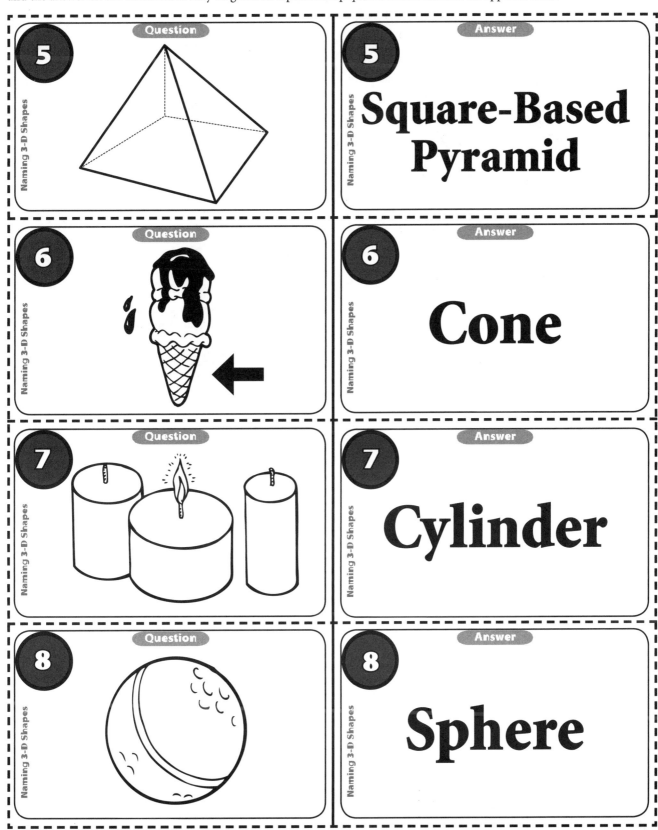

# Naming 3-D Shapes

**Instructions:** Cut out each card along the dotted line. Fold each card along the solid line so you have the question on one side and the answer on the other. Cards may be glued or taped to keep questions and answers on opposite sides.

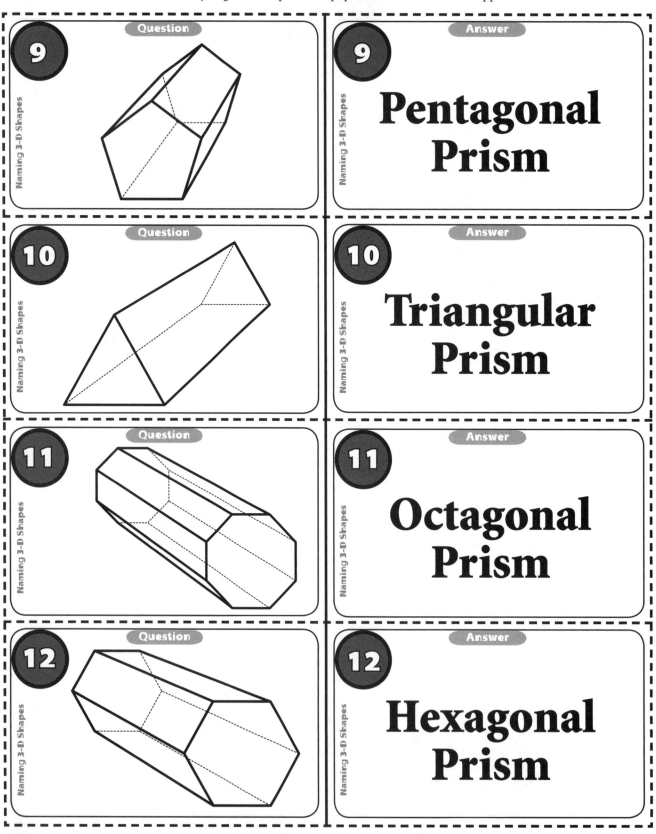

**9** Question — Naming 3-D Shapes

**9** Answer — Naming 3-D Shapes

**Pentagonal Prism**

**10** Question — Naming 3-D Shapes

**10** Answer — Naming 3-D Shapes

**Triangular Prism**

**11** Question — Naming 3-D Shapes

**11** Answer — Naming 3-D Shapes

**Octagonal Prism**

**12** Question — Naming 3-D Shapes

**12** Answer — Naming 3-D Shapes

**Hexagonal Prism**

# Naming 3-D Shapes

**Instructions:** Cut out each card along the dotted line. Fold each card along the solid line so you have the question on one side and the answer on the other. Cards may be glued or taped to keep questions and answers on opposite sides.

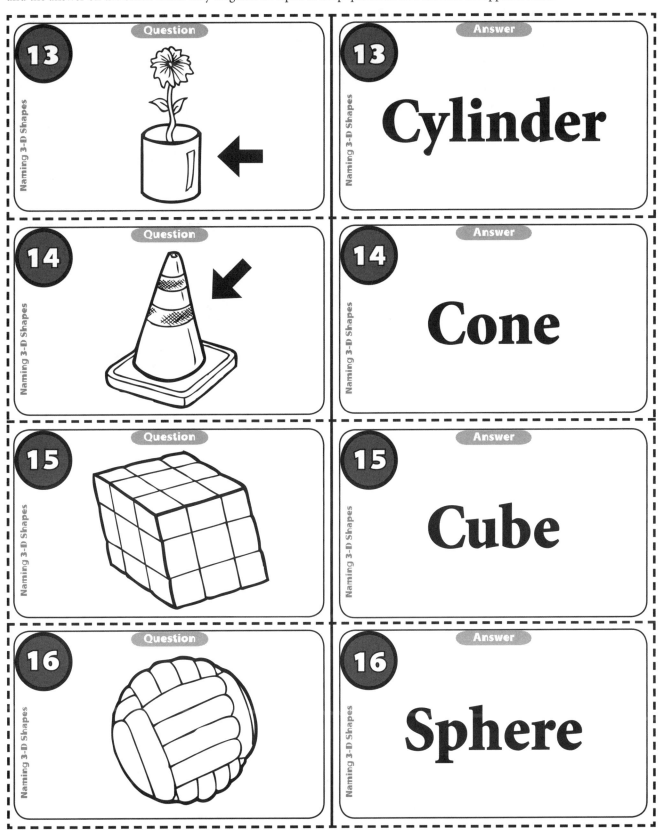

**13** Question — Naming 3-D Shapes

**13** Answer — Naming 3-D Shapes — **Cylinder**

**14** Question — Naming 3-D Shapes

**14** Answer — Naming 3-D Shapes — **Cone**

**15** Question — Naming 3-D Shapes

**15** Answer — Naming 3-D Shapes — **Cube**

**16** Question — Naming 3-D Shapes

**16** Answer — Naming 3-D Shapes — **Sphere**

# Naming 3-D Shapes

**Instructions:** Cut out each card along the dotted line. Fold each card along the solid line so you have the question on one side and the answer on the other. Cards may be glued or taped to keep questions and answers on opposite sides.

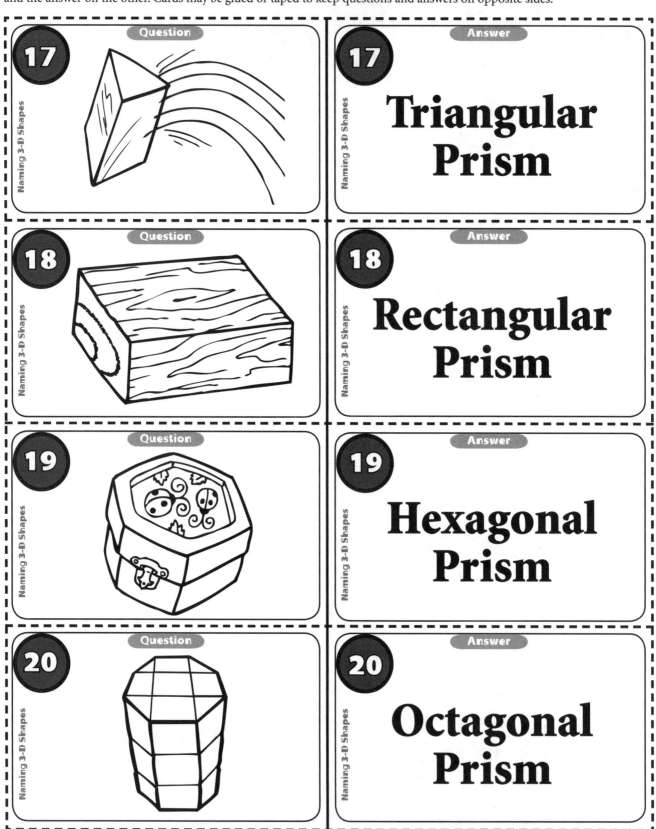

**17** Question — Naming 3-D Shapes

**17** Answer — Naming 3-D Shapes

## Triangular Prism

**18** Question — Naming 3-D Shapes

**18** Answer — Naming 3-D Shapes

## Rectangular Prism

**19** Question — Naming 3-D Shapes

**19** Answer — Naming 3-D Shapes

## Hexagonal Prism

**20** Question — Naming 3-D Shapes

**20** Answer — Naming 3-D Shapes

## Octagonal Prism

# Coordinate Points

**Instructions:** Cut out each card along the dotted line. Fold each card along the solid line so you have the question on one side and the answer on the other. Cards may be glued or taped to keep questions and answers on opposite sides.

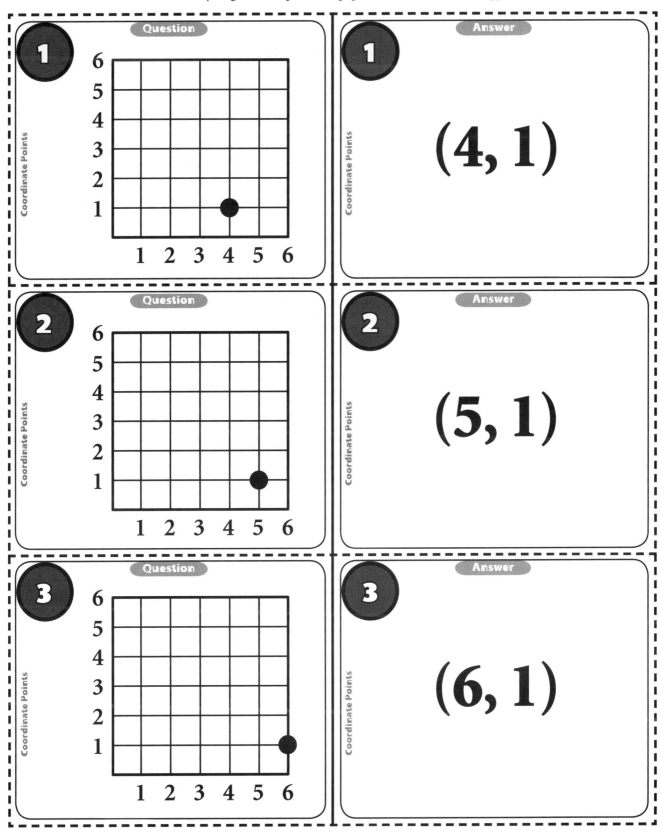

# Coordinate Points

**Instructions:** Cut out each card along the dotted line. Fold each card along the solid line so you have the question on one side and the answer on the other. Cards may be glued or taped to keep questions and answers on opposite sides.

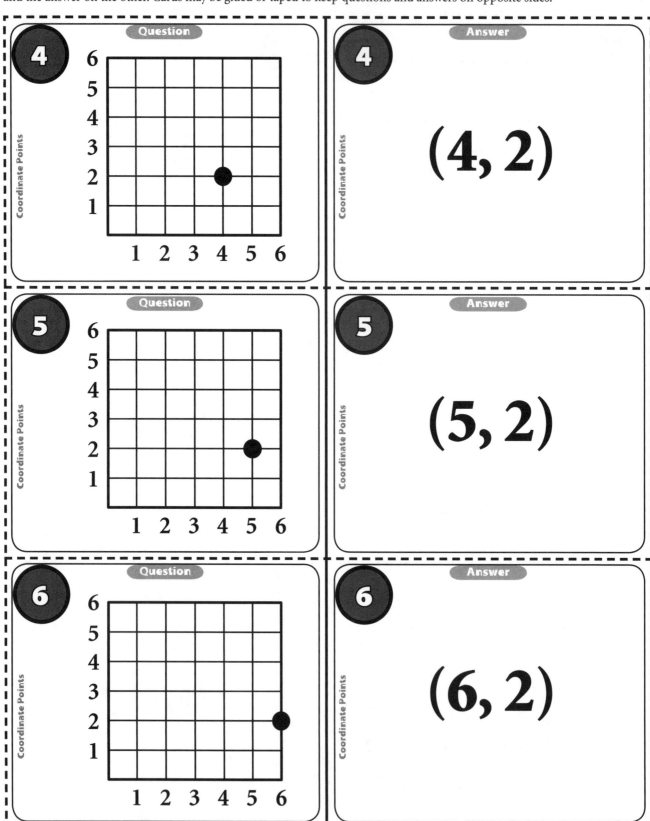

# Coordinate Points

**Instructions:** Cut out each card along the dotted line. Fold each card along the solid line so you have the question on one side and the answer on the other. Cards may be glued or taped to keep questions and answers on opposite sides.

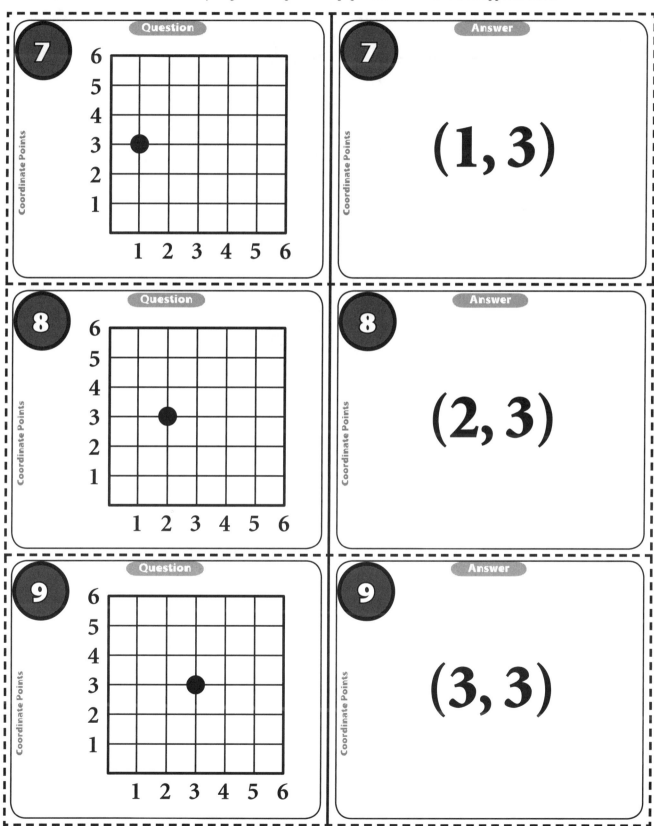

**7** Question — Coordinate Points

**7** Answer — Coordinate Points

(1, 3)

**8** Question — Coordinate Points

**8** Answer — Coordinate Points

(2, 3)

**9** Question — Coordinate Points

**9** Answer — Coordinate Points

(3, 3)

# Coordinate Points

**Instructions:** Cut out each card along the dotted line. Fold each card along the solid line so you have the question on one side and the answer on the other. Cards may be glued or taped to keep questions and answers on opposite sides.

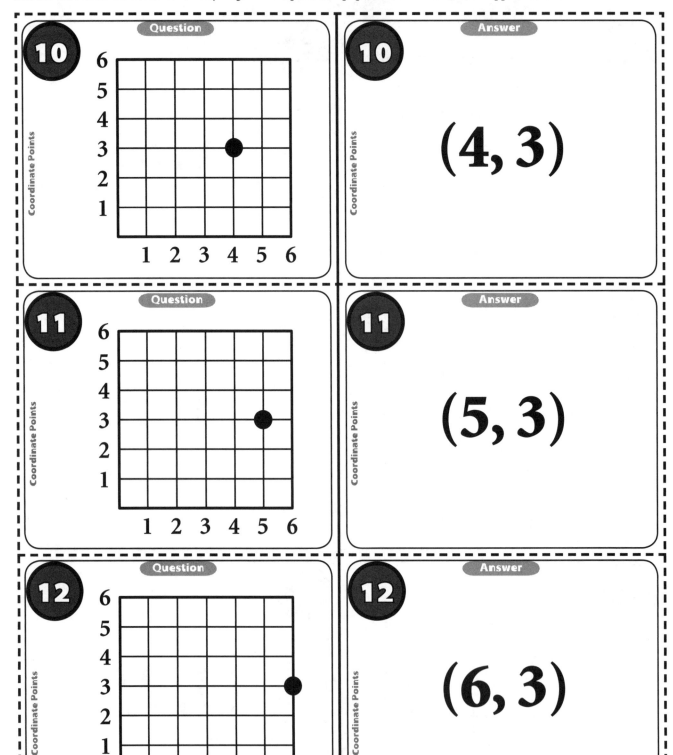

# Coordinate Points

**Instructions:** Cut out each card along the dotted line. Fold each card along the solid line so you have the question on one side and the answer on the other. Cards may be glued or taped to keep questions and answers on opposite sides.

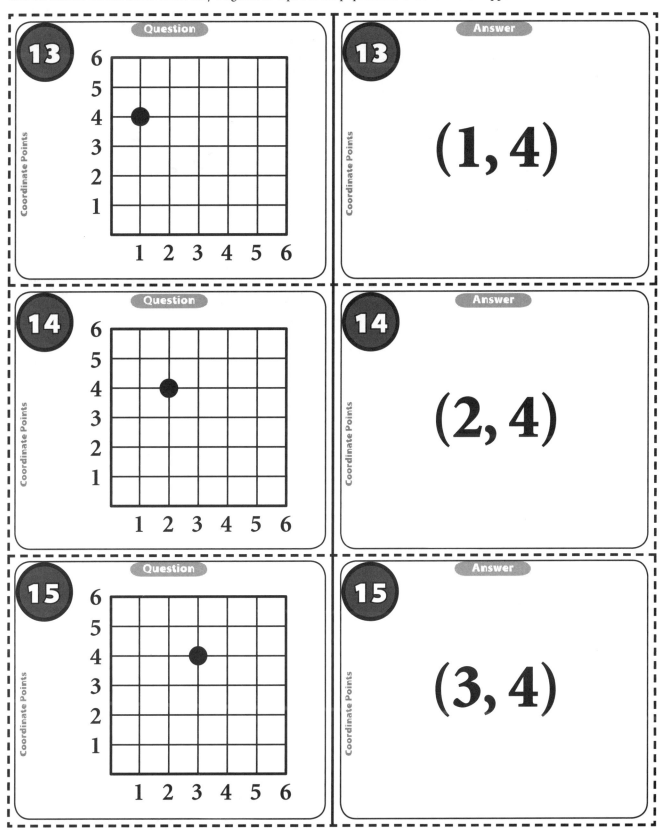

**13** Question

**13** Answer

$$(1, 4)$$

**14** Question

**14** Answer

$$(2, 4)$$

**15** Question

**15** Answer

$$(3, 4)$$

# Coordinate Points

**Instructions:** Cut out each card along the dotted line. Fold each card along the solid line so you have the question on one side and the answer on the other. Cards may be glued or taped to keep questions and answers on opposite sides.

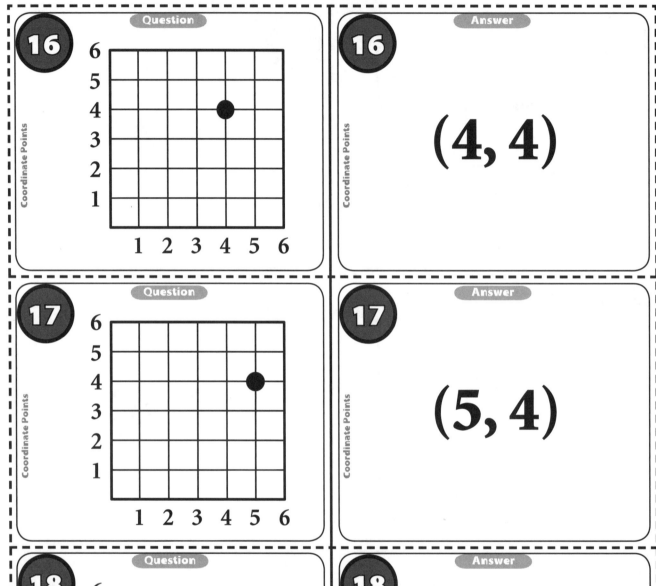

**Question**

**16**

Coordinate Points

**Answer**

**16**

Coordinate Points

(4, 4)

**Question**

**17**

Coordinate Points

**Answer**

**17**

Coordinate Points

(5, 4)

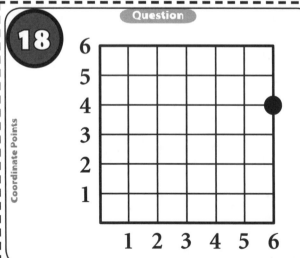

**Question**

**18**

Coordinate Points

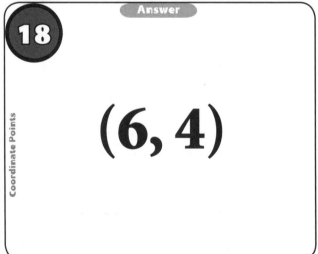

**Answer**

**18**

Coordinate Points

(6, 4)

# Coordinate Points

**Instructions:** Cut out each card along the dotted line. Fold each card along the solid line so you have the question on one side and the answer on the other. Cards may be glued or taped to keep questions and answers on opposite sides.

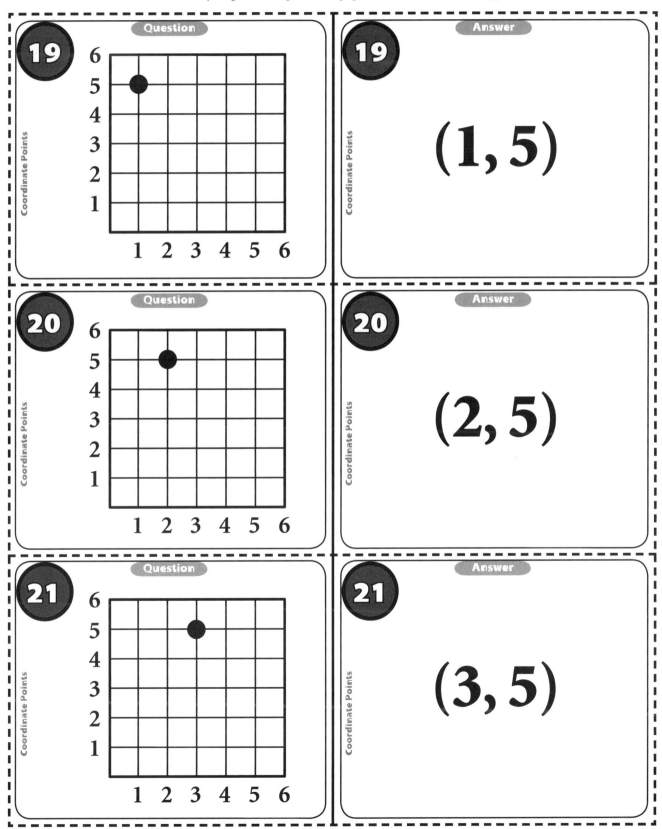

**19** Question — Coordinate Points

**19** Answer — Coordinate Points

$$(1, 5)$$

**20** Question — Coordinate Points

**20** Answer — Coordinate Points

$$(2, 5)$$

**21** Question — Coordinate Points

**21** Answer — Coordinate Points

$$(3, 5)$$

# Coordinate Points

**Instructions:** Cut out each card along the dotted line. Fold each card along the solid line so you have the question on one side and the answer on the other. Cards may be glued or taped to keep questions and answers on opposite sides.

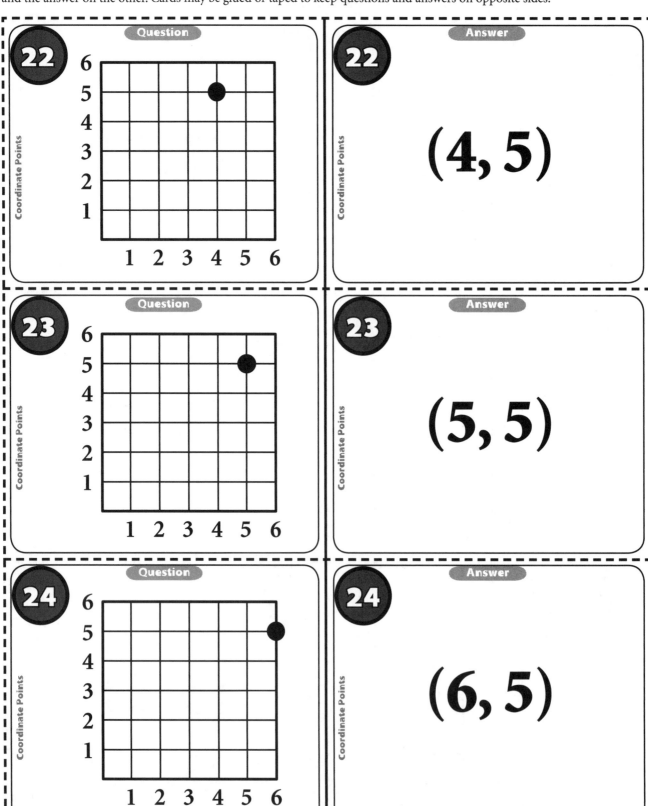

**22** Question

**22** Answer

$(4, 5)$

**23** Question

**23** Answer

$(5, 5)$

**24** Question

**24** Answer

$(6, 5)$

# Coordinate Points

**Instructions:** Cut out each card along the dotted line. Fold each card along the solid line so you have the question on one side and the answer on the other. Cards may be glued or taped to keep questions and answers on opposite sides.

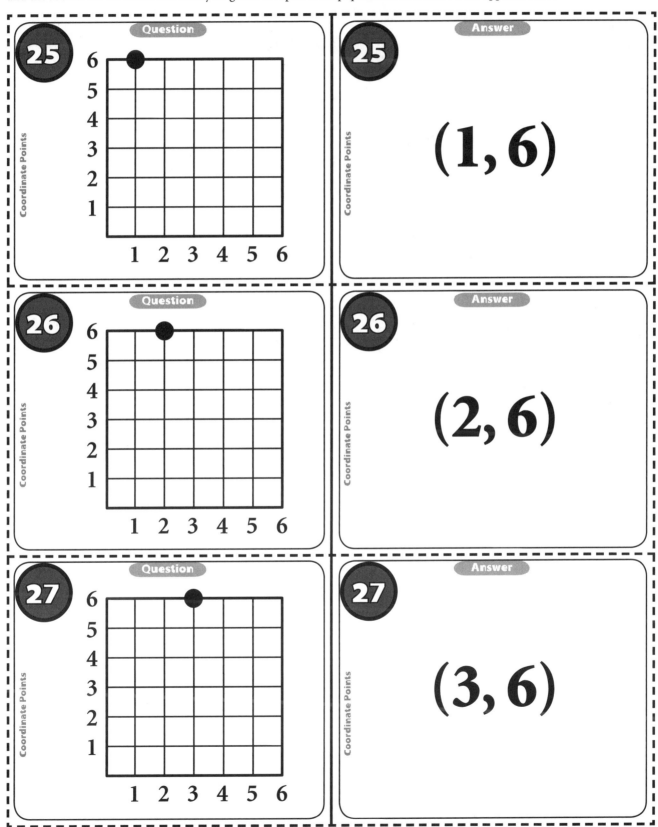

**25** Question

Coordinate Points

**25** Answer

Coordinate Points

$(1, 6)$

**26** Question

Coordinate Points

**26** Answer

Coordinate Points

$(2, 6)$

**27** Question

Coordinate Points

**27** Answer

Coordinate Points

$(3, 6)$

# Coordinate Points

**Instructions:** Cut out each card along the dotted line. Fold each card along the solid line so you have the question on one side and the answer on the other. Cards may be glued or taped to keep questions and answers on opposite sides.

**28** Question

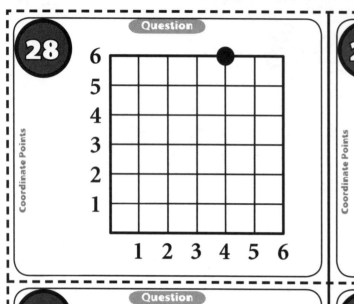

**28** Answer

Coordinate Points

$(4, 6)$

**29** Question

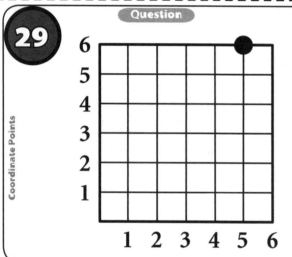

**29** Answer

Coordinate Points

$(5, 6)$

**30** Question

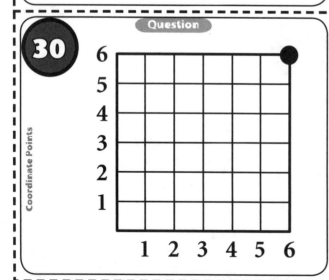

**30** Answer

Coordinate Points

$(6, 6)$

# Coordinate Points

**Instructions:** Cut out each card along the dotted line. Fold each card along the solid line so you have the question on one side and the answer on the other. Cards may be glued or taped to keep questions and answers on opposite sides.

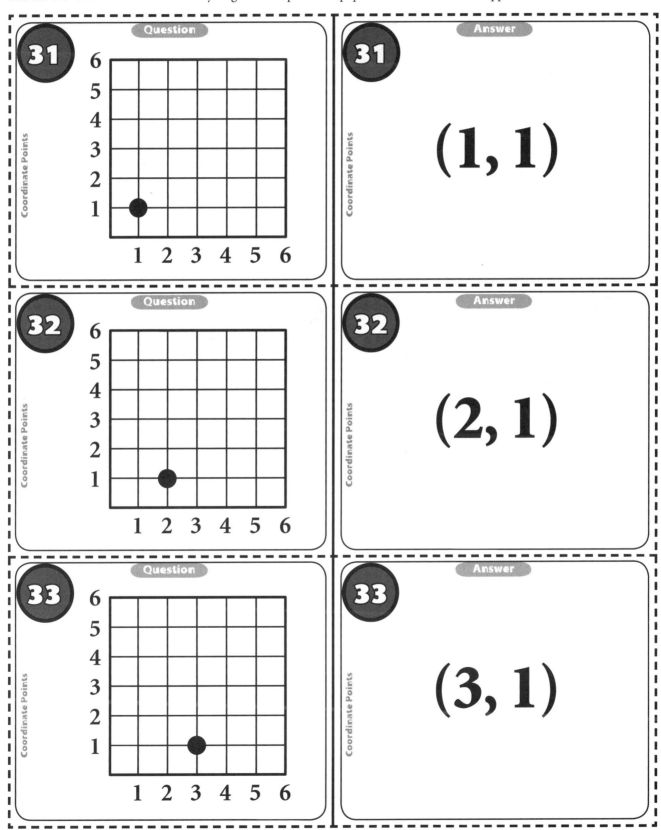

**31** Question

Coordinate Points

6
5
4
3
2
1
1 2 3 4 5 6

**31** Answer

Coordinate Points

$(1, 1)$

**32** Question

Coordinate Points

6
5
4
3
2
1
1 2 3 4 5 6

**32** Answer

Coordinate Points

$(2, 1)$

**33** Question

Coordinate Points

6
5
4
3
2
1
1 2 3 4 5 6

**33** Answer

Coordinate Points

$(3, 1)$

# Coordinate Points

**Instructions:** Cut out each card along the dotted line. Fold each card along the solid line so you have the question on one side and the answer on the other. Cards may be glued or taped to keep questions and answers on opposite sides.

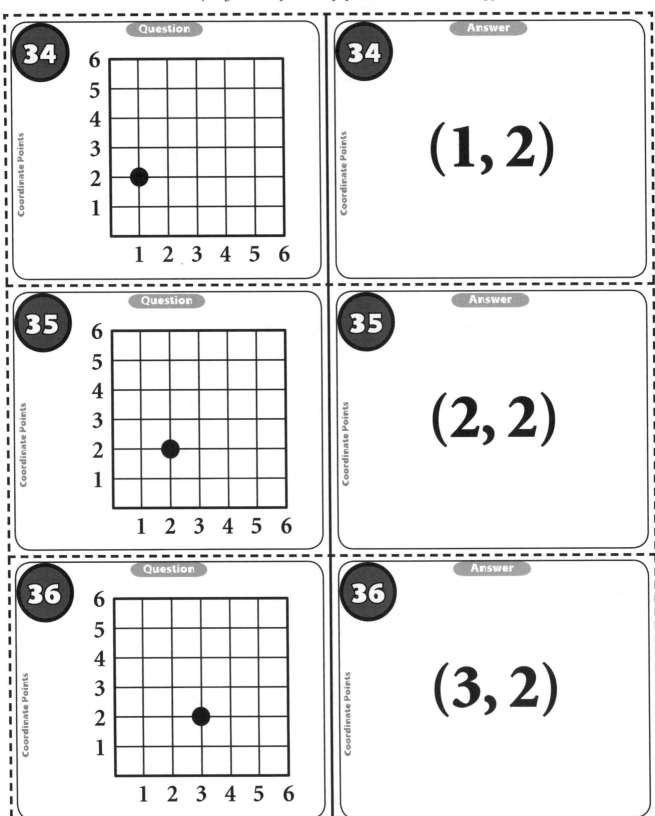

**34** Question — Coordinate Points

**34** Answer — Coordinate Points

$$(1, 2)$$

**35** Question — Coordinate Points

**35** Answer — Coordinate Points

$$(2, 2)$$

**36** Question — Coordinate Points

**36** Answer — Coordinate Points

$$(3, 2)$$

# Likely or Unlikely?

**Instructions:** Cut out each card along the dotted line. Fold each card along the solid line so you have the question on one side and the answer on the other. Cards may be glued or taped to keep questions and answers on opposite sides.

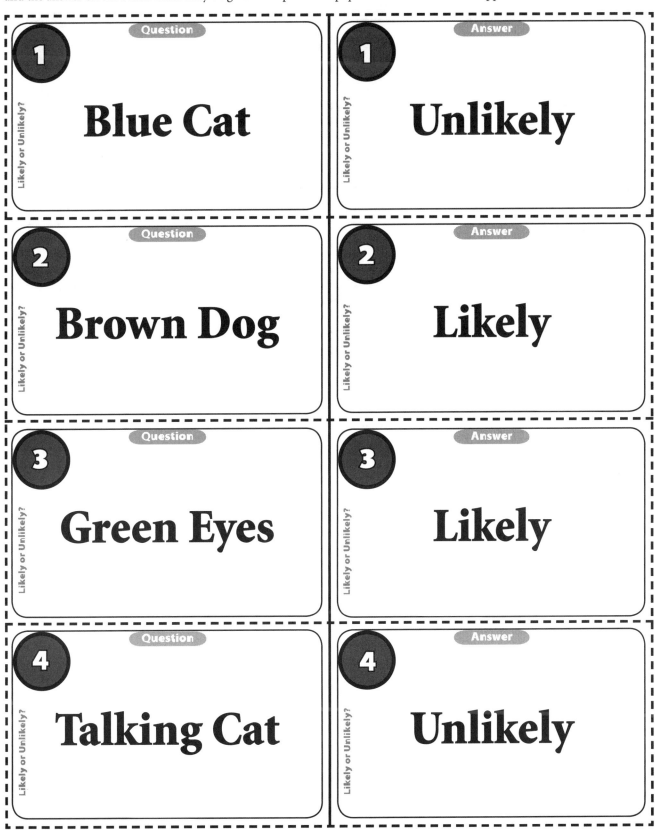

| Question 1 | Answer 1 |
|---|---|
| Blue Cat | Unlikely |
| **Question 2** | **Answer 2** |
| Brown Dog | Likely |
| **Question 3** | **Answer 3** |
| Green Eyes | Likely |
| **Question 4** | **Answer 4** |
| Talking Cat | Unlikely |

# Likely or Unlikely?

**Instructions:** Cut out each card along the dotted line. Fold each card along the solid line so you have the question on one side and the answer on the other. Cards may be glued or taped to keep questions and answers on opposite sides.

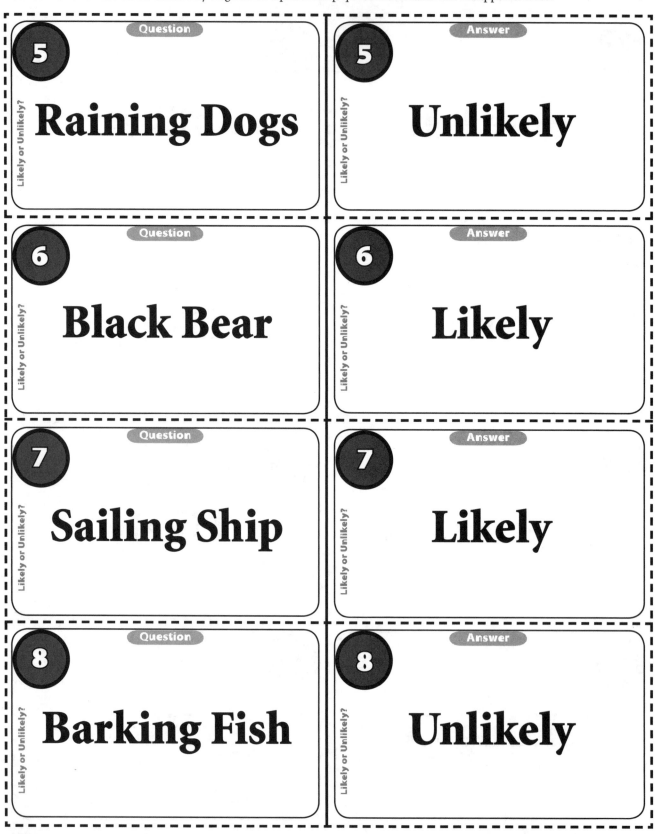

| Question | Answer |
|---|---|
| **5** Likely or Unlikely? **Raining Dogs** | **5** Likely or Unlikely? **Unlikely** |
| **6** Likely or Unlikely? **Black Bear** | **6** Likely or Unlikely? **Likely** |
| **7** Likely or Unlikely? **Sailing Ship** | **7** Likely or Unlikely? **Likely** |
| **8** Likely or Unlikely? **Barking Fish** | **8** Likely or Unlikely? **Unlikely** |

# Likely or Unlikely?

**Instructions:** Cut out each card along the dotted line. Fold each card along the solid line so you have the question on one side and the answer on the other. Cards may be glued or taped to keep questions and answers on opposite sides.

| | |
|---|---|
| **Question** 9 — Likely or Unlikely? **Flying Pigs** | **Answer** 9 — Likely or Unlikely? **Unlikely** |
| **Question** 10 — Likely or Unlikely? **Jumping Frog** | **Answer** 10 — Likely or Unlikely? **Likely** |
| **Question** 11 — Likely or Unlikely? **Mooing Cow** | **Answer** 11 — Likely or Unlikely? **Likely** |
| **Question** 12 — Likely or Unlikely? **Talking Rabbit** | **Answer** 12 — Likely or Unlikely? **Unlikely** |

# Likely or Unlikely?

**Instructions:** Cut out each card along the dotted line. Fold each card along the solid line so you have the question on one side and the answer on the other. Cards may be glued or taped to keep questions and answers on opposite sides.

| Question 13 — Likely or Unlikely? | Answer 13 — Likely or Unlikely? |
|---|---|
| **Snowing Ice Cream** | **Unlikely** |
| Question 14 — Likely or Unlikely? | Answer 14 — Likely or Unlikely? |
| **Purple Crayon** | **Likely** |
| Question 15 — Likely or Unlikely? | Answer 15 — Likely or Unlikely? |
| **Barking Dog** | **Likely** |
| Question 16 — Likely or Unlikely? | Answer 16 — Likely or Unlikely? |
| **Running Rock** | **Unlikely** |

# Likely or Unlikely?

**Instructions:** Cut out each card along the dotted line. Fold each card along the solid line so you have the question on one side and the answer on the other. Cards may be glued or taped to keep questions and answers on opposite sides.

**Question**

17

*Likely or Unlikely?*

## Purple Pig

**Answer**

17

*Likely or Unlikely?*

## Unlikely

**Question**

18

*Likely or Unlikely?*

## Screaming Baby

**Answer**

18

*Likely or Unlikely?*

## Likely

**Question**

19

*Likely or Unlikely?*

## Flying Bird

**Answer**

19

*Likely or Unlikely?*

## Likely

**Question**

20

*Likely or Unlikely?*

## Flying Ship

**Answer**

20

*Likely or Unlikely?*

## Unlikely

# Quiz-Quiz-Trade Answer Key

## 5.1 How Many?

| | | | | |
|---|---|---|---|---|
| 1. | 30 | | 21. | 18 |
| 2. | 40 | | 22. | 19 |
| 3. | 50 | | 23. | 20 |
| 4. | 80 | | 24. | 21 |
| 5. | 2 | | 25. | 22 |
| 6. | 4 | | 26. | 23 |
| 7. | 6 | | 27. | 24 |
| 8. | 8 | | 28. | 25 |
| 9. | 3 | | 29. | 32 |
| 10. | 5 | | 30. | 24 |
| 11. | 7 | | 31. | 28 |
| 12. | 9 | | 32. | 36 |
| 13. | 10 | | 33. | 50 |
| 14. | 11 | | 34. | 55 |
| 15. | 12 | | 35. | 60 |
| 16. | 13 | | 36. | 70 |
| 17. | 14 | | 37. | 25 |
| 18. | 15 | | 38. | 50 |
| 19. | 16 | | 39. | 75 |
| 20. | 17 | | 40. | 100 |

## 5.2 Addition Facts

| | | | | | | | |
|---|---|---|---|---|---|---|---|
| 1. | 1 | | 14. | 3 | | 27. | 5 |
| 2. | 2 | | 15. | 4 | | 28. | 6 |
| 3. | 3 | | 16. | 5 | | 29. | 7 |
| 4. | 4 | | 17. | 6 | | 30. | 8 |
| 5. | 5 | | 18. | 7 | | 31. | 9 |
| 6. | 6 | | 19. | 8 | | 32. | 10 |
| 7. | 7 | | 20. | 9 | | 33. | 11 |
| 8. | 8 | | 21. | 10 | | 34. | 12 |
| 9. | 9 | | 22. | 11 | | 35. | 13 |
| 10. | 10 | | 23. | 12 | | 36. | 14 |
| 11. | 11 | | 24. | 13 | | 37. | 4 |
| 12. | 12 | | 25. | 3 | | 38. | 5 |
| 13. | 2 | | 26. | 4 | | 39. | 6 |

## 5.2 Addition Facts (cont.)

| | | | | | |
|---|---|---|---|---|---|
| 40. | 7 | 72. | 17 | 104. | 16 |
| 41. | 8 | 73. | 7 | 105. | 17 |
| 42. | 9 | 74. | 8 | 106. | 18 |
| 43. | 10 | 75. | 9 | 107. | 19 |
| 44. | 11 | 76. | 10 | 108. | 20 |
| 45. | 12 | 77. | 11 | 109. | 10 |
| 46. | 13 | 78. | 12 | 110. | 11 |
| 47. | 14 | 79. | 13 | 111. | 12 |
| 48. | 15 | 80. | 14 | 112. | 13 |
| 49. | 5 | 81. | 15 | 113. | 14 |
| 50. | 6 | 82. | 16 | 114. | 15 |
| 51. | 7 | 83. | 17 | 115. | 16 |
| 52. | 8 | 84. | 18 | 116. | 17 |
| 53. | 9 | 85. | 8 | 117. | 18 |
| 54. | 10 | 86. | 9 | 118. | 19 |
| 55. | 11 | 87. | 10 | 119. | 20 |
| 56. | 12 | 88. | 11 | 120. | 21 |
| 57. | 13 | 89. | 12 | 121. | 11 |
| 58. | 14 | 90. | 13 | 122. | 12 |
| 59. | 15 | 91. | 14 | 123. | 13 |
| 60. | 16 | 92. | 15 | 124. | 14 |
| 61. | 6 | 93. | 16 | 125. | 15 |
| 62. | 7 | 94. | 17 | 126. | 16 |
| 63. | 8 | 95. | 18 | 127. | 17 |
| 64. | 9 | 96. | 19 | 128. | 18 |
| 65. | 10 | 97. | 9 | 129. | 19 |
| 66. | 11 | 98. | 10 | 130. | 20 |
| 67. | 12 | 99. | 11 | 131. | 21 |
| 68. | 13 | 100. | 12 | 132. | 22 |
| 69. | 14 | 101. | 13 | | |
| 70. | 15 | 102. | 14 | | |
| 71. | 16 | 103. | 15 | | |

# Quiz-Quiz-Trade Answer Key

## 5.3 Subtraction Facts

| # | Ans | | # | Ans |
|---|-----|---|---|-----|
| 1. | 0 | | 33. | 2 |
| 2. | 1 | | 34. | 3 |
| 3. | 2 | | 35. | 4 |
| 4. | 3 | | 36. | 5 |
| 5. | 4 | | 37. | 6 |
| 6. | 5 | | 38. | 7 |
| 7. | 6 | | 39. | 0 |
| 8. | 7 | | 40. | 1 |
| 9. | 8 | | 41. | 2 |
| 10. | 9 | | 42. | 3 |
| 11. | 10 | | 43. | 4 |
| 12. | 0 | | 44. | 5 |
| 13. | 1 | | 45. | 6 |
| 14. | 2 | | 46. | 0 |
| 15. | 3 | | 47. | 1 |
| 16. | 4 | | 48. | 2 |
| 17. | 5 | | 49. | 3 |
| 18. | 6 | | 50. | 4 |
| 19. | 7 | | 51. | 5 |
| 20. | 8 | | 52. | 0 |
| 21. | 9 | | 53. | 1 |
| 22. | 0 | | 54. | 2 |
| 23. | 1 | | 55. | 3 |
| 24. | 2 | | 56. | 4 |
| 25. | 3 | | 57. | 0 |
| 26. | 4 | | 58. | 1 |
| 27. | 5 | | 59. | 2 |
| 28. | 6 | | 60. | 3 |
| 29. | 7 | | 61. | 0 |
| 30. | 8 | | 62. | 1 |
| 31. | 0 | | 63. | 2 |
| 32. | 1 | | 64. | 0 |

# Quiz-Quiz-Trade Answer Key

## 5.4 Naming 2-D Shapes

1. Rectangle
2. Square
3. Rhombus
4. Trapezoid
5. Octagon
6. Triangle
7. Oval
8. Circle
9. Hexagon
10. Pentagon
11. Octagon
12. Triangle
13. Circle
14. Oval
15. Square
16. Rhombus
17. Rectangle
18. Pentagon
19. Hexagon
20. Trapezoid

## 5.5 Naming 3-D Shapes

1. Cylinder
2. Cube
3. Rectangular Prism
4. Sphere
5. Square-Based Pyramid
6. Cone
7. Cylinder
8. Sphere
9. Pentagonal Prism
10. Triangular Prism
11. Octagonal Prism
12. Hexagonal Prism
13. Cylinder
14. Cone
15. Cube
16. Sphere
17. Triangular Prism
18. Rectangular Prism
19. Hexagonal Prism
20. Octagonal Prism

# Quiz-Quiz-Trade Answer Key

## 5.6 Coordinate Points

| | | | |
|---|---|---|---|
| 1. | (4, 1) | 19. | (1, 5) |
| 2. | (5, 1) | 20. | (2, 5) |
| 3. | (6, 1) | 21. | (3, 5) |
| 4. | (4, 2) | 22. | (4, 5) |
| 5. | (5, 2) | 23. | (5, 5) |
| 6. | (6, 2) | 24. | (6, 5) |
| 7. | (1, 3) | 25. | (1, 6) |
| 8. | (2, 3) | 26. | (2, 6) |
| 9. | (3, 3) | 27. | (3, 6) |
| 10. | (4, 3) | 28. | (4, 6) |
| 11. | (5, 3) | 29. | (5, 6) |
| 12. | (6, 3) | 30. | (6, 6) |
| 13. | (1, 4) | 31. | (1, 1) |
| 14. | (2, 4) | 32. | (2, 1) |
| 15. | (3, 4) | 33. | (3, 1) |
| 16. | (4, 4) | 34. | (1, 2) |
| 17. | (5, 4) | 35. | (2, 2) |
| 18. | (6, 4) | 36. | (3, 2) |

## 5.7 Likely or Unlikely?

| | | | |
|---|---|---|---|
| 1. | Unlikely | 11. | Likely |
| 2. | Likely | 12. | Unlikely |
| 3. | Likely | 13. | Unlikely |
| 4. | Unlikely | 14. | Likely |
| 5. | Unlikely | 15. | Likely |
| 6. | Likely | 16. | Unlikely |
| 7. | Likely | 17. | Unlikely |
| 8. | Unlikely | 18. | Likely |
| 9. | Unlikely | 19. | Likely |
| 10. | Likely | 20. | Unlikely |

# COOPERATIVE MATH

# Structure **6**
## Sage-N-Scribe

## Structure 6

# Sage-N-Scribe

**Partners take turns being the Sage and Scribe.**

## Instructions

*In pairs, Partner A is the Sage; Partner B is the Scribe. Partners receive a worksheet with problems for each partner.*

**1** The Sage gives the Scribe step-by-step instructions how to perform a task or solve a problem. For example, "Write the first fact family, 5 + 4 = 9."

**2** The Scribe records the Sage's solution step-by-step in writing, coaching if necessary.

**3** The Scribe praises the Sage for his or her directions.

**4** Students switch roles for the next problem or task.

Sage-N-Scribe creates a high level of participation and is ideal for peer tutoring in math. Both partners have an active role for each problem. The Sage verbalizes his or her mathematical thinking while the Scribe records the thinking and the answer. By hearing their partners talk through problems, peers have ready access to the thinking of others. This makes it easy to emulate others and quickly detect where things are going wrong. Plus, repeatedly teaching others reinforces students' retention of the problem-solving strategy.

# Sage-N-Scribe Activities

## Number and Operations

## Algebra

## Geometry

## Measurement

## Data Analysis and Probability

## Answer Key .................. 298

# Sage-N-Scribe
# Primary Tips

## General Tips

- Limit number of concepts being reviewed. It is okay for primary students to practice concepts multiple times.
- Use problems that require students to explain their thinking out loud.
- Designate a Partner A and Partner B in each pair.
- The students should sit side-by-side with one paper and one pencil between them so they need to take turns.
- Content should be a review of material previously taught.
- Make sure there is plenty of space to write on the worksheet.

## Before
### Teaching the Structure

- Start with a visual of the structure. Use the visual to explain the steps.
- Model with students how to sit, explain their thinking, record answer, and praise their partner.
  - ★ Tips on "How to sit"
    - Model with two students. Demonstrate how to sit side-by-side with the paper and pencil in between them so that both students can see the paper at all times.
      - ★ Tips for the Scribe
        - Model how to write only what the Sage tells them to.

## Before
**Teaching the Structure** *(continued)*

★ **Tips on "Coaching"**
- Give students examples of coaching phrases without giving their partner the answer. For example: "Count with me." Coaching is always specific to the task so the teacher must model specific coaching phrases that match the content. Phrases like "keep trying" or "try again" are encouraging statements, not coaching.
- Student coaches could also use manipulatives to help show things such as addition/subtraction, counting, etc.

★ **Tip on "Praising"**
- Give specific praise or cheer that all students do when done quizzing/answering (examples: high five, a round of applause, thumbs up, "Great job!"). Watch to make sure the praising does not distract students from the content.

## During
**Doing the Structure**

- Start with short amounts of time. If the structure continues for too long, students start to get loud and off task.
- Listen for good coaching and praising. Stop the group if appropriate and hold up a pair as models. Do this during the structure so that other students can practice what you have emphasized.

## After
**Processing the Structure**

- Talk about what went well. Demonstrate if needed.
- Note any problems.
- Set goals for next time.

# Sage-N-Scribe Activities

## Activity 6.1

### Fact Families

A *fact family* is a set of numbers sentences that relate addition and subtraction. Each number sentence in the fact family has the same numbers. Students pair up: one is the Sage, the other is the Scribe. Pairs receive a fact family worksheet. The Sage gives the Scribe step-by-step directions to answer the problem. The Scribe writes the Sage's answer, and coaches if necessary. Students agree on answer, celebrate, and switch roles.

**NCTM Standard: Number and Operations Standard PreK–2**
★ Understand meanings of operations and how they relate to one another.
 • Understand various meanings of addition and subtraction of whole numbers and the relationship between the two operations.

**pp. 284–285**

## Activity 6.2

### Addition Situations

Identify a sage and a scribe. The sage talks out loud while answering the problem. The scribe writes the answer that was said by the sage and coaches if necessary. Students agree on answer, celebrate, and switch roles.

**NCTM Standard: Numbers and Operations Standard PreK–2**
★ Understand meanings of operations and how they relate to one another.
 • Understand various meanings of addition and subtraction of whole numbers and the relationship between the two operations.

**pp. 286–287**

## Activity 6.3

# Estimate and Calculate

Identify a sage and a scribe. The sage talks out loud while answering the problem. The scribe writes the answer that was said by the sage and coaches if necessary. Students agree on answer, celebrate, and switch roles.

**NCTM Standard: Number and Operations Standard PreK–2**
★ Compute fluently and make reasonable estimates.
  • Develop and use strategies for whole-number computations, with focus on addition and subtraction.

**pp. 288–289**

## Activity 6.4

# Growing Patterns

Identify a sage and a scribe. The sage talks out loud while answering the problem by continuing the pattern. The scribe writes the answer that was said by the sage and coaches if necessary. Students agree on answer, celebrate, and switch roles.

**NCTM Standard: Algebra Standard PreK–2**
★ Understand patterns, relations, and functions.
  • Recognize, describe, and extend patterns, such as sequences of sounds and shapes or simple numeric patterns, and translate from one representation to another.

**pp. 290–291**

## Activity 6.5

# Direction and Distance

Identify a sage and a scribe. The sage talks out loud while answering the problem. The scribe writes the answer that was said by the sage and coaches if necessary. Students agree on answer, celebrate, and switch roles.

**NCTM Standard: Geometry Standard PreK–2**
★ Specify locations and describe spatial relationships using coordinate geometry and other representational systems.
  • Describe, name, and interpret direction and distance in navigating space and apply ideas about direction and distance.

**p. 292**

# Sage-N-Scribe
## Activities continued

## Activity 6.6

### Symmetry #1

Identify a sage and a scribe. The sage talks out loud while answering the problem. The scribe writes the answer that was said by the sage and coaches if necessary. Students agree on answer, celebrate, and switch roles.

**NCTM Standard: Geometry Standard PreK–2**
★ Apply transformations and use symmetry to analyze mathematical situations.
• Recognize and create shapes that have symmetry.

p. 293

## Activity 6.7

### Symmetry #2

Identify a sage and a scribe. The sage talks out loud while answering the problem. The scribe writes the answer that was said by the sage and coaches if necessary. Students agree on answer, celebrate, and switch roles.

**NCTM Standard: Geometry Standard PreK–2**
★ Apply transformations and use symmetry to analyze mathematical situations.
• Recognize and create shapes that have symmetry.

p. 294

## Activity 6.8

### Match the Time

Identify a sage and a scribe. The sage talks out loud while answering the problem. The scribe writes the answer that was said by the sage and coaches if necessary. Students agree on answer, celebrate, and switch roles.

**NCTM Standard: Measurement Standard PreK–2**
★ Understand measurable attributes of objects and the units, systems, and processes of measurement.
• Recognize the attributes of length, volume, weight, area, and time.

p. 295

## Activity 6.9

# Measuring with Dinosaurs

Identify a sage and a scribe. The sage talks out loud while answering the problem. The scribe writes the answer that was said by the sage and coaches if necessary. Students agree on answer, celebrate, and switch roles.

**NCTM Standard: Measurement Standard PreK–2**
★ Apply appropriate techniques, tools, and formulas to determine measurements.
　• Measure with multiple copies of units of the same size, such as paper clips laid end to end.

**p. 296**

## Activity 6.10

# Graphs

Identify a sage and a scribe. The sage talks out loud while answering the problem. The scribe writes the answer that was said by the sage and coaches if necessary. Students agree on answer, celebrate, and switch roles.

**NCTM Standard: Data Analysis and Probability Standard PreK–2**
★ Select and use appropriate statistical methods to analyze data.
　• Describe parts of the data and the set of data as a whole to determine what the data show.

**p. 297**

# Fact Families

**Instructions:** Write the three remaining number sentences that belong with the given fact.

**A** Sage _____

Scribe _____

**1** 4 + 5 = 9

★ _____

★ _____

★ _____

**2** 5 + 2 = 7

★ _____

★ _____

★ _____

**3** 2 + 3 = 5

★ _____

★ _____

★ _____

**4** 4 − 1 = 3

★ _____

★ _____

★ _____

**5** 6 + 3 = 9

★ _____

★ _____

★ _____

**B** Sage _____

Scribe _____

**1** 2 + 1 = 3

★ _____

★ _____

★ _____

**2** 4 + 2 = 6

★ _____

★ _____

★ _____

**3** 5 − 2 = 3

★ _____

★ _____

★ _____

**4** 9 + 1 = 10

★ _____

★ _____

★ _____

**5** 1 + 4 = 5

★ _____

★ _____

★ _____

# Fact Families

**Instructions:** Write the three remaining number sentences that belong with the given fact.

**A** Sage _____
   Scribe _____

**6** 8 + 5 = 13

★ _____
★ _____
★ _____

**7** 10 − 8 = 2

★ _____
★ _____
★ _____

**8** 8 + 6 = 14

★ _____
★ _____
★ _____

**9** 9 + 6 = 15

★ _____
★ _____
★ _____

**10** 5 + 6 = 11

★ _____
★ _____
★ _____

**B** Sage _____
   Scribe _____

**6** 15 − 5 = 10

★ _____
★ _____
★ _____

**7** 7 + 4 = 11

★ _____
★ _____
★ _____

**8** 12 − 7 = 5

★ _____
★ _____
★ _____

**9** 13 − 2 = 11

★ _____
★ _____
★ _____

**10** 9 − 6 = 3

★ _____
★ _____
★ _____

# Addition Situations

**Instructions:** Solve each problem and write the answer.

## A

Sage _____

Scribe _____

**1**  ⬭⬭⬭ ✚ ⬭⬭

_____

**2** ▢▢▢ ✚ ▢▢▢

_____

**3** ◎◎ ✚ ◎◎

_____

**4** ⬜⬜⬜ ✚ ⬜⬜ ⬜⬜

_____

**5** ◇◇ ✚ ◇◇ ◇◇

_____

## B

Sage _____

Scribe _____

**1** ◯ ✚ ◯◯

_____

**2** ♡♡ ✚ ♡♡♡

_____

**3** ⌒ ✚ ⌒

_____

**4** ▯▯▯▯▯ ✚ ▯

_____

**5** ▯▯▯ ✚ ▯▯▯

_____

# Addition Situations

**Instructions:** Solve each problem and write the answer.

**A**  Sage _____
   Scribe _____

**6** ▯▯▯▯▯ + ▯▯
_____

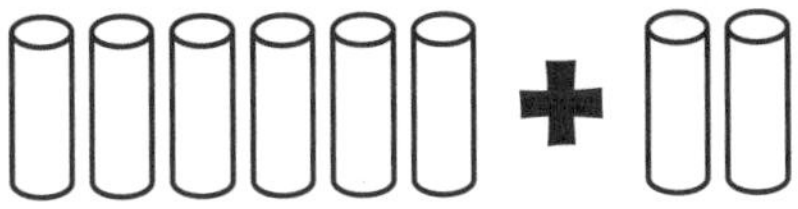

**7** ▯▯▯▯▯ + ▯▯
_____

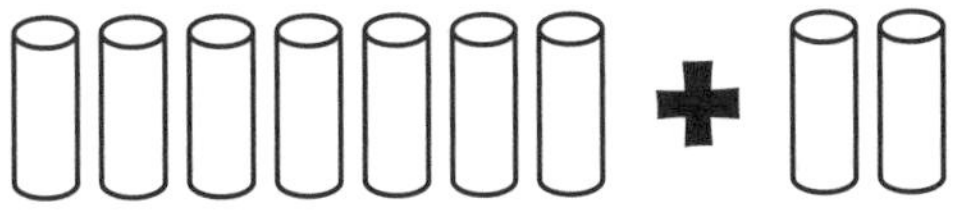

**8** △△△△△△ + △△△△
_____

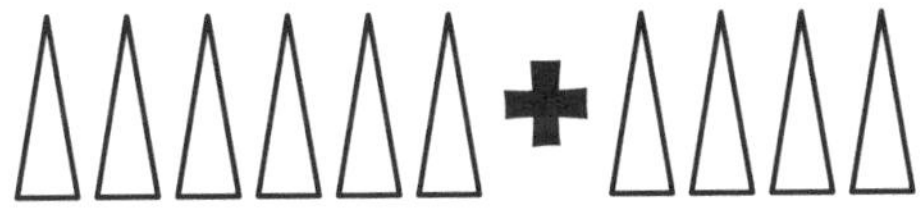

**9** ▱▱▱ + ▱▱▱▱▱
_____

**10** ▯▯▯▯▯ + ▯▯▯▯
_____

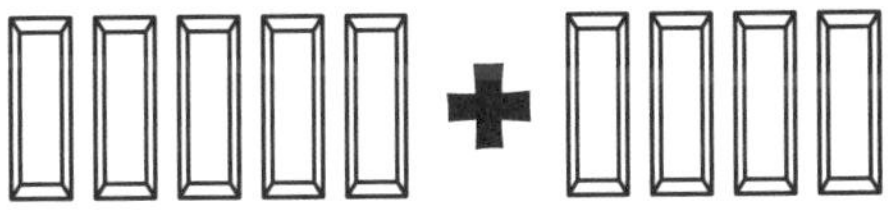

**B**  Sage _____
   Scribe _____

**6** ▯▯▯▯▯ + ▯▯▯
_____

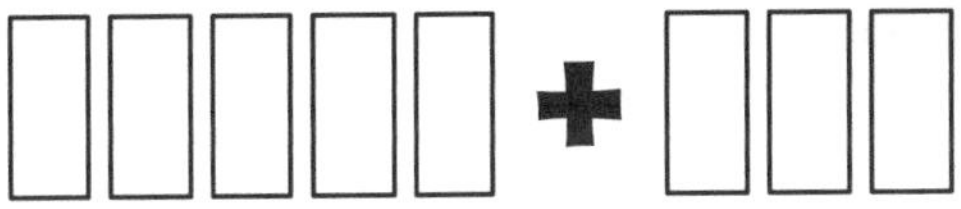

**7** ○○○○○ + ○
_____

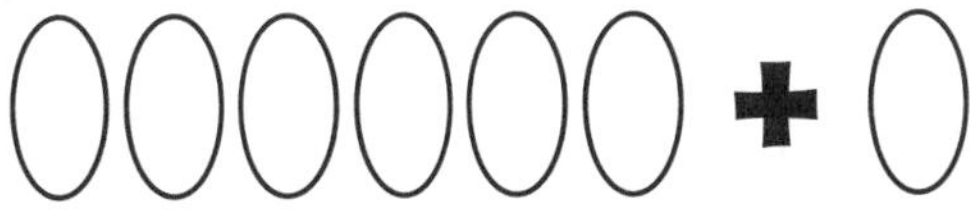

**8** ▯▯▯ + ▯▯▯▯▯
_____

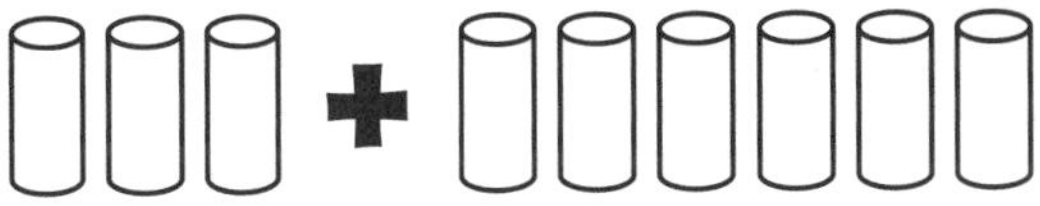

**9** ☆☆☆☆ + ☆☆☆
_____

**10** ▯▯▯▯▯▯▯ + ▯
_____

# Estimate and Calculate

**Instructions:** Estimate the answer and write your guess. Then solve and write the answer.

## A  Sage _____
### Scribe _____

 **1** 25 + 15

Guess _____

Check _____

 **2** 13 + 17

Guess _____

Check _____

 **3** 33 + 42

Guess _____

Check _____

 **4** 91 + 12

Guess _____

Check _____

 **5** 35 + 27

Guess _____

Check _____

## B  Sage _____
### Scribe _____

 **1** 46 + 39

Guess _____

Check _____

 **2** 39 + 21

Guess _____

Check _____

 **3** 38 + 14

Guess _____

Check _____

 **4** 55 + 25

Guess _____

Check _____

 **5** 64 + 26

Guess _____

Check _____

# Estimate and Calculate

**Instructions:** Estimate the answer and write your guess. Then solve and write the answer.

## A

Sage _____

Scribe _____

**6** 10 + 15

Guess _____

Check _____

**7** 15 + 15

Guess _____

Check _____

**8** 40 + 22

Guess _____

Check _____

**9** 32 + 20

Guess _____

Check _____

**10** 9 + 30

Guess _____

Check _____

## B

Sage _____

Scribe _____

**6** 21 + 20

Guess _____

Check _____

**7** 30 + 10

Guess _____

Check _____

**8** 25 + 25

Guess _____

Check _____

**9** 14 + 10

Guess _____

Check _____

**10** 10 + 15

Guess _____

Check _____

# Growing Patterns

**Instructions:** Continue each number pattern.

**A**  Sage _____
       Scribe _____

**1** 1, 2, 3, 4, _____, _____, _____

**2** 10, 11, 12, 13, _____, _____, _____

**3** 5, 6, 7, 8, _____, _____, _____

**4** 1, 3, 5, 7, _____, _____, _____

**5** 11, 12, 13, 14, _____, _____, _____

**B**  Sage _____
       Scribe _____

**1** 7, 8, 9, 10, _____, _____, _____

**2** 5, 6, 7, 8, _____, _____, _____

**3** 7, 9, 11, 13, _____, _____, _____

**4** 2, 4, 6, 8, _____, _____, _____

**5** 6, 7, 8, 9, _____, _____, _____

# Growing Patterns

**Instructions:** Continue each number pattern.

 **Sage** _____

**Scribe** _____

**6** 5, 10, 15, 20, _____, _____, _____

**7** 10, 20, 30, 40, _____, _____, _____

**8** 6, 8, 10, 12, _____, _____, _____

**9** 1, 4, 7, 10, _____, _____, _____

**10** 12, 14, 16, 18, _____, _____, _____

 **Sage** _____

**Scribe** _____

**6** 15, 20, 25, 30, _____, _____, _____

**7** 20, 22, 24, 26, _____, _____, _____

**8** 14, 15, 16, 17, _____, _____, _____

**9** 30, 40, 50, 60, _____, _____, _____

**10** 12, 15, 18, 21, _____, _____, _____

# Direction and Distance

**Instructions:** Use the graph to answer the questions.

| | A | B | C | D | E | F |
|---|---|---|---|---|---|---|
| **4** | | | | | | 🦀 |
| **3** | 🦊 | | | | | 🐄 |
| **2** | | 🐸 | | | | |
| **1** | | | | | 🐕 | |

## A

Sage _____

Scribe _____

**1** Where is the crab? (F, ___)

**2** What animal is in (B, 2)?

_____

**3** What animal is one square south of the crab?

_____

**4** What animal is one square south and three squares east of the frog?

_____

**5** Where is the fox? (___, 3)

## B

Sage _____

Scribe _____

**1** Where is the dog? (E, ___)

**2** What animal is in (F, 3)?

_____

**3** What animal is one square north of the cow?

_____

**4** What animal is two squares north and four squares west of the dog?

_____

**5** Where is the cow? (___, 3)

# Symmetry #1

**Instructions:** Draw one line of symmetry for each shape or object.

**A** Sage _____
Scribe _____

1
2
3
4
5

**B** Sage _____
Scribe _____

1
2
3
4
5

# Symmetry #2

**Instructions:** Circle the pictures with symmetry. Put an X on the pictures that do not have symmetry.

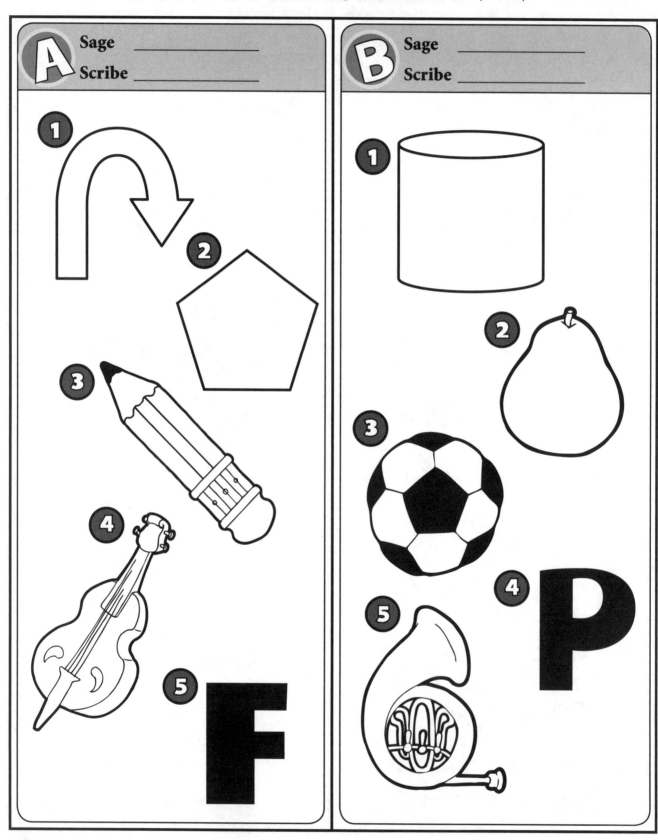

**A** Sage _____
Scribe _____

1
2
3
4
5 F

**B** Sage _____
Scribe _____

1
2
3
4 P
5

# Match the Time

**Instructions:** Read the clock and write the correct time.

| | |
|---|---|
| **6:00** | |
| **9:00** | |
| **3:00** | |
| **2:00** | |
| **10:30** | |
| **12:30** | |
| **5:30** | |
| **3:30** | |
| **1:00** | |
| **7:00** | |

# Measuring with Dinosaurs

**Instructions:** Cut out the dinosaur. Use the dinosaur to measure the lines.
Measure to the nearest half dinosaur. Write the answer above the line.

**A**

Sage _____

Scribe _____

**1** ·················

**2** ································

**3** ··········

**4** ·····························

**5** ·····························

**B**

Sage _____

Scribe _____

**1** – – – – – – –

**2** – – – – – – – – –

**3** – – – – – – – – – – – – – – –

**4** – – – – – – – – – – – – – –

**5** – – – – – – – – – – – – – – – –

# Graphs

**Instructions:** Use the graph to answer the questions.

## Our Favorite Foods

**A**

Sage _____

Scribe _____

**1** What is the title of this graph?

_____

**2** Which food is liked the most?

_____

**3** How many people like fruit?

_____

**4** How many more students like hot dogs than ice cream?

_____

**B**

Sage _____

Scribe _____

**1** Which food is liked the least?

_____

**2** How many people like pizza?

_____

**3** Which two foods were liked by the same number of students?

_____

**4** How many more people liked fruit than vegetables?

_____

# Sage-N-Scribe Answer Key

## 6.1 Fact Families

**Partner A**

1. $5 + 4 = 9$, $9 - 4 = 5$, $9 - 5 = 4$
2. $2 + 5 = 7$, $7 - 2 = 5$, $7 - 5 = 2$
3. $3 + 2 = 5$, $5 - 3 = 2$, $5 - 2 = 3$
4. $4 - 3 = 1$, $3 + 1 = 4$, $1 + 3 = 4$
5. $3 + 6 = 9$, $9 - 3 = 6$, $9 - 6 = 3$
6. $5 + 8 = 13$, $13 - 5 = 8$, $13 - 8 = 5$
7. $10 - 2 = 8$, $8 + 2 = 10$, $2 + 8 = 10$
8. $6 + 8 = 14$, $14 - 8 = 6$, $14 - 6 = 8$
9. $6 + 9 = 15$, $15 - 6 = 9$, $15 - 9 = 6$
10. $6 + 5 = 11$, $11 - 5 = 6$, $11 - 6 = 5$

**Partner B**

1. $1 + 2 = 3$, $3 - 1 = 2$, $3 - 2 = 1$
2. $2 + 4 = 6$, $6 - 2 = 4$, $6 - 4 = 2$
3. $5 - 3 = 2$, $3 + 2 = 5$, $2 + 3 = 5$
4. $1 + 9 = 10$, $10 - 1 = 9$, $10 - 9 = 1$
5. $4 + 1 = 5$, $5 - 1 = 4$, $5 - 4 = 1$
6. $15 - 10 = 5$, $5 + 10 = 15$, $10 + 5 = 15$
7. $4 + 7 = 11$, $11 - 4 = 7$, $11 - 7 = 4$
8. $12 - 5 = 7$, $5 + 7 = 12$, $7 + 5 = 12$
9. $13 - 11 = 2$, $2 + 11 = 13$, $11 + 2 = 13$
10. $9 - 3 = 6$, $3 + 6 = 9$, $6 + 3 = 9$

## 6.2 Addition Situations

**Partner A**

1. 5
2. 6
3. 4
4. 7
5. 6
6. 8
7. 9
8. 10
9. 8
10. 9

**Partner B**

1. 3
2. 5
3. 2
4. 7
5. 7
6. 8
7. 7
8. 9
9. 7
10. 9

# Sage-N-Scribe Answer Key

## 6.3 Estimate and Calculate

**Partner A**
1. 40
2. 30
3. 75
4. 103
5. 62
6. 25
7. 30
8. 62
9. 52
10. 39

**Partner B**
1. 85
2. 60
3. 52
4. 80
5. 90
6. 41
7. 40
8. 50
9. 24
10. 25

## 6.4 Growing Patterns

**Partner A**
1. 5, 6, 7
2. 14, 15, 16
3. 9, 10, 11
4. 9, 11, 13
5. 15, 16, 17
6. 25, 30, 35
7. 50, 60, 70
8. 14, 16, 18
9. 13, 16, 19
10. 20, 22, 24

**Partner B**
1. 11, 12, 13
2. 9, 10, 11
3. 15, 17, 19
4. 10, 12, 14
5. 10, 11, 12
6. 35, 40, 45
7. 28, 30, 32
8. 18, 19, 20
9. 70, 80, 90
10. 24, 27, 30

## 6.5 Direction and Distance

**Partner A**
1. 4
2. Frog
3. Cow
4. Dog
5. A

**Partner B**
1. 1
2. Cow
3. Crab
4. Fox
5. F

# Sage-N-Scribe Answer Key

## 6.6 Symmetry #1

**Partner A**
Answers may vary for #2!

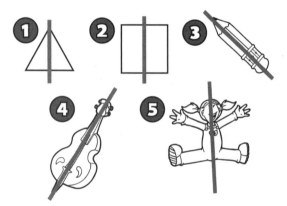

**Partner B**
Answers may vary for #1 and #2!

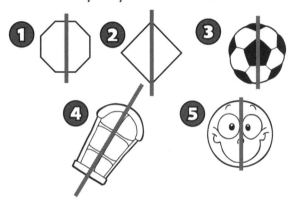

## 6.7 Symmetry #2

**Partner A**

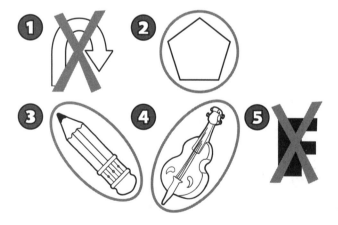

**Partner B**

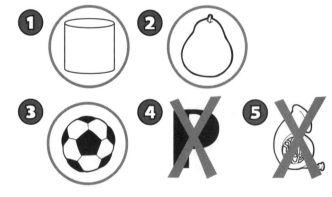

## 6.8 Match the Time

**Partner A**
1. 7:00
2. 6:00
3. 3:00
4. 10:30
5. 12:30

**Partner B**
1. 9:00
2. 1:00
3. 2:00
4. 5:30
5. 3:30

## 6.9 Measuring with Dinosaurs

**Partner A**
1. 1
2. 2
3. $^1/_2$
4. 3
5. 2 $^1/_2$

**Partner B**
1. 1
2. 1 $^1/_2$
3. 3
4. 2 $^1/_2$
5. 3 $^1/_2$

## 6.10 Graphs

**Partner A**
1. Our Favorite Foods
2. Pizza
3. 3
4. 1

**Partner B**
1. Vegetables
2. 6
3. Fruit and Ice Cream
4. 2

COOPERATIVE MATH

Structure 7

Showdown

## Structure 7

# Showdown

**When the Showdown Captain calls, "Showdown!" teammates all display their own answers. Teammates either celebrate or tutor, and then celebrate.**

## Instructions

*Teams each have a set of question cards stacked facedown in the center of the table.*

**1** The teacher selects one student on each team to be the Showdown Captain for the first round.

**2** The Showdown Captain draws the top card, reads the question, and provides think time.

**3** Working alone, all students, including the Showdown Captain, write their answers.

**4** When finished, teammates signal they're ready.

**5** The Showdown Captain calls, "Showdown."

**6** Teammates show and discuss their answers.

**7** The Showdown Captain leads the checking.

**8** If correct, the team celebrates; if not, teammates tutor, then celebrate.

**9** The person on the left of the Showdown Captain becomes the Showdown Captain for the next round.

*Modifications: Rather than cards, students can play Showdown with oral questions from the teacher, or from questions on a handout or questions displayed by a projector.*

Showdown keeps everyone on their toes. Students hold a math showdown with every problem. Every student is accountable to their teammates for solving each problem and participating. If a teammate misses a problem, then he or she receives immediate feedback and tutoring. Students see themselves on the same side with this friendly showdown as teams celebrate their math success!

# Showdown Activities

 **Number and Operations**

 **Algebra**

 **Geometry**

 **Measurement**

 **Data Analysis and Probability**

 **Answer Key** .............. **365**

# Showdown Primary Tips

## General Tips

- Limit number of concepts being reviewed. It is okay for primary students to practice concepts multiple times.
- Laminate cards for durability.
- Content should be a review of material previously taught.
- Use whiteboards to have students work out their answers.
- Use visuals on cards.
- Make sure answers are accessible.
- For extra help, have the answer key rotate with the "Showdown Captain."

## Before
### Teaching the Structure

- Start with a visual of the structure. Use the visual to explain the steps.
- Create a signal that tells the "Showdown Captain" that the question is answered, such as turning the paper/whiteboard over, or putting pencils down.
- Model with four students. Demonstrate how to place the cards in the middle of the group.
  - ★ **Tips for Showdown Captain**
    - Model how the Showdown Captain picks the top card and reads/shows the group.
    - Model asking. Demonstrate how to hold the card and ask the question. If the answer is on the back, remind students to show the question side only.
    - Model how to wait for the signal to show all group members are done.
    - Model how to show answers when the Showdown Captain says, "Showdown."
    - Remind them that the Captain answers the questions, too.

## Before
### Teaching the Structure *(continued)*

★ **Tips on "Coaching"**
- Give students examples of coaching phrases without giving their partner the answer. For example: "Count with me." Coaching is always specific to the task so the teacher must model specific coaching phrases that match the content. Phrases like "keep trying" or "try again" are encouraging statements not coaching.
- Student coaches could also use manipulatives to help show things such as addition/subtraction, counting, etc.
- Watch for hogs. The Showdown Captain should "lead" checking.

★ **Tip on "Praising"**
- Give specific praise or cheer that all students do when done quizzing/answering (examples: high five, a round of applause, thumbs up, "Great job!"). Watch to make sure the praising does not distract students from the content.

## During
### Doing the Structure

- Start with short amounts of time. If the structure continues for too long, students start to get loud and off task.
- For primary students, the teacher can be the "Showdown Captain" each time.
- Listen for good coaching and praising. Stop the group if appropriate and hold up a pair as models. Do this during the structure so that other students can practice what you have emphasized.

## After
### Processing the Structure

- Talk about what went well. Demonstrate if needed.
- Note any problems.
- Set goals for next time.

# Showdown Activities

## Activity 7.1

# Number Words and Numerals

Students write the numeral that matches the number word. Assign a "Showdown Captain." The Captain chooses a card and shows to the group. Group members work alone and write the numeral that matches the word. When finished, teammates signal when they're ready.

The Captain calls, "Showdown." Teammates show and state their answers. The Captain checks, coaches, and praises the other members. If correct, the team celebrates; if not, teammates coach, then celebrate. When everyone is finished, Showdown Captain role is rotated clockwise.

**NCTM Standard: Number and Operations Standard PreK–2**
★ Understand numbers, ways of representing numbers, relationships among numbers, and number systems.
   • Connect number words and numerals to the quantities they represent, using various physical models and representations.

pp. 312–317

## Activity 7.2

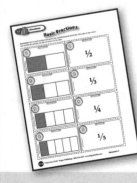

# Basic Fractions

Students write the fraction shown. Assign a "Showdown Captain." The Captain chooses a card and shows to the group. Group members work alone and write the fraction. When finished, teammates signal when they're ready. The Captain

calls, "Showdown." Teammates show and state their answers. The Captain checks, coaches, and praises the other members. If correct, the team celebrates; if not, teammates coach, then celebrate. When everyone is finished, Showdown Captain role is rotated clockwise.

**NCTM Standard: Number and Operations Standard PreK–2**
★ Understand numbers, ways of representing numbers, relationships among numbers, and number systems.
   • Understand and represent commonly used fractions.

pp. 318–325

# Activity 7.3

## Equal Groups

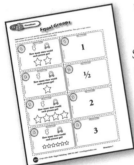

Students are given a card with a number of objects and a number of people. Assign a "Showdown Captain." The Captain chooses a card and shows to the group. Group members work alone and answer the question. When finished, teammates signal when they're ready. The Captain calls, "Showdown." Teammates show and state their answers. The Captain checks, coaches, and praises the other members. If correct, the team celebrates; if not, teammates coach, then celebrate. When everyone is finished, Showdown Captain role is rotated clockwise.

**NCTM Standard: Number and Operations Standard PreK–2**
★ Understand meanings of operations and how they relate to one another.
  • Understand situations that entail multiplication and division, such as equal groupings of objects and sharing equally.

pp. 324–329

# Activity 7.4

## Addition and Subtraction

Students are given a card with an addition or subtraction number sentence or situation. Assign a "Showdown Captain." The Captain chooses a card and shows to the group. Group members work alone and write the answer to the number sentence or situation. When finished, teammates signal when they're ready. The Captain calls, "Showdown." Teammates show and state their answers. The Captain checks, coaches, and praises the other members. If correct, the team celebrates; if not, teammates coach, then celebrate. When everyone is finished, Showdown Captain role is rotated clockwise.

**NCTM Standard: Number and Operations Standard PreK–2**
★ Understand meanings of operations and how they relate to one another.
  • Understand various meanings of addition and subtraction of whole numbers and the relationship between the two operations.

pp. 330–340

# Showdown
## Activities continued

---

## Activity 7.5

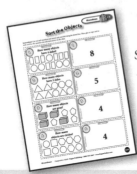

### Sort the Objects

Students are shown a card with objects. Assign a "Showdown Captain." The Captain chooses a card and shows to the group. Group members work alone and answer the question. When finished, teammates signal when they're ready. The Captain calls, "Showdown."

Teammates show and state their answers. The Captain checks, coaches, and praises the other members. If correct, the team celebrates; if not, teammates coach, then celebrate. When everyone is finished, Showdown Captain role is rotated clockwise.

**NCTM Standard: Algebra Standard PreK–2**
★ Understand patterns, relations, and functions.
  • Sort, classify, and order objects by size, number, and other properties.

pp. 341–346

---

## Activity 7.6

### Is It Symmetrical?

Students look at a picture and look for symmetry. Assign a "Showdown Captain." The Captain chooses a card and shows to the group. Group members work alone and write the answer to the question. When finished, teammates signal when they're ready. The Captain calls, "Showdown."

Teammates show and state their answers. The Captain checks, coaches, and praises the other members. If correct, the team celebrates; if not, teammates coach, then celebrate. When everyone is finished, Showdown Captain role is rotated clockwise.

**NCTM Standard: Geometry Standard PreK–2**
★ Apply transformations and use symmetry to analyze mathematical situations.
  • Recognize and create shapes that have symmetry.

pp. 347–350

---

## Activity 7.7

# What Time Is It?

Students are shown a card with a clock. Assign a "Showdown Captain." The Captain chooses a card and shows to the group. Group members work alone and write the time on the clock. When finished, teammates signal when they're ready. The Captain calls, "Showdown."

Teammates show and state their answers. The Captain checks, coaches, and praises the other members. If correct, the team celebrates; if not, teammates coach, then celebrate. When everyone is finished, Showdown Captain role is rotated clockwise.

**NCTM Standard: Measurement Standard PreK–2**
★ Understand measurable attributes of objects and the units, systems, and processes of measurement.
  • Recognize the attributes of length, volume, weight, area, and time.

**pp. 351–362**

## Activity 7.8

# Make a Graph

All students on the team receive a blank graph. Assign a "Showdown Captain." The Captain chooses a card and shows to the group. Group members work alone and write the answer to the graph. When finished, teammates signal when they're ready. The Captain calls, "Showdown."

Teammates show and state their answers. The Captain checks, coaches, and praises the other members. If correct, the team celebrates; if not, teammates coach, then celebrate. When everyone is finished, Showdown Captain role is rotated clockwise.

**NCTM Standard: Data Analysis and Probability Standard PreK–2**
★ Formulate questions that can be addressed with data and collect, organize, and display relevant data to answer them.
  • Represent data using concrete objects, pictures, and graphs.

**pp. 363–364**

# Number Words and Numerals

**Instructions:** Cut out each question and answer pair and fold along the dotted line. Then, glue or tape card so each card has the question one side and answer on the other.

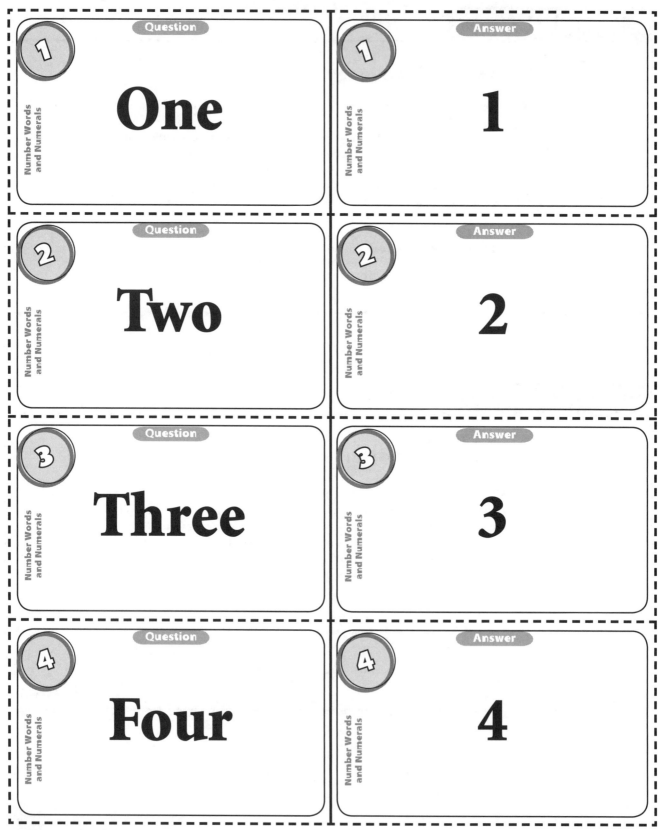

**Question 1** — Number Words and Numerals — **One**

**Answer 1** — Number Words and Numerals — **1**

**Question 2** — Number Words and Numerals — **Two**

**Answer 2** — Number Words and Numerals — **2**

**Question 3** — Number Words and Numerals — **Three**

**Answer 3** — Number Words and Numerals — **3**

**Question 4** — Number Words and Numerals — **Four**

**Answer 4** — Number Words and Numerals — **4**

# Number Words and Numerals

**Instructions:** Cut out each question and answer pair and fold along the dotted line. Then, glue or tape card so each card has the question one side and answer on the other.

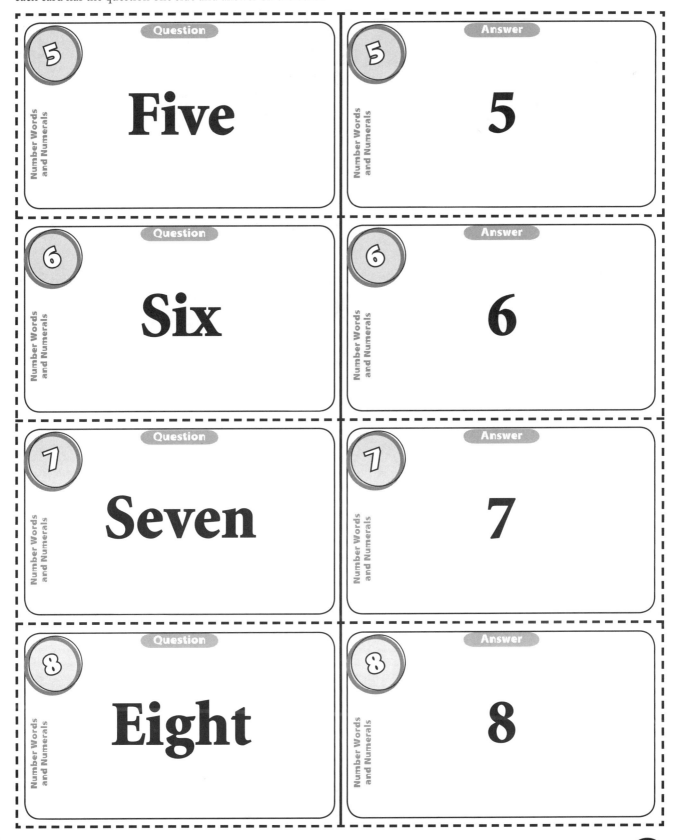

| | |
|---|---|
| **Question** ⑤ Number Words and Numerals **Five** | **Answer** ⑤ Number Words and Numerals **5** |
| **Question** ⑥ Number Words and Numerals **Six** | **Answer** ⑥ Number Words and Numerals **6** |
| **Question** ⑦ Number Words and Numerals **Seven** | **Answer** ⑦ Number Words and Numerals **7** |
| **Question** ⑧ Number Words and Numerals **Eight** | **Answer** ⑧ Number Words and Numerals **8** |

# Number Words and Numerals

**Instructions:** Cut out each question and answer pair and fold along the dotted line. Then, glue or tape card so each card has the question one side and answer on the other.

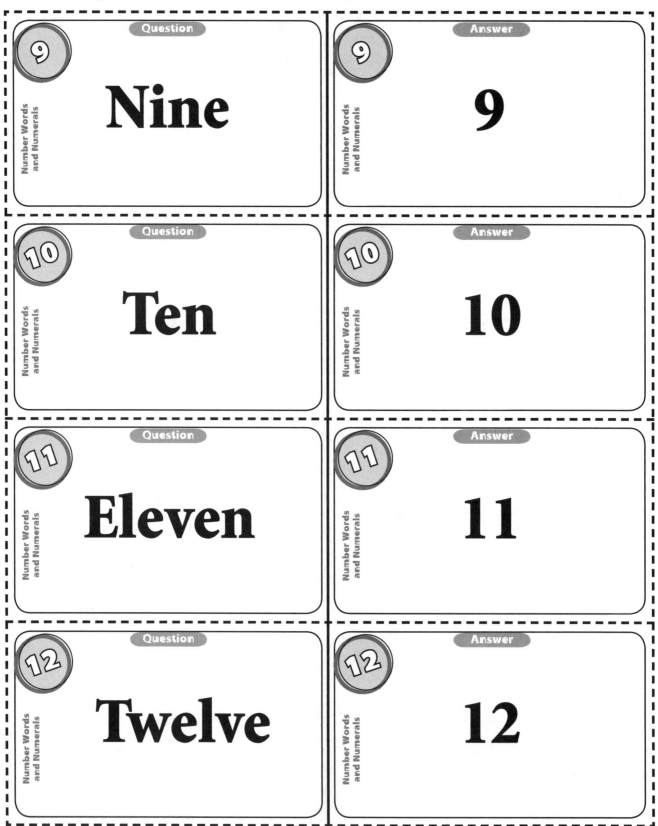

# Number Words and Numerals

**Instructions:** Cut out each question and answer pair and fold along the dotted line. Then, glue or tape card so each card has the question one side and answer on the other.

| Question | Answer |
|----------|--------|
| **13** Number Words and Numerals **Fifteen** | **13** Number Words and Numerals **15** |
| **14** Number Words and Numerals **Seventeen** | **14** Number Words and Numerals **17** |
| **15** Number Words and Numerals **Twenty** | **15** Number Words and Numerals **20** |
| **16** Number Words and Numerals **Twenty-five** | **16** Number Words and Numerals **25** |

# Number Words and Numerals

**Instructions:** Cut out each question and answer pair and fold along the dotted line. Then, glue or tape card so each card has the question one side and answer on the other.

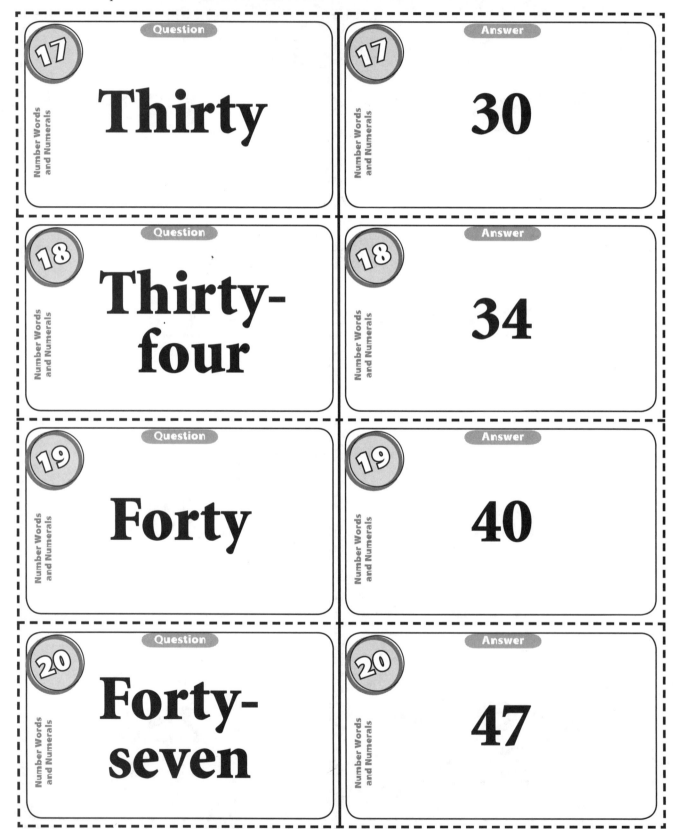

| Question 17 | Answer 17 |
|---|---|
| **Thirty** | **30** |

| Question 18 | Answer 18 |
|---|---|
| **Thirty-four** | **34** |

| Question 19 | Answer 19 |
|---|---|
| **Forty** | **40** |

| Question 20 | Answer 20 |
|---|---|
| **Forty-seven** | **47** |

# Number Words and Numerals

**Instructions:** Cut out each question and answer pair and fold along the dotted line. Then, glue or tape card so each card has the question one side and answer on the other.

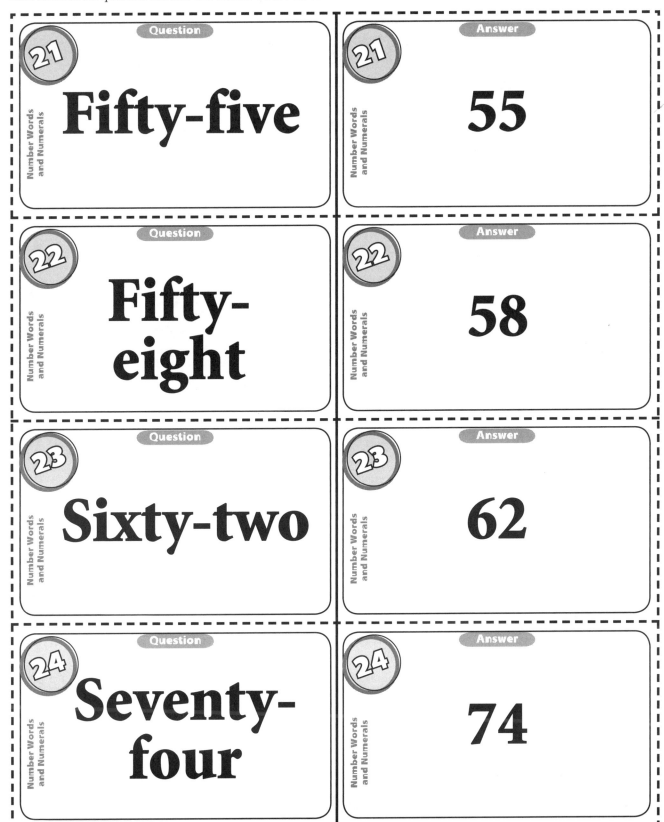

**Question**
21
Number Words and Numerals
**Fifty-five**

**Answer**
21
Number Words and Numerals
**55**

**Question**
22
Number Words and Numerals
**Fifty-eight**

**Answer**
22
Number Words and Numerals
**58**

**Question**
23
Number Words and Numerals
**Sixty-two**

**Answer**
23
Number Words and Numerals
**62**

**Question**
24
Number Words and Numerals
**Seventy-four**

**Answer**
24
Number Words and Numerals
**74**

# Basic Fractions

**Instructions:** Cut out each question and answer pair and fold along the dotted line. Then, glue or tape card so each card has the question one side and answer on the other.

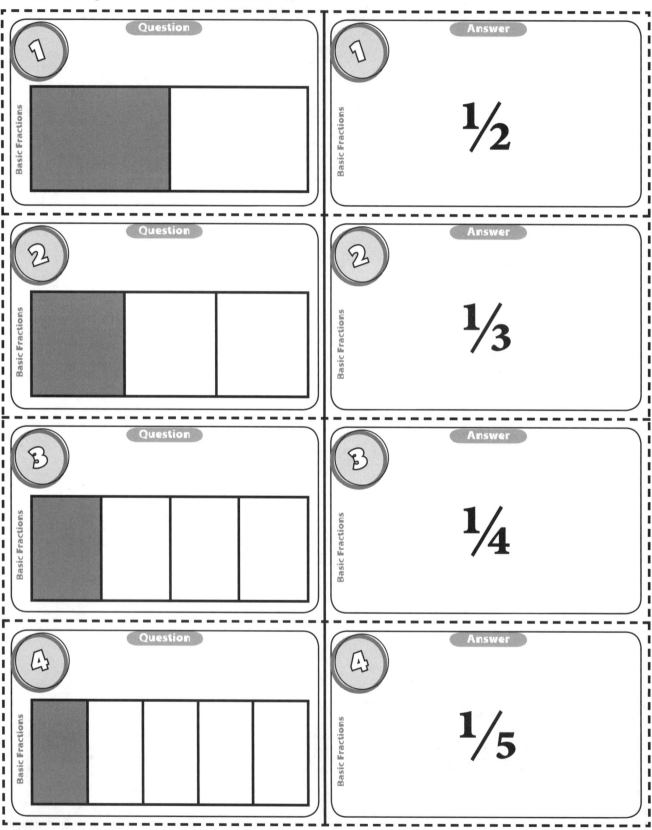

# Basic Fractions

**Instructions:** Cut out each question and answer pair and fold along the dotted line. Then, glue or tape card so each card has the question one side and answer on the other.

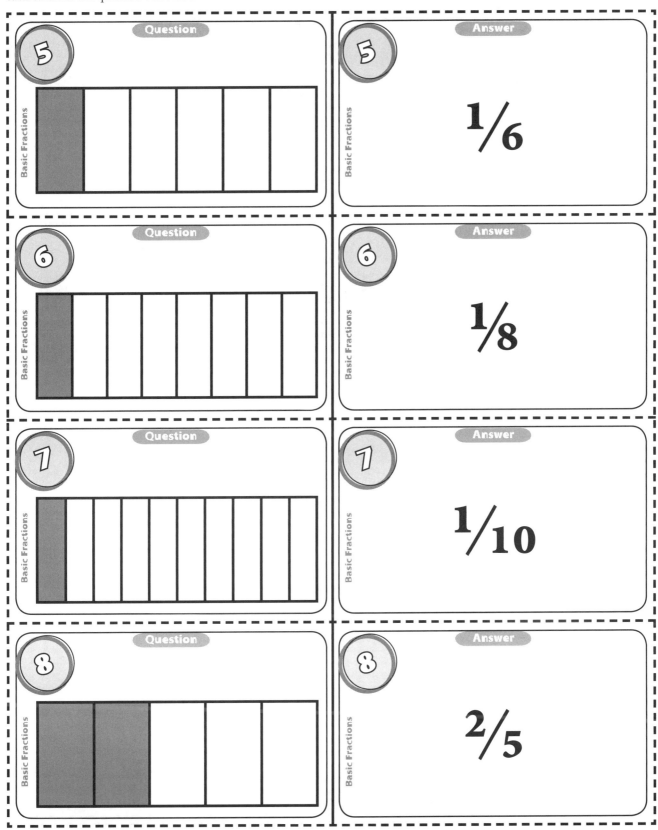

**5** Question — Basic Fractions

**5** Answer — Basic Fractions

$$\dfrac{1}{6}$$

**6** Question — Basic Fractions

**6** Answer — Basic Fractions

$$\dfrac{1}{8}$$

**7** Question — Basic Fractions

**7** Answer — Basic Fractions

$$\dfrac{1}{10}$$

**8** Question — Basic Fractions

**8** Answer — Basic Fractions

$$\dfrac{2}{5}$$

# Basic Fractions

**Instructions:** Cut out each question and answer pair and fold along the dotted line. Then, glue or tape card so each card has the question one side and answer on the other.

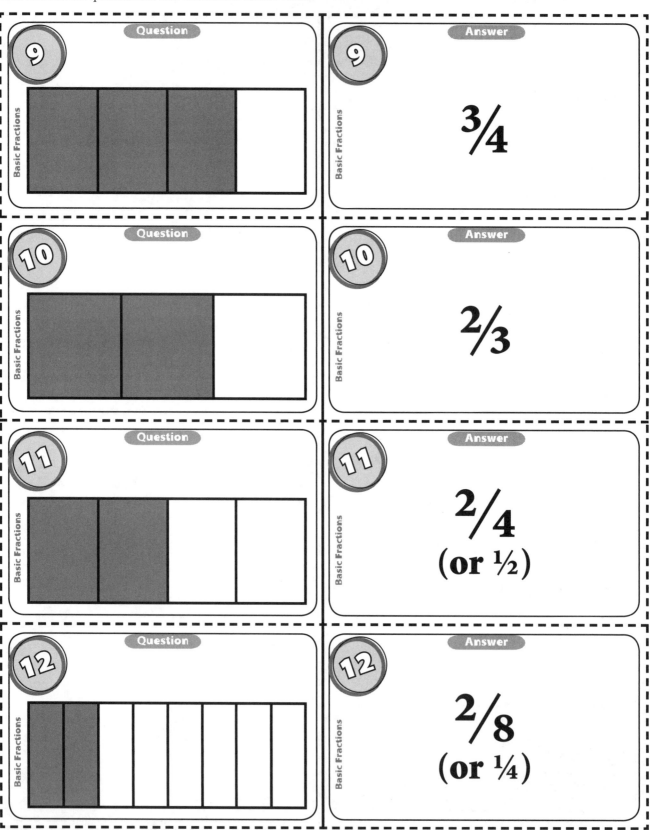

# Basic Fractions

**Instructions:** Cut out each question and answer pair and fold along the dotted line. Then, glue or tape card so each card has the question one side and answer on the other.

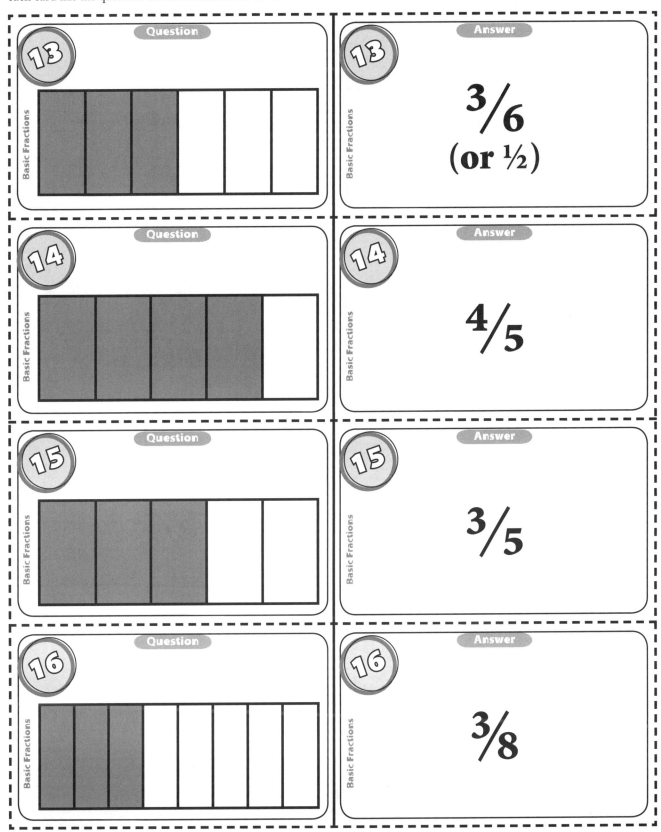

**13** Question — Basic Fractions

**13** Answer — Basic Fractions

$$\frac{3}{6}$$
(or ½)

**14** Question — Basic Fractions

**14** Answer — Basic Fractions

$$\frac{4}{5}$$

**15** Question — Basic Fractions

**15** Answer — Basic Fractions

$$\frac{3}{5}$$

**16** Question — Basic Fractions

**16** Answer — Basic Fractions

$$\frac{3}{8}$$

# Basic Fractions

**Instructions:** Cut out each question and answer pair and fold along the dotted line. Then, glue or tape card so each card has the question one side and answer on the other.

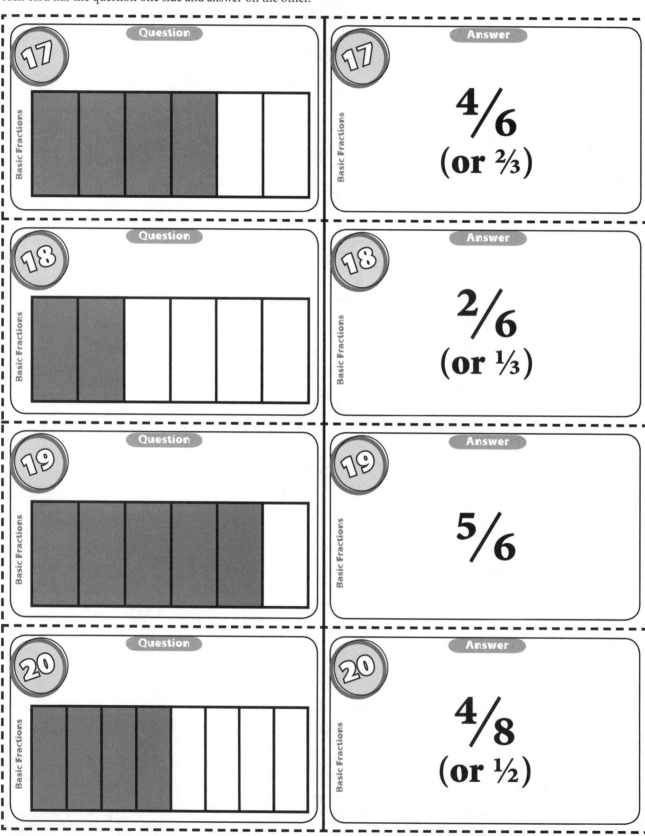

**Question 17** — Basic Fractions

**Answer 17:** 4/6 (or ⅔)

**Question 18** — Basic Fractions

**Answer 18:** 2/6 (or ⅓)

**Question 19** — Basic Fractions

**Answer 19:** 5/6

**Question 20** — Basic Fractions

**Answer 20:** 4/8 (or ½)

# Basic Fractions

**Instructions:** Cut out each question and answer pair and fold along the dotted line. Then, glue or tape card so each card has the question one side and answer on the other.

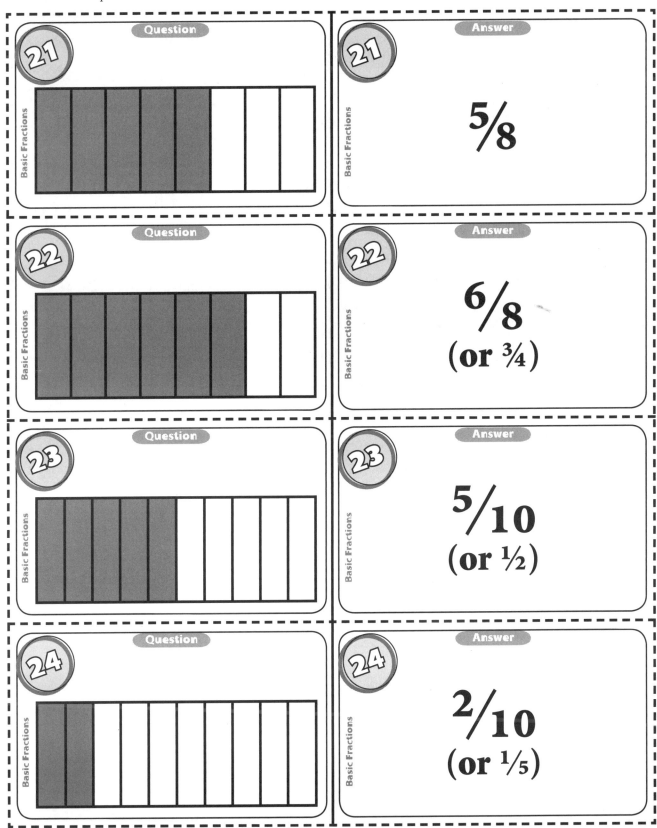

# Equal Groups

**Instructions:** Cut out each question and answer pair and fold along the dotted line. Then, glue or tape card so each card has the question one side and answer on the other.

# Equal Groups

**Instructions:** Cut out each question and answer pair and fold along the dotted line. Then, glue or tape card so each card has the question one side and answer on the other.

**Question**

5 — Equal Groups

How many stars would each person get?

**Answer**

5 — Equal Groups

**1**

**Question**

6 — Equal Groups

How many stars would each person get?

**Answer**

6 — Equal Groups

**3**

**Question**

7 — Equal Groups

How many stars would each person get?

**Answer**

7 — Equal Groups

**4**

**Question**

8 — Equal Groups

How many stars would each person get?

**Answer**

8 — Equal Groups

**2**

# Equal Groups

**Instructions:** Cut out each question and answer pair and fold along the dotted line. Then, glue or tape card so each card has the question one side and answer on the other.

**9** | Question
Equal Groups
How many stars would each person get?

**9** | Answer
Equal Groups
1

**10** | Question
Equal Groups
How many stars would each person get?

**10** | Answer
Equal Groups
2

**11** | Question
Equal Groups
How many stars would each person get?

**11** | Answer
Equal Groups
3

**12** | Question
Equal Groups
How many stars would each person get?

**12** | Answer
Equal Groups
4

# Equal Groups

**Instructions:** Cut out each question and answer pair and fold along the dotted line. Then, glue or tape card so each card has the question one side and answer on the other.

| | |
|---|---|
| **13** Question — Equal Groups — How many stars would each person get? | **13** Answer — Equal Groups — **1** |
| **14** Question — Equal Groups — How many stars would each person get? | **14** Answer — Equal Groups — **2** |
| **15** Question — Equal Groups — How many stars would each person get? | **15** Answer — Equal Groups — **3** |
| **16** Question — Equal Groups — How many stars would each person get? | **16** Answer — Equal Groups — **9** |

# Equal Groups

**Instructions:** Cut out each question and answer pair and fold along the dotted line. Then, glue or tape card so each card has the question one side and answer on the other.

**17** **Question**

How many stars would each person get?

**17** **Answer**

**2**

**18** **Question**

How many stars would each person get?

**18** **Answer**

**5**

**19** **Question**

How many stars would each person get?

**19** **Answer**

**7**

**20** **Question**

How many stars would each person get?

**20** **Answer**

**6**

# Equal Groups

**Instructions:** Cut out each question and answer pair and fold along the dotted line. Then, glue or tape card so each card has the question one side and answer on the other.

**Question 21** — Equal Groups — How many stars would each person get?

**Answer 21** — Equal Groups — **8**

**Question 22** — Equal Groups — How many stars would each person get?

**Answer 22** — Equal Groups — **4**

**Question 23** — Equal Groups — How many stars would each person get?

**Answer 23** — Equal Groups — **1**

**Question 24** — Equal Groups — How many stars would each person get?

**Answer 24** — Equal Groups — **1½**

# Addition and Subtraction

**Instructions:** Cut out each question and answer pair and fold along the dotted line. Then, glue or tape card so each card has the question one side and answer on the other.

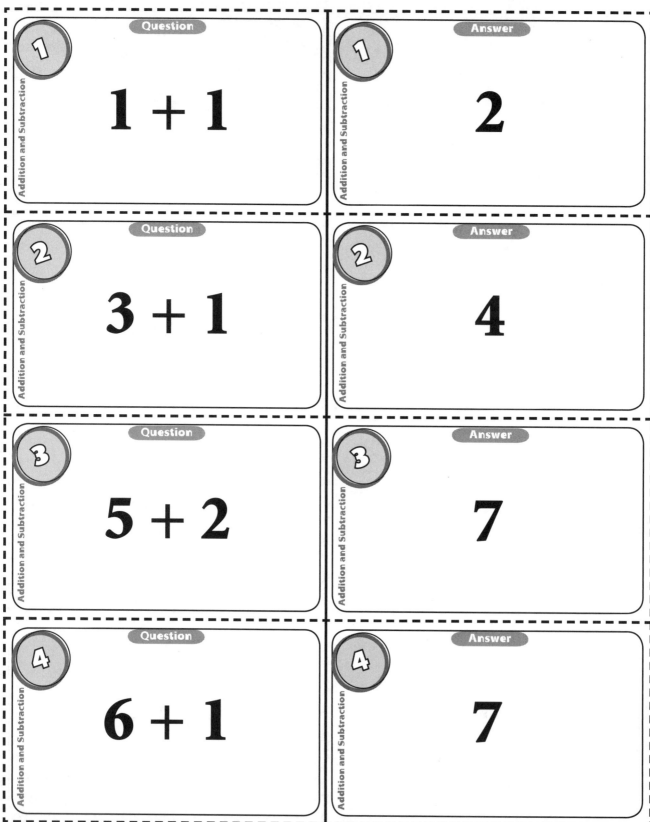

| **Question** | **Answer** |
| --- | --- |
| **1** $1 + 1$ | **1** $2$ |
| **2** $3 + 1$ | **2** $4$ |
| **3** $5 + 2$ | **3** $7$ |
| **4** $6 + 1$ | **4** $7$ |

# Addition and Subtraction

**Instructions:** Cut out each question and answer pair and fold along the dotted line. Then, glue or tape card so each card has the question one side and answer on the other.

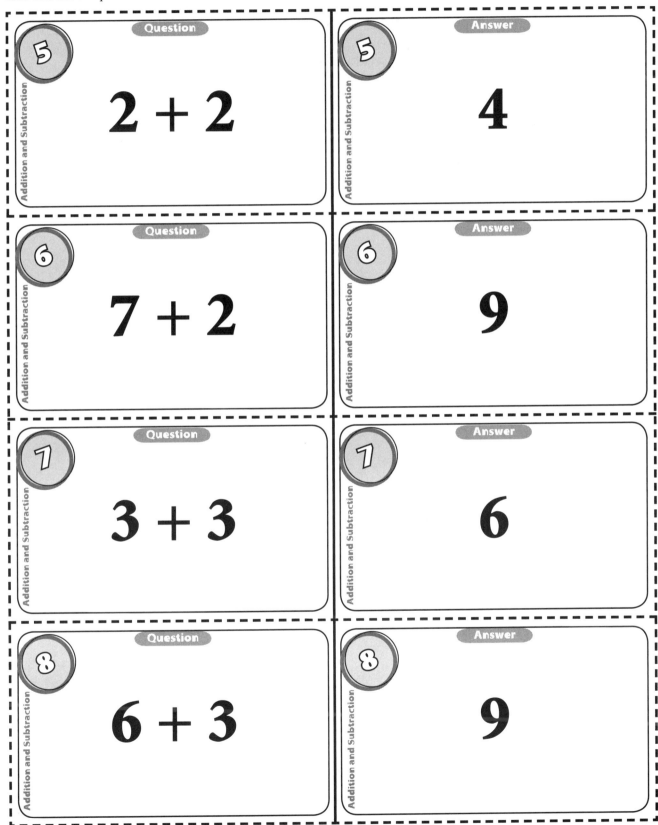

| Question 5 | Answer 5 |
|---|---|
| $2 + 2$ | $4$ |

| Question 6 | Answer 6 |
|---|---|
| $7 + 2$ | $9$ |

| Question 7 | Answer 7 |
|---|---|
| $3 + 3$ | $6$ |

| Question 8 | Answer 8 |
|---|---|
| $6 + 3$ | $9$ |

Addition and Subtraction

# Addition and Subtraction

**Instructions:** Cut out each question and answer pair and fold along the dotted line. Then, glue or tape card so each card has the question one side and answer on the other.

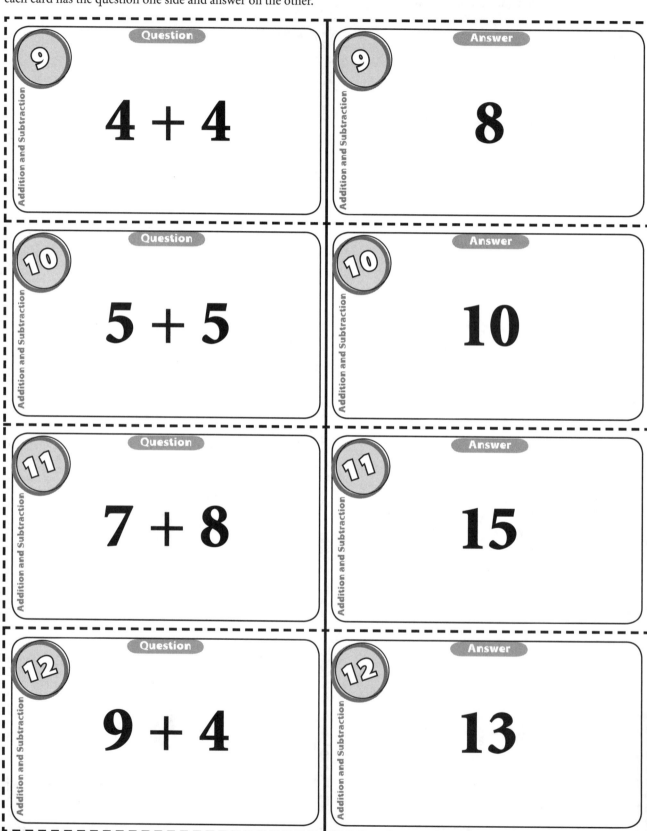

| Question 9 | Answer 9 |
|:---:|:---:|
| $4 + 4$ | $8$ |

Addition and Subtraction

| Question 10 | Answer 10 |
|:---:|:---:|
| $5 + 5$ | $10$ |

Addition and Subtraction

| Question 11 | Answer 11 |
|:---:|:---:|
| $7 + 8$ | $15$ |

Addition and Subtraction

| Question 12 | Answer 12 |
|:---:|:---:|
| $9 + 4$ | $13$ |

Addition and Subtraction

# Addition and Subtraction

**Instructions:** Cut out each question and answer pair and fold along the dotted line. Then, glue or tape card so each card has the question one side and answer on the other.

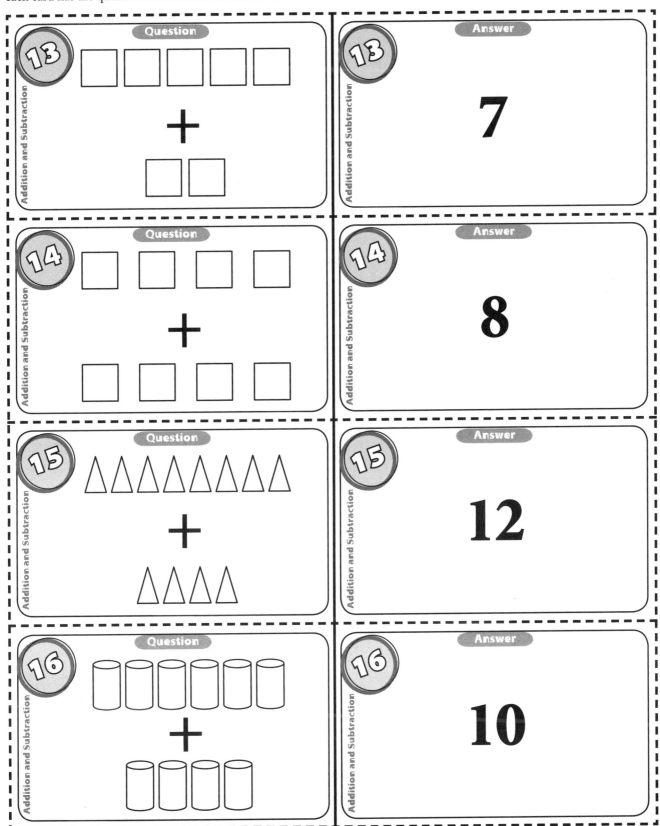

# Addition and Subtraction

**Instructions:** Cut out each question and answer pair and fold along the dotted line. Then, glue or tape card so each card has the question one side and answer on the other.

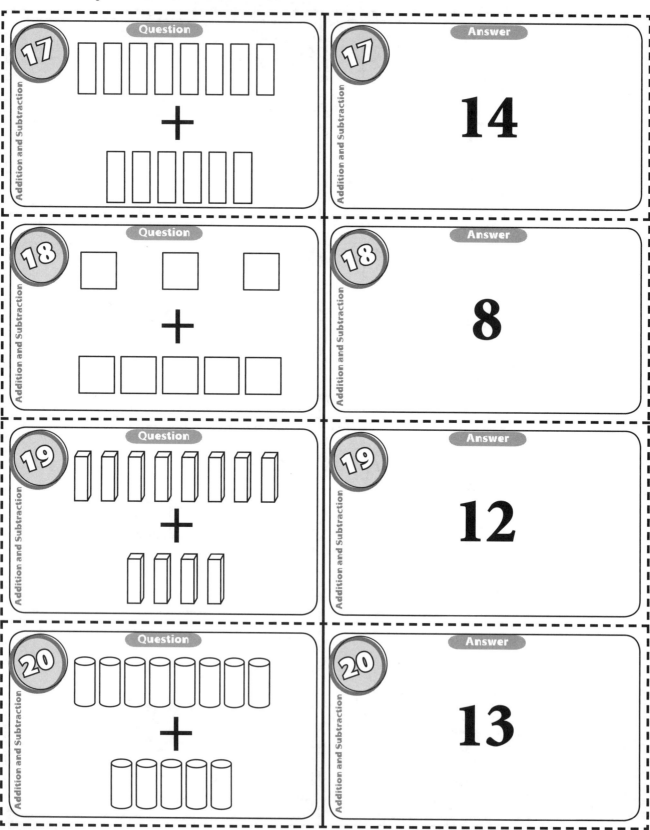

# Addition and Subtraction

**Instructions:** Cut out each question and answer pair and fold along the dotted line. Then, glue or tape card so each card has the question one side and answer on the other.

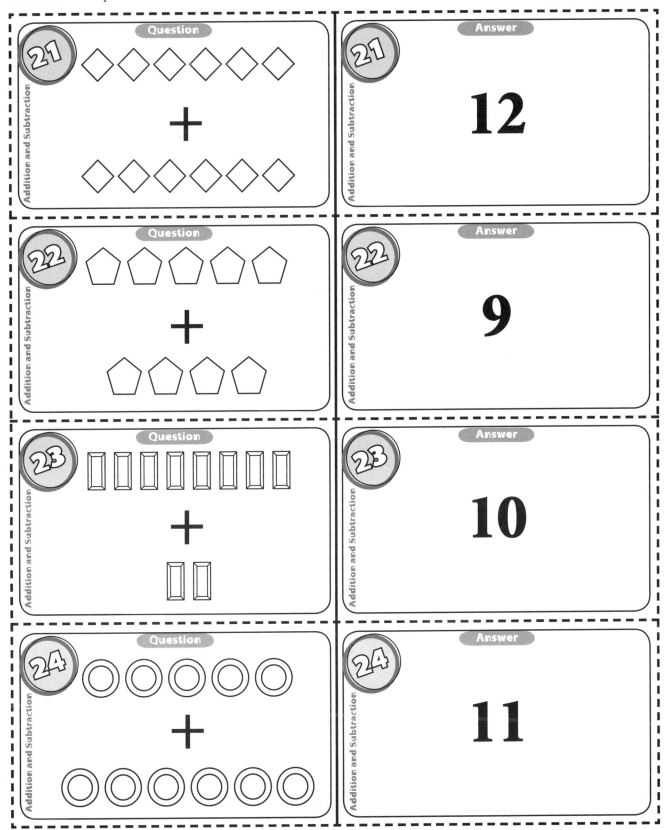

# Addition and Subtraction

**Instructions:** Cut out each question and answer pair and fold along the dotted line. Then, glue or tape card so each card has the question one side and answer on the other.

| | |
|---|---|
| **Question** 25 — Addition and Subtraction | **Answer** 25 — Addition and Subtraction |
| $2 - 1$ | $1$ |
| **Question** 26 — Addition and Subtraction | **Answer** 26 — Addition and Subtraction |
| $3 - 1$ | $2$ |
| **Question** 27 — Addition and Subtraction | **Answer** 27 — Addition and Subtraction |
| $5 - 2$ | $3$ |
| **Question** 28 — Addition and Subtraction | **Answer** 28 — Addition and Subtraction |
| $6 - 1$ | $5$ |

# Addition and Subtraction

**Instructions:** Cut out each question and answer pair and fold along the dotted line. Then, glue or tape card so each card has the question one side and answer on the other.

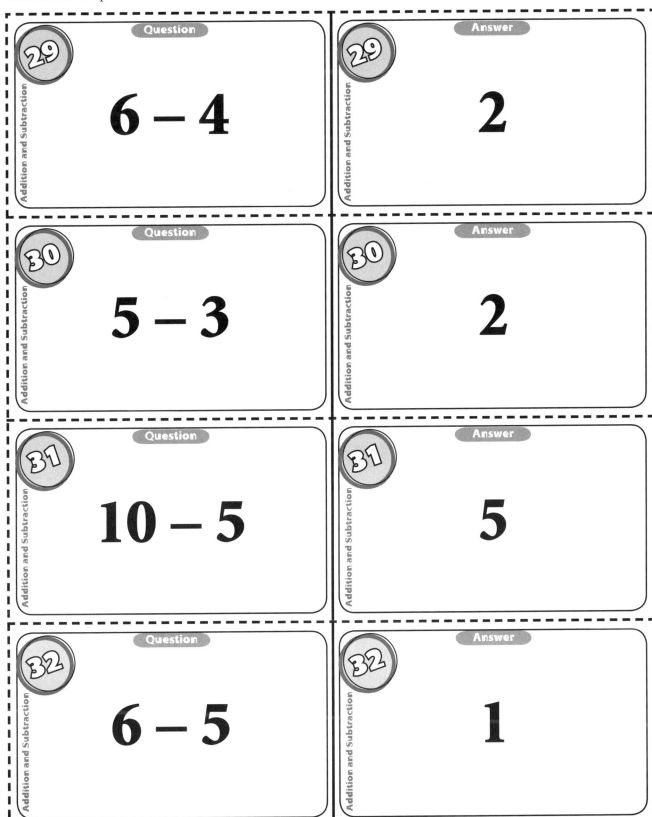

**29** Question

$$6 - 4$$

**29** Answer

$$2$$

**30** Question

$$5 - 3$$

**30** Answer

$$2$$

**31** Question

$$10 - 5$$

**31** Answer

$$5$$

**32** Question

$$6 - 5$$

**32** Answer

$$1$$

# Addition and Subtraction

**Instructions:** Cut out each question and answer pair and fold along the dotted line. Then, glue or tape card so each card has the question one side and answer on the other.

| | |
|---|---|
| **33** Question<br>Addition and Subtraction<br><br>## 15 – 5 | **33** Answer<br>Addition and Subtraction<br><br>## 10 |
| **34** Question<br>Addition and Subtraction<br><br>## 11 – 2 | **34** Answer<br>Addition and Subtraction<br><br>## 9 |
| **35** Question<br>Addition and Subtraction<br><br>## 9 – 5 | **35** Answer<br>Addition and Subtraction<br><br>## 4 |
| **36** Question<br>Addition and Subtraction<br><br>## 12 – 4 | **36** Answer<br>Addition and Subtraction<br><br>## 8 |

# Addition and Subtraction

**Instructions:** Cut out each question and answer pair and fold along the dotted line. Then, glue or tape card so each card has the question one side and answer on the other.

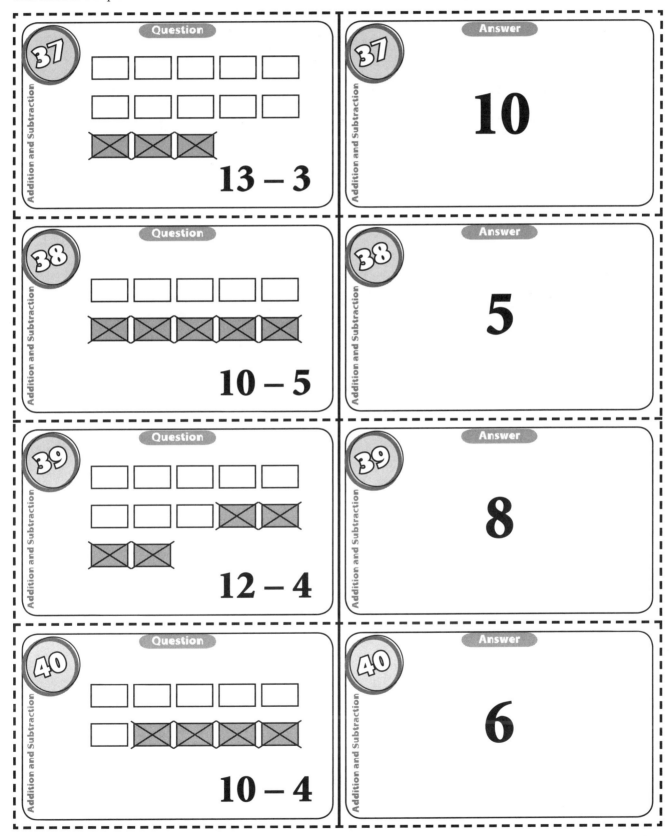

| | |
|---|---|
| **37** Question — 13 – 3 | **37** Answer — **10** |
| **38** Question — 10 – 5 | **38** Answer — **5** |
| **39** Question — 12 – 4 | **39** Answer — **8** |
| **40** Question — 10 – 4 | **40** Answer — **6** |

# Addition and Subtraction

**Instructions:** Cut out each question and answer pair and fold along the dotted line. Then, glue or tape card so each card has the question one side and answer on the other.

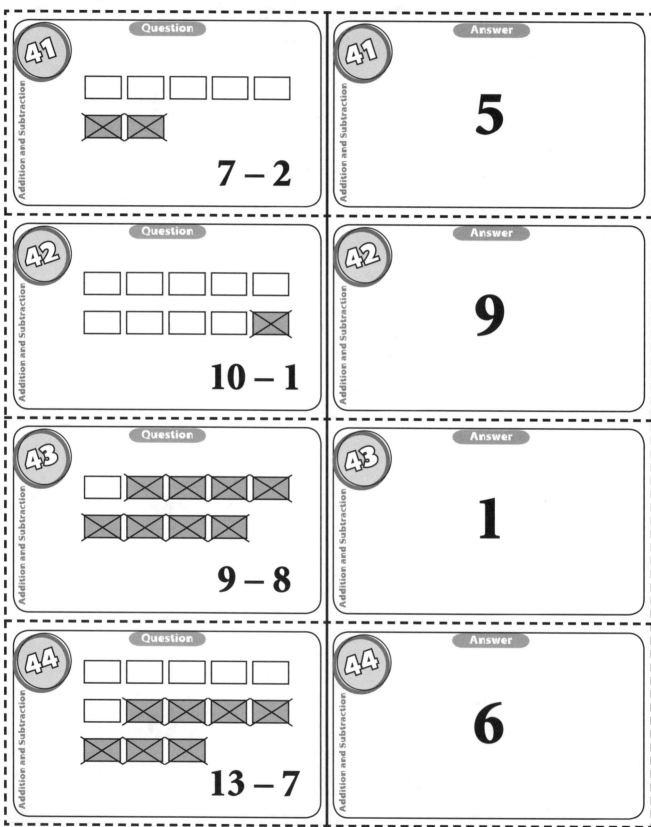

**Question 41**

$7 - 2$

**Answer 41**

$5$

**Question 42**

$10 - 1$

**Answer 42**

$9$

**Question 43**

$9 - 8$

**Answer 43**

$1$

**Question 44**

$13 - 7$

**Answer 44**

$6$

# Sort the Objects

**Instructions:** Cut out each question and answer pair and fold along the dotted line. Then, glue or tape card so each card has the question one side and answer on the other.

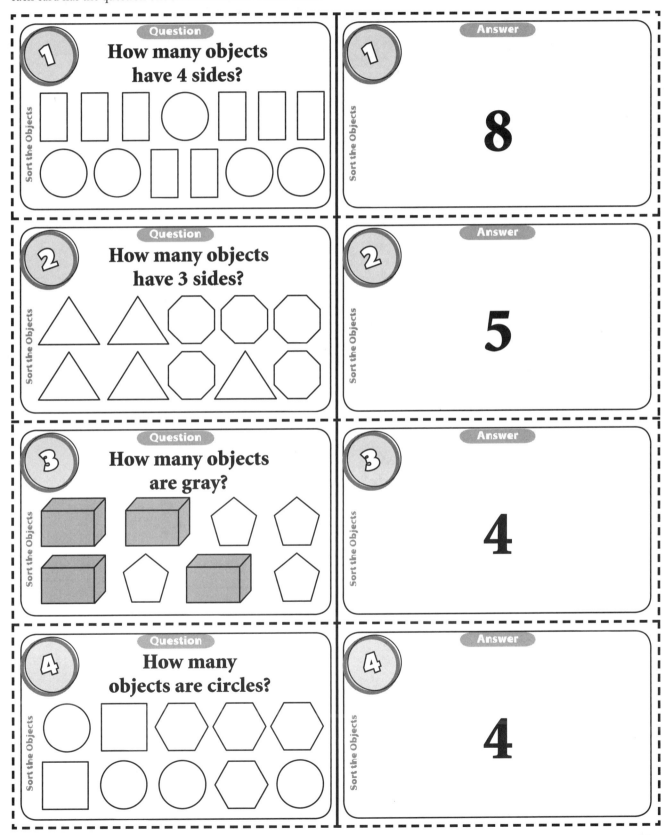

**Question 1** — Sort the Objects

How many objects have 4 sides?

**Answer 1** — Sort the Objects

8

**Question 2** — Sort the Objects

How many objects have 3 sides?

**Answer 2** — Sort the Objects

5

**Question 3** — Sort the Objects

How many objects are gray?

**Answer 3** — Sort the Objects

4

**Question 4** — Sort the Objects

How many objects are circles?

**Answer 4** — Sort the Objects

4

# Sort the Objects

**Instructions:** Cut out each question and answer pair and fold along the dotted line. Then, glue or tape card so each card has the question one side and answer on the other.

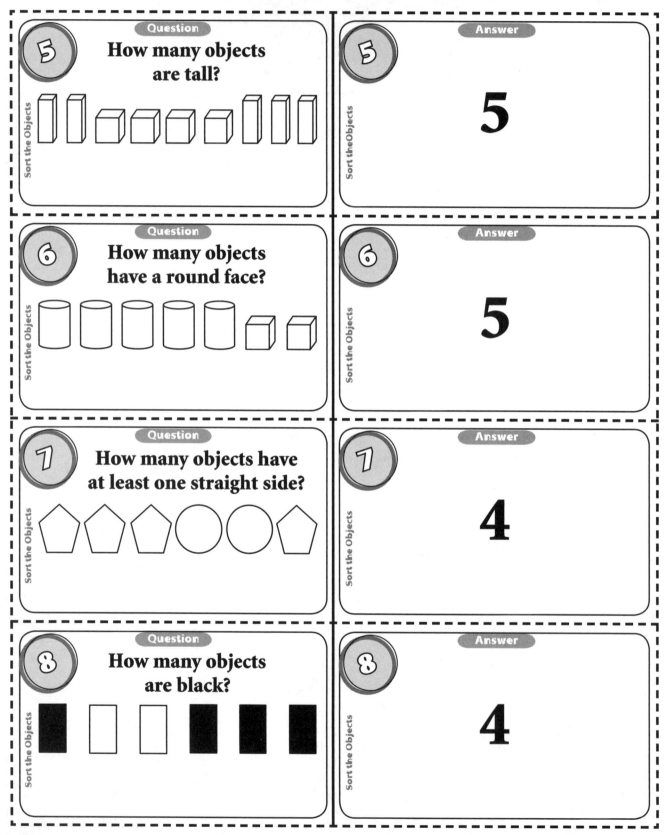

**Question**

5 **How many objects are tall?**

Sort the Objects

**Answer**

5 **5**

Sort the Objects

**Question**

6 **How many objects have a round face?**

Sort the Objects

**Answer**

6 **5**

Sort the Objects

**Question**

7 **How many objects have at least one straight side?**

Sort the Objects

**Answer**

7 **4**

Sort the Objects

**Question**

8 **How many objects are black?**

Sort the Objects

**Answer**

8 **4**

Sort the Objects

# Sort the Objects

**Instructions:** Cut out each question and answer pair and fold along the dotted line. Then, glue or tape card so each card has the question one side and answer on the other.

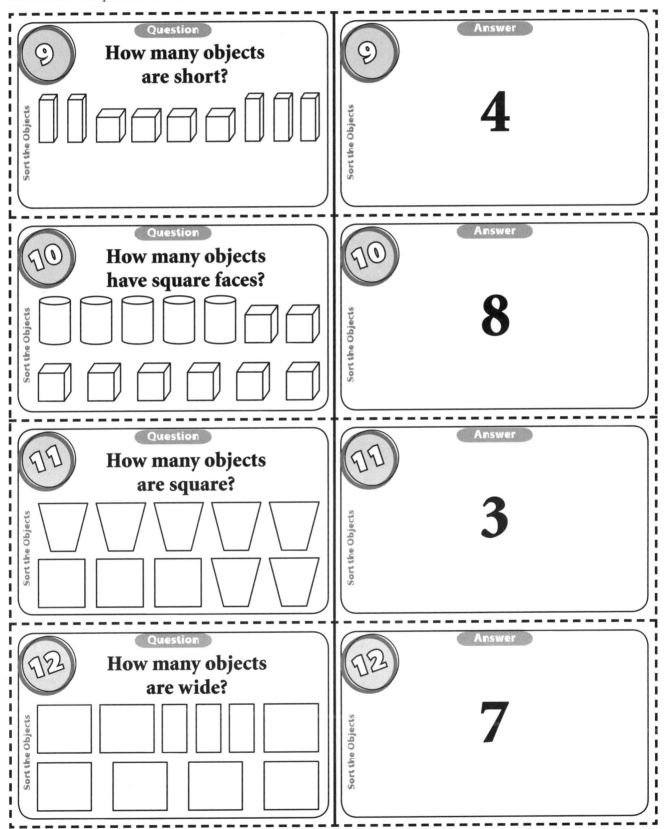

**Question**
9
How many objects are short?

Sort the Objects

**Answer**
9

**4**

Sort the Objects

**Question**
10
How many objects have square faces?

Sort the Objects

**Answer**
10

**8**

Sort the Objects

**Question**
11
How many objects are square?

Sort the Objects

**Answer**
11

**3**

Sort the Objects

**Question**
12
How many objects are wide?

Sort the Objects

**Answer**
12

**7**

Sort the Objects

# Sort the Objects

**Instructions:** Cut out each question and answer pair and fold along the dotted line. Then, glue or tape card so each card has the question one side and answer on the other.

**13** **Question**
## How many objects are little?

Sort the Objects

**13** **Answer**

Sort the Objects

# 16

---

**14** **Question**
## How many objects have 4 sides?

Sort the Objects

**14** **Answer**

Sort the Objects

# 5

---

**15** **Question**
## How many objects have 3 sides?

Sort the Objects

**15** **Answer**

Sort the Objects

# 13

---

**16** **Question**
## How many objects are big?

Sort the Objects

**16** **Answer**

Sort the Objects

# 5

# Sort the Objects

**Instructions:** Cut out each question and answer pair and fold along the dotted line. Then, glue or tape card so each card has the question one side and answer on the other.

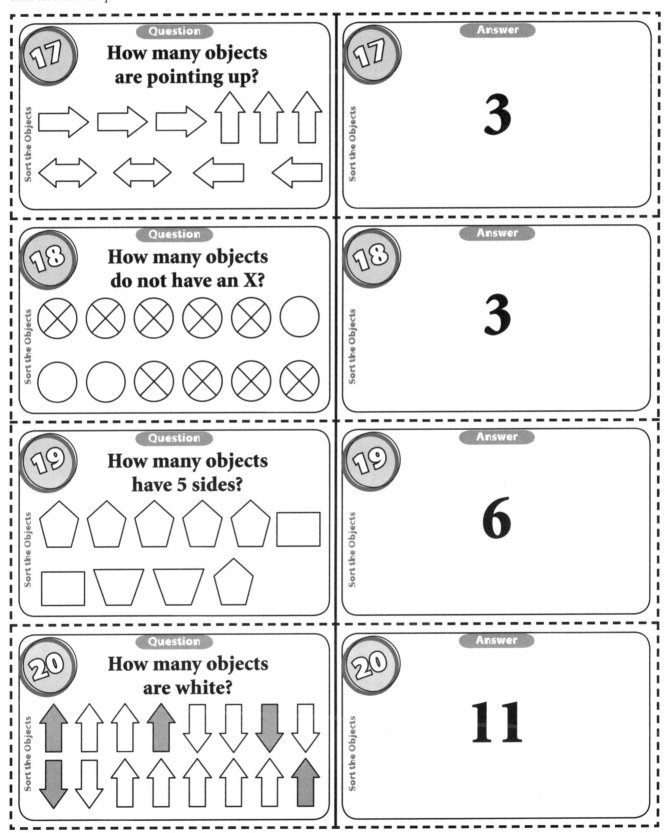

**Question** 17 — How many objects are pointing up? — **Answer** 17 — **3**

**Question** 18 — How many objects do not have an X? — **Answer** 18 — **3**

**Question** 19 — How many objects have 5 sides? — **Answer** 19 — **6**

**Question** 20 — How many objects are white? — **Answer** 20 — **11**

# Sort the Objects

**Instructions:** Cut out each question and answer pair and fold along the dotted line. Then, glue or tape card so each card has the question one side and answer on the other.

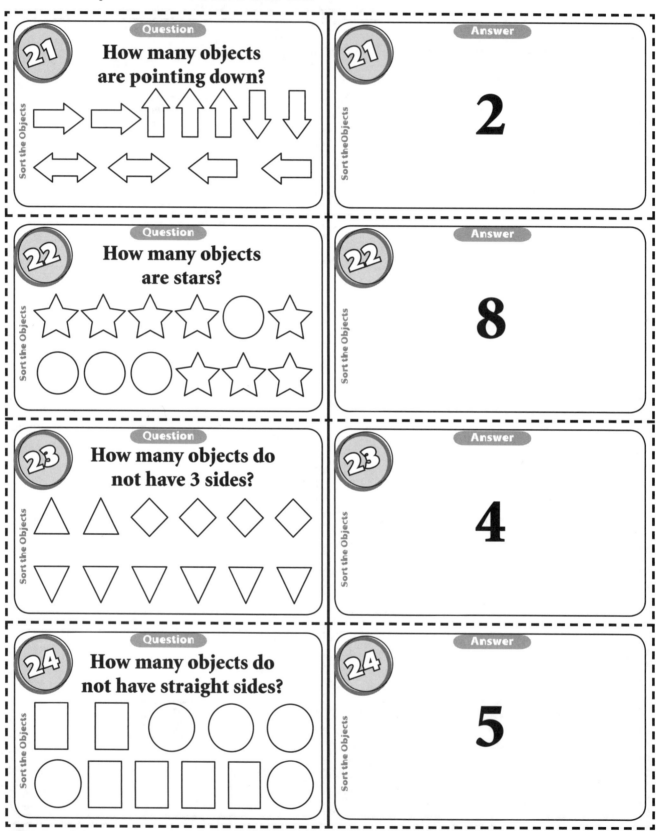

**Question**

**21** How many objects are pointing down?

**Answer**

**21** **2**

**Question**

**22** How many objects are stars?

**Answer**

**22** **8**

**Question**

**23** How many objects do not have 3 sides?

**Answer**

**23** **4**

**Question**

**24** How many objects do not have straight sides?

**Answer**

**24** **5**

# Is It Symmetrical?

**Instructions:** Cut out each question and answer pair and fold along the dotted line. Then, glue or tape card so each card has the question one side and answer on the other.

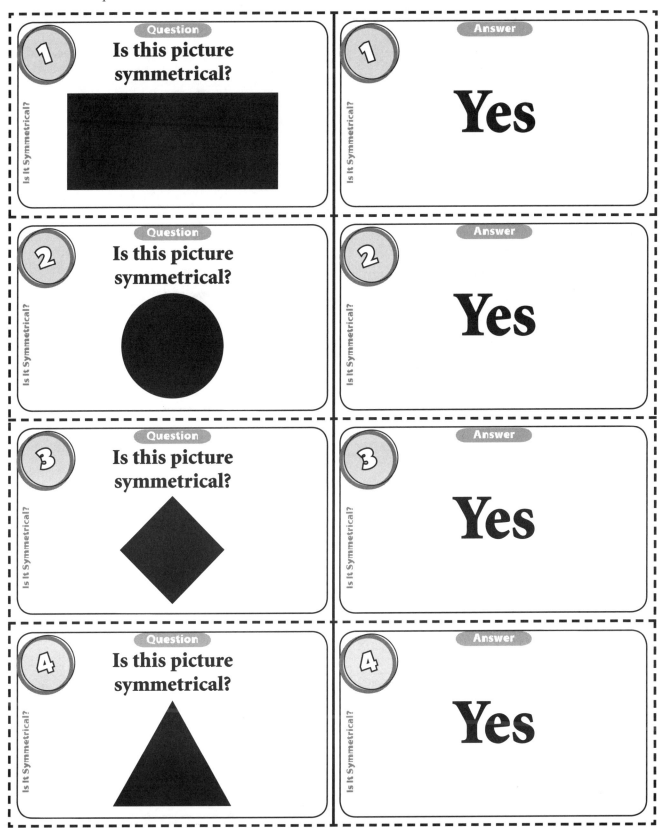

# Is It Symmetrical?

**Instructions:** Cut out each question and answer pair and fold along the dotted line. Then, glue or tape card so each card has the question one side and answer on the other.

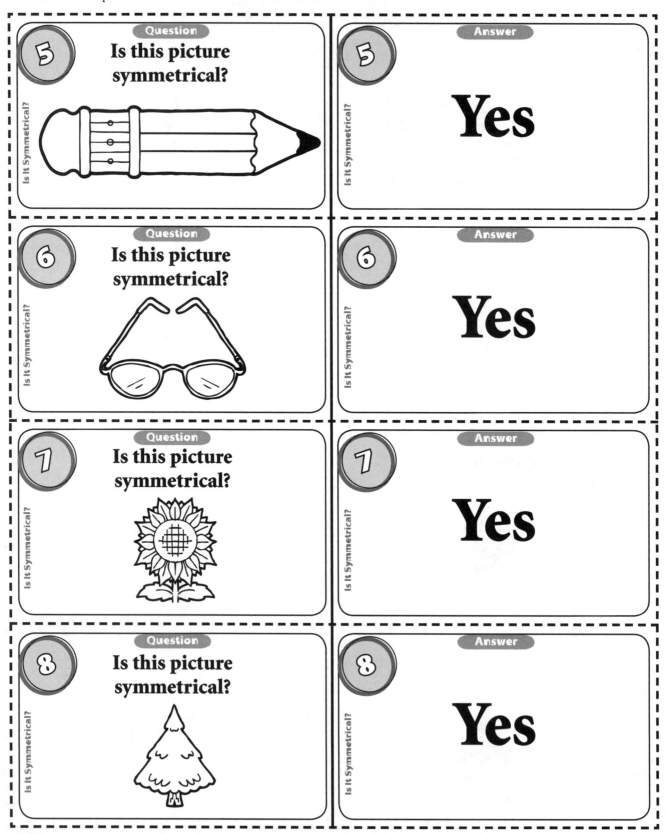

| Question | Answer |
|---|---|
| **5** Is this picture symmetrical? | **5** Yes |
| **6** Is this picture symmetrical? | **6** Yes |
| **7** Is this picture symmetrical? | **7** Yes |
| **8** Is this picture symmetrical? | **8** Yes |

# Is It Symmetrical?

**Instructions:** Cut out each question and answer pair and fold along the dotted line. Then, glue or tape card so each card has the question one side and answer on the other.

# Is It Symmetrical?

**Instructions:** Cut out each question and answer pair and fold along the dotted line. Then, glue or tape card so each card has the question one side and answer on the other.

# What Time Is It?

**Instructions:** Cut out each question and answer pair and fold along the dotted line. Then, glue or tape card so each card has the question one side and answer on the other.

**Question 1**

What time does the clock show?

**Answer 1**

**1:00**

**Question 2**

What time does the clock show?

**Answer 2**

**2:00**

**Question 3**

What time does the clock show?

**Answer 3**

**3:00**

**Question 4**

What time does the clock show?

**Answer 4**

**4:00**

# What Time Is It?

**Instructions:** Cut out each question and answer pair and fold along the dotted line. Then, glue or tape card so each card has the question one side and answer on the other.

**5** Question — What Time Is It? **What time does the clock show?**

**5** Answer — What Time Is It? **5:00**

**6** Question — What Time Is It? **What time does the clock show?**

**6** Answer — What Time Is It? **6:00**

**7** Question — What Time Is It? **What time does the clock show?**

**7** Answer — What Time Is It? **7:00**

**8** Question — What Time Is It? **What time does the clock show?**

**8** Answer — What Time Is It? **8:00**

# What Time Is It?

**Instructions:** Cut out each question and answer pair and fold along the dotted line. Then, glue or tape card so each card has the question one side and answer on the other.

| Question | Answer |
|---|---|
| 9 — What time does the clock show? | 9 — **9:00** |
| 10 — What time does the clock show? | 10 — **10:00** |
| 11 — What time does the clock show? | 11 — **11:00** |
| 12 — What time does the clock show? | 12 — **12:00** |

# What Time Is It?

**Instructions:** Cut out each question and answer pair and fold along the dotted line. Then, glue or tape card so each card has the question one side and answer on the other.

**13** Question — What time does the clock show?

**13** Answer — **1:30**

**14** Question — What time does the clock show?

**14** Answer — **2:30**

**15** Question — What time does the clock show?

**15** Answer — **3:30**

**16** Question — What time does the clock show?

**16** Answer — **4:30**

# What Time Is It?

**Instructions:** Cut out each question and answer pair and fold along the dotted line. Then, glue or tape card so each card has the question one side and answer on the other.

**17** Question — What Time Is It? — **What time does the clock show?**

**17** Answer — What Time Is It? — **5:30**

**18** Question — What Time Is It? — **What time does the clock show?**

**18** Answer — What Time Is It? — **6:30**

**19** Question — What Time Is It? — **What time does the clock show?**

**19** Answer — What Time Is It? — **7:30**

**20** Question — What Time Is It? — **What time does the clock show?**

**20** Answer — What Time Is It? — **8:30**

# What Time Is It?

**Instructions:** Cut out each question and answer pair and fold along the dotted line. Then, glue or tape card so each card has the question one side and answer on the other.

| | |
|---|---|
| **21** Question | **21** Answer |
| What time does the clock show? | **9:30** |
| **22** Question | **22** Answer |
| What time does the clock show? | **10:30** |
| **23** Question | **23** Answer |
| What time does the clock show? | **11:30** |
| **24** Question | **24** Answer |
| What time does the clock show? | **12:30** |

# What Time Is It?

**Instructions:** Cut out each question and answer pair and fold along the dotted line. Then, glue or tape card so each card has the question one side and answer on the other.

**25** Question
What time does the clock show?

**25** Answer
## 1:15

**26** Question
What time does the clock show?

**26** Answer
## 2:15

**27** Question
What time does the clock show?

**27** Answer
## 3:15

**28** Question
What time does the clock show?

**28** Answer
## 4:15

# What Time Is It?

**Instructions:** Cut out each question and answer pair and fold along the dotted line. Then, glue or tape card so each card has the question one side and answer on the other.

**29** | Question — What Time Is It? — **What time does the clock show?**

**29** | Answer — What Time Is It? — **5:15**

**30** | Question — What Time Is It? — **What time does the clock show?**

**30** | Answer — What Time Is It? — **6:15**

**31** | Question — What Time Is It? — **What time does the clock show?**

**31** | Answer — What Time Is It? — **7:15**

**32** | Question — What Time Is It? — **What time does the clock show?**

**32** | Answer — What Time Is It? — **8:15**

# What Time Is It?

**Instructions:** Cut out each question and answer pair and fold along the dotted line. Then, glue or tape card so each card has the question one side and answer on the other.

**33** Question
What time does the clock show?

**33** Answer
**9:15**

**34** Question
What time does the clock show?

**34** Answer
**10:15**

**35** Question
What time does the clock show?

**35** Answer
**11:15**

**36** Question
What time does the clock show?

**36** Answer
**12:15**

# What Time Is It?

**Instructions:** Cut out each question and answer pair and fold along the dotted line. Then, glue or tape card so each card has the question one side and answer on the other.

**37** Question — What time does the clock show?

**37** Answer — **1:45**

**38** Question — What time does the clock show?

**38** Answer — **2:45**

**39** Question — What time does the clock show?

**39** Answer — **3:45**

**40** Question — What time does the clock show?

**40** Answer — **4:45**

# What Time Is It?

**Instructions:** Cut out each question and answer pair and fold along the dotted line. Then, glue or tape card so each card has the question one side and answer on the other.

**41** Question — What Time Is It? — What time does the clock show?

**41** Answer — What Time Is It? — **5:45**

**42** Question — What Time Is It? — What time does the clock show?

**42** Answer — What Time Is It? — **6:45**

**43** Question — What Time Is It? — What time does the clock show?

**43** Answer — What Time Is It? — **7:45**

**44** Question — What Time Is It? — What time does the clock show?

**44** Answer — What Time Is It? — **8:45**

# What Time Is It?

**Instructions:** Cut out each question and answer pair and fold along the dotted line. Then, glue or tape card so each card has the question one side and answer on the other.

**45** Question

What time does the clock show?

What Time Is It?

**45** Answer

**9:45**

What Time Is It?

**46** Question

What time does the clock show?

What Time Is It?

**46** Answer

**10:45**

What Time Is It?

**47** Question

What time does the clock show?

What Time Is It?

**47** Answer

**11:45**

What Time Is It?

**48** Question

What time does the clock show?

What Time Is It?

**48** Answer

**12:45**

What Time Is It?

# Make a Graph

**Instructions:** Cut out each card along the dotted line. Teams stack the cards facedown and use the cards and Showdown to complete the blank graph on the following page.

**1**

Make a Graph

## Put a title on the graph.

**2**

Make a Graph

## Label the *x*-axis "Favorite Animals."

**3**

Make a Graph

## Label the *y*-axis "Number of People."

**4**

Make a Graph

## Ten students liked cats.

**5**

Make a Graph

## Three students liked crabs.

**6**

Make a Graph

## Eight students liked cows.

**7**

Make a Graph

## Five students liked fish.

**8**

Make a Graph

## Seven students liked frogs.

# Make a Graph

**Instructions:** Use the Make a Graph Cards to complete this graph.

| | cat | crab | cow | fish | frog |
|---|---|---|---|---|---|
| 12 | | | | | |
| 10 | | | | | |
| 8 | | | | | |
| 6 | | | | | |
| 4 | | | | | |
| 2 | | | | | |

cat     crab     cow     fish     frog

# Showdown Answer Key

## 7.1 Number Words and Numerals

1. 1
2. 2
3. 3
4. 4
5. 5
6. 6
7. 7
8. 8
9. 9
10. 10
11. 11
12. 12

13. 15
14. 17
15. 20
16. 25
17. 30
18. 34
19. 40
20. 47
21. 55
22. 58
23. 62
24. 74

## 7.2 Basic Fractions

1. ½
2. ⅓
3. ¼
4. ⅕
5. ⅙
6. ⅛
7. ¹⁄₁₀
8. ⅖
9. ¾
10. ⅔
11. ²⁄₄ (or ½)
12. ²⁄₈ (or ¼)

13. ³⁄₆ (or ½)
14. ⅘
15. ⅗
16. ⅜
17. ⁴⁄₆ (or ⅔)
18. ²⁄₆ (or ⅓)
19. ⅚
20. ⁴⁄₈ (or ½)
21. ⅝
22. ⁶⁄₈ (or ¾)
23. ⁵⁄₁₀ (or ½)
24. ²⁄₁₀ (or ⅕)

# Showdown Answer Key

## 7.3 Equal Groups

| | | | |
|---|---|---|---|
| 1. | 1 | 13. | 1 |
| 2. | ½ | 14. | 2 |
| 3. | 2 | 15. | 3 |
| 4. | 3 | 16. | 9 |
| 5. | 1 | 17. | 2 |
| 6. | 3 | 18. | 5 |
| 7. | 4 | 19. | 7 |
| 8. | 2 | 20. | 6 |
| 9. | 1 | 21. | 8 |
| 10. | 2 | 22. | 4 |
| 11. | 3 | 23. | 1 |
| 12. | 4 | 24. | 1½ |

## 7.4 Addition and Subtraction

| | | | | | |
|---|---|---|---|---|---|
| 1. | 2 | 16. | 10 | 31. | 5 |
| 2. | 4 | 17. | 14 | 32. | 1 |
| 3. | 7 | 18. | 8 | 33. | 10 |
| 4. | 7 | 19. | 12 | 34. | 9 |
| 5. | 4 | 20. | 13 | 35. | 4 |
| 6. | 9 | 21. | 12 | 36. | 8 |
| 7. | 6 | 22. | 9 | 37. | 10 |
| 8. | 9 | 23. | 10 | 38. | 5 |
| 9. | 8 | 24. | 11 | 39. | 8 |
| 10. | 10 | 25. | 1 | 40. | 6 |
| 11. | 15 | 26. | 2 | 41. | 5 |
| 12. | 13 | 27. | 3 | 42. | 9 |
| 13. | 7 | 28. | 5 | 43. | 1 |
| 14. | 8 | 29. | 2 | 44. | 6 |
| 15. | 12 | 30. | 2 | | |

# Showdown Answer Key

## 7.5 Sort the Objects

1. 8
2. 5
3. 4
4. 4
5. 5
6. 5
7. 4
8. 4
9. 4
10. 8
11. 3
12. 7

13. 16
14. 5
15. 13
16. 5
17. 3
18. 3
19. 6
20. 11
21. 2
22. 8
23. 4
24. 5

## 7.6 Is It Symmetrical?

1. Yes
2. Yes
3. Yes
4. Yes
5. Yes
6. Yes
7. Yes
8. Yes

9. No
10. No
11. No
12. No
13. No
14. No
15. No
16. No

# Showdown Answer Key

## 7.7 What Time Is It?

1. 1:00
2. 2:00
3. 3:00
4. 4:00
5. 5:00
6. 6:00
7. 7:00
8. 8:00
9. 9:00
10. 10:00
11. 11:00
12. 12:00
13. 1:30
14. 2:30
15. 3:30
16. 4:30
17. 5:30
18. 6:30
19. 7:30
20. 8:30
21. 9:30
22. 10:30
23. 11:30
24. 12:30

25. 1:15
26. 2:15
27. 3:15
28. 4:15
29. 5:15
30. 6:15
31. 7:15
32. 8:15
33. 9:15
34. 10:15
35. 11:15
36. 12:15
37. 1:45
38. 2:45
39. 3:45
40. 4:45
41. 5:45
42. 6:45
43. 7:45
44. 8:45
45. 9:45
46. 10:45
47. 11:45
48. 12:45

# Showdown Answer Key

## 7.8 Make a Graph

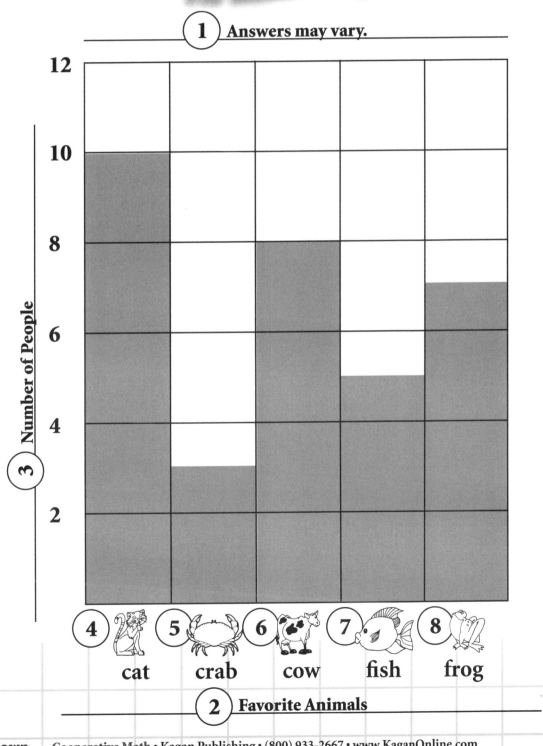

① Answers may vary.

③ Number of People

④ cat   ⑤ crab   ⑥ cow   ⑦ fish   ⑧ frog

② Favorite Animals

# Notes

# Notes

# Notes